RONMENTAL POLLUTION

GING CLIMATE

Presented to Parliament by Command of Her Majesty
June 2000

Cm 4749   £27

Recycled paper

Previous Reports by the Royal Commission on Environmental Pollution

Information about the current work of the Royal Commission can be obtained from its website at http://www.rcep.org.uk or from the Secretariat at Steel House, 11 Tothill Street, London SW1H 9RE

ROYAL COMMISSION ON ENVIRONMENTAL POLLUTION

TWENTY-SECOND REPORT

To the Queen's Most Excellent Majesty

MAY IT PLEASE YOUR MAJESTY

We, the undersigned Commissioners, having been appointed 'to advise on matters, both national and international, concerning the pollution of the environment; on the adequacy of research in this field; and the future possibilities of danger to the environment';

And to enquire into any such matters referred to us by one of Your Majesty's Secretaries of State or by one of Your Majesty's Ministers, or any other such matters on which we ourselves shall deem it expedient to advise:

HUMBLY SUBMIT TO YOUR MAJESTY THE FOLLOWING REPORT.

Material goods have gained an increasing and finally an inexorable power over the lives of men as at no previous period in history.... The tremendous cosmos of the modern economic order is now bound to the technical and economic conditions of machine production which to-day determine the lives of all the individuals who are born into this mechanism, not only those directly concerned with economic acquisition, with irresistible force. Perhaps it will so determine them until the last ton of fossilized fuel is burnt.

> Max Weber. *The protestant ethic and the spirit of capitalism.* 1920. Translated by Talcott Parsons.

Are these the shadows of the things that Will be,
or are they shadows of things that May be, only?

> Charles Dickens. *A Christmas carol.*

CONTENTS

Part II   *The United Kingdom's response*

Chapter 5

Chapter 6

REDUCING ENERGY USE   85

INFORMATION BOXES

TABLES

FIGURES

Photographs between pages 84 and 85

I	Sizewell B nuclear power station
II	Didcot coal-fired power station
III	Deeside combined cycle gas turbine power station
IV	Supermarket in Greenwich
V	University building at Norwich

Photographs between pages 130 and 131

VI	Zero energy housing development in London
VII	Tidal stream turbine
VIII	Severn tidal barrage
IX	Offshore wind farm in the Baltic Sea
X	Onshore wind farm in Wales

Photographs between pages 142 and 143

XI	Hydro power scheme in Scotland
XII	Harbour wall wind farm in Northumberland
XIII	Large photovoltaic installation in Wales
XIV	Short rotation willow coppice
XV	Scale model of wave power machine
XVI	Dinorwig pumped storage scheme

SUMMARY

1.   Access to abundant and instantly available energy underlies our entire way of life, yet its impact on the environment is growing. This poses a radical challenge for the UK; a challenge that cannot be met successfully unless the government's energy policies and its environmental policies are coherent. A sustainable energy policy for the UK should protect the interests of generations to come, but it must also seek to achieve social justice, a higher quality of life and industrial competitiveness today. Achieving the right balance is formidably difficult; current policies do not strike it.

2.   All energy supplies have substantial effects on the environment. Some have impacts on human health and they all change the natural world to some extent. Damaging air pollutants from fossil fuels, large, intrusive wind farms in upland scenery, radioactive emissions from the reprocessing of spent nuclear fuel and the destruction of woodlands to supply cooking fuel and warmth in poor countries are all well known examples of this broad range of concerns.

CLIMATE CHANGE – THE NEED FOR GLOBAL AGREEMENT

3.   One effect of energy supply has now come to assume special importance, though it was barely in the consciousness of politicians or the public 20 years ago. This is human-induced climate change which is threatening to impose very significant shifts in temperatures, rainfall, extremes of weather and sea levels in this century and those that follow. The principal cause is that the concentration of carbon dioxide in the atmosphere has been rising, mainly because of humanity's growing use of fossil fuels, and trapping more solar warmth. The concentration of carbon dioxide is already higher than at any time for millions of years and we seem to be experiencing the first effects.

4.   Some human-induced climate change now seems inevitable. There will, therefore, be a need for adaptation by nations and communities. But the larger challenge is to halt the steady rise in the concentrations of carbon dioxide and other greenhouse gases, limiting further change and reducing the risks of catastrophic alterations in climate. Given the present state of knowledge of the climate system, we support the proposal that an atmospheric carbon dioxide concentration of 550 parts per million by volume (ppmv) – approximately double the pre-industrial level – should be regarded as an upper limit that should not be exceeded. The current concentration is some 370 ppmv.

5.   Fossil fuels are finite, so people will eventually have to stop consuming them – but if they were all burnt during the course of this century and the next the resulting build up of carbon dioxide would go well above 550 ppmv and would be likely to lead to dangerous and destructive climate change. Even if the global use of coal, oil and gas was prevented from rising and held at current levels the climate would change markedly. To limit the damage beyond that already in train, large reductions in global emissions will be necessary during this century and the next. Strong and effective action has to start immediately.

6.   Countering the threat of major changes in climate is a task for the entire world community. Developing nations produce much less carbon dioxide *per capita* than developed countries like the UK. But the developing world's consumption of fossil fuels is rising rapidly as it industrialises and living standards rise. It seems highly likely that its emissions will overtake the combined emissions of the developed countries within a few decades. International agreement on a means of limiting each country's emissions is needed, so that the global total is kept to a level which prevents intolerable and dangerous climate change.

7.   The most promising, and just, basis for securing long-term agreement is to allocate emission rights to nations on a *per capita* basis – enshrining the idea that every human is entitled to release into the atmosphere the same quantity of greenhouse gases. But because of the very wide differences between *per capita* emission levels around the world, and because current global emissions are already above safe levels, there will have to be an adjustment period covering several decades in which nations' quotas converge on the same *per capita* level. This is the principle of contraction and convergence, which we support.

8.   International trading in emissions quotas could play a crucial role in enabling such an agreement to be obtained and adhered to, as could partnership agreements under which developed nations help to achieve clean development in industrialising countries. Nations which found it costly and difficult to make the required emission reductions would be willing to purchase quota at a negotiated price from states which found it relatively cheap to emit less than their quota.

THE UK'S ROLE

9.   For the UK, an international agreement along these lines which prevented carbon dioxide concentrations in the atmosphere from exceeding 550 ppmv and achieved convergence by 2050 could imply a reduction of 60% from current annual carbon dioxide emissions by 2050 and perhaps of 80% by 2100. These are massive changes. But the government should implement short, medium and long term strategies which are sufficiently coherent and effective to achieve these reductions. Action at home would help the UK, as part of the European Union, to argue strongly for significant action by other nations; only if the majority of nations act can there be any hope of stabilising carbon dioxide concentrations at a tolerable level.

10.   Major benefits, unrelated to reducing climate change, would flow from policies to reduce our use of fossil fuels. Among the benefits are a reduction in the air pollution which harms human health and causes acid rain and photochemical smogs and a reduction in the congestion, noise and environmental degradation caused by rising levels of road traffic. If the package of policies included raising the very low levels of energy efficiency in UK housing, this could be tied to urban regeneration and the elimination of fuel poverty.

11.   UK governments have played an important and constructive role in obtaining, first, general recognition that climate change is an issue of fundamental importance and, second, commitments from the developed countries to cut their rising emissions of greenhouse gases. Reaching agreement on further necessary actions by the entire world community will probably be much harder, and take much longer, without continued leadership from the UK and other European nations.

12.   International leadership must have a firm basis in effective and appropriate national policies. The UK has recently made substantial reductions in its greenhouse gas emissions, and has referred to these while exhorting other nations to act. However, the amount of energy the UK uses is still increasing and the factors that have led to emission reductions over the last decade are largely coincidental. Chief among these is the substitution of gas for coal as fuel in power stations. This will contribute to further reductions in this decade but, at this stage, it looks as if making further substantial cuts in carbon dioxide emissions will become much more difficult for the UK after 2010.

13.   The UK is therefore poorly prepared, as yet, to face the long-term challenge of reducing emissions from coal, oil and gas to far below present levels. The government's goal of a 20% reduction in carbon dioxide emissions by 2010 (compared to their 1990 level) is much more ambitious than the UK's international legal obligation under the UN's Kyoto Protocol of a 12.5% reduction in greenhouse gas emissions. If the former can be achieved, this will represent

valuable and world-beating progress. The government has now produced a draft climate change programme. This goes beyond meeting the Kyoto obligation, but it is not yet sufficient to achieve a 20% carbon dioxide reduction by 2010. Looking further ahead, a programme for more radical changes will be required.

14.   We have considered what needs to be done in the longer term. We have sought to relate that directly to actions that can and should be taken by the government and by other parties in the UK now. We have examined the scope for reducing the demand for energy. We have assessed the extent to which new and renewable energy sources – which produce either no carbon dioxide, or far less than existing fossil fuel technologies – can substitute for coal, oil and gas. We have considered the wider economic, social and environmental aspects of reducing demand and developing alternatives to fossil fuels, as well as their technical feasibility.

LOCKING UP CARBON DIOXIDE

15.   We have also considered other approaches to the problem which involve locking the extra carbon dioxide produced by humanity away from the atmosphere. Trees and other vegetation take up carbon dioxide when they grow and release it when they burn or rot, so wise management of the Earth's forests is desirable. Globally, forest re-growth could only compensate for a small part of the rising carbon dioxide emissions; simplistic suggestions that climate change can be prevented by planting trees are wide of the mark. The priority should be to prevent deforestation making things worse, while at the same time meeting other essential needs for land in developing countries.

16.   The land area of the UK is too small for tree planting to make a significant contribution to removing its own fossil fuel emissions from the atmosphere. The UK should, however, conserve its existing forests and seize opportunities to expand them for the sake of protecting wildlife, enhancing landscapes and improving amenity. It must also conserve other major carbon sinks, particularly soils and peat bogs, in ways which prevent them from becoming significant carbon sources.

17.   The oceans are a huge reservoir for carbon. But not enough is known about their internal processes to be sure that either stimulating the growth of microscopic marine plants or injecting liquid carbon dioxide directly into seawater would be an effective way of keeping greenhouse gases out of the atmosphere. Either might have major unintended consequences, particularly for marine life.

18.   There is considerable potential for disposing of carbon dioxide in deep geological strata with minimal environmental impact. If the present high cost of removing carbon dioxide from emissions were regarded as acceptable, or could be reduced, removal and disposal might make a significant contribution to reducing emissions. Disposal in geological formations beneath the sea-bed may be safer and more secure than in those below dry land. But this approach can only be applied to emissions from large installations such as power stations, not to the larger share of emissions which come from vehicles and homes. Further research into the safety of this disposal technology is required. If it proves safe and cost-effective then a substantial proportion of UK electricity could continue to be produced by fossil-fuel burning plant with capture and isolation of the carbon dioxide produced. But reductions in the demand for energy and the deployment of non-fossil fuel energy sources have the leading role to play in reducing emissions over the coming decades.

REDUCING ENERGY USE

19.   The demand for energy in the UK has been rising steadily. This increase is linked to the growing output of goods and services associated with economic growth, increasing travel, the rising number of households and the gradual increase in population. Energy consumption has risen more slowly than economic activity (as measured by gross domestic product), reflecting the tendency of organisations and individuals to find ways of using energy more efficiently.

20.   But there is ample opportunity for further, large efficiency improvements in the use of energy by manufacturing industry, commercial and public services, households and transport. The scope for improvements in buildings of all kinds, but especially housing, is particularly large. Every house should have an energy label and energy efficiency standards for new buildings, as set out in the building regulations, should be drastically improved over the next few years. The need for improvements in transport is particularly pressing, given the rapid growth in this sector's energy consumption.

21.   It should be possible to reduce the UK's overall energy consumption without damaging its international competitiveness or causing hardship. Such a reduction would make a major contribution to achieving long-term reductions in carbon dioxide emissions.

22.   To bring this about will require government to give much higher priority to energy efficiency, a change in public attitudes with people linking their own day to day use of energy with fossil fuel consumption and the threat of climate change, and a new cultural and institutional framework within which individuals will feel that they can make a difference. To these ends, government should build on its existing energy efficiency policies and campaigns and introduce new ones. Further incentives are required, as are new and strengthened regulations.

A CARBON TAX

23.   The prices consumers pay for fossil fuels do not, for the most part, reflect the harm their use is doing and will continue to do as the impacts of increasing climate change make themselves felt. Fossil fuel and electricity prices in the UK have, for the most part, been falling during the last decade, reducing the incentives to improve energy efficiency. This is partly a reflection of global price shifts, and partly the result of government policy in privatising major energy suppliers and then regulating the liberalised markets. The government now plans to introduce an energy tax called the climate change levy to stimulate efficiency improvements and reduce energy consumption. Some energy sources and some consumers will be exempted, either partially or entirely. Households will not have to pay the tax, on the grounds that if they did this would increase fuel poverty. Some of the revenues raised will be used to promote energy efficiency improvements and alternatives to fossil fuels.

24.   We welcome this approach but we favour a general carbon tax based on the quantity of carbon dioxide emitted per unit of energy supplied. It should be applied upstream, when fossil fuels are first purchased. This would give producers, distributors and consumers of energy an incentive to switch to sources which produced fewer emissions. It would lead to higher energy prices downstream, stimulating efficiency improvements and reducing consumption. Other environmentally harmful aspects of energy supply and use are already covered, to some extent, by regulation and taxation. Emissions of carbon dioxide are not; hence the need for a carbon tax.

25.   We accept that such a tax would, without mitigation, tend to increase fuel poverty. This ought to be eradicated; we find it unacceptable that in a relatively wealthy nation like the UK, millions of vulnerable people cannot afford adequate warmth in their homes. The first call on the revenues from a carbon tax, which we envisage being introduced initially at a relatively low rate, would be to prevent any overall increase in fuel poverty and to reduce it further. This should be done through increases in benefits and through an enhanced programme to improve radically the energy efficiency of the worst of the UK housing stock.

26.   Some of the carbon tax revenues should fund other measures for reducing emissions, such as subsidies and tax relief for energy efficiency improvements and research and development of low carbon and carbon free energy sources. The remaining revenues should be used to offset the adverse effects of the tax on the international competitiveness of UK commerce and industry; reducing taxes on employment is one option.

ALTERNATIVE ENERGY SOURCES

27.   Many sources of energy have emerged as potential alternatives to fossil fuels. Exploiting these also gives rise to a wide range of impacts on the environment. Such impacts ought to be taken into account from the outset in deciding what role alternative energy sources can play. Some alternatives to fossil fuels are associated with indirect emissions of carbon dioxide; an example would be the emissions from road transport taking energy crops from fields to power stations. However, the overall emissions from the alternative energy sources are much lower than those of fossil fuels.

28.   The strong growth in air travel and road traffic indicates that much more needs to be done to control their rising emissions. But aircraft and road vehicles are likely to continue to depend on fossil fuels for some decades to come. Some reduction in carbon dioxide emissions from road transport can be achieved by reformulating oil and gas into hydrogen-rich fuels which can be used in on-board fuel cells powering electric motors. In the longer term, much larger reductions in transport emissions might be achieved by switching to hydrogen produced from water using non-fossil fuel energy.

29.   The large-scale non-carbon energy sources that are already well established and available in large quantities in the UK are nuclear power and hydro power, both of which supply only electricity. There is only a limited potential for further large-scale exploitation of hydro power in the UK and environmental concerns may rule out further major schemes. Further growth in the number of small-scale hydro schemes is possible, but not to the extent that it could make a substantial contribution to UK energy needs.

NUCLEAR POWER

30.   Nuclear power is a significant source of carbon-free energy for the UK, having enjoyed four decades of extensive state support in research, development and operation. But unless new plant is built, nuclear power will almost have ceased by 2020. New nuclear power stations should not be built until the problem of managing nuclear waste has been solved to the satisfaction both of the scientific community and the general public. Irrespective of the future role of nuclear power, an effective long-term repository needs to be provided to accommodate the wastes that already exist.

31.   Nuclear power could continue to play an important role in reducing UK greenhouse gas emissions. We do not, however, accept the arguments of those who hold that it is indispensable. We do not believe public opinion will permit the construction of new nuclear power stations unless they are part of a strategy which delivers radical improvements in energy efficiency and an equal opportunity for the deployment of other alternatives to fossil fuels which can compete in terms of cost and reduced environmental impacts. The procedures for weighing up these issues will need to allow for debate of a high standard, and at the same time be capable of articulating deeply held values and beliefs. We have suggested in our previous report, on environmental standards, how that might be achieved.

32.   A priority for government should be to set out a programme demonstrating the new non-fossil fuel resources (which may or may not include nuclear power) and/or the reductions in energy demand that could compensate for the expected closure of almost all existing UK nuclear plant over the next two decades. This needs to be done within the next five years, because of the long period required to implement a programme on this scale. If the nuclear plants were replaced by fossil fuel power stations without carbon dioxide capture and isolation then all of the emission reductions achieved so far would be undone. If renewables and demand reduction cannot be brought forward on the scale required, and if capture and isolation of carbon dioxide proves unsafe or prohibitively expensive, the case for building new nuclear stations will be strengthened.

33.   There is no foreseeable prospect of some magic source of almost unlimited energy with negligible environmental impact. Nuclear fusion has sometimes been advocated as that, but it is still at the research stage and a commercial-scale demonstration plant seems unlikely to be constructed before 2050. Its environmental impact, as well as its economic viability, have yet to be clarified.

TIDES, WINDS, WAVES AND SUNSHINE

34.   Tidal barrages could generate large quantities of electricity on a predictable but intermittent basis. There are none operating in the UK but the technology is proven. They would be expensive to construct and are likely to have major impacts on the wildlife and ecology of estuaries. Their economic viability might be increased if they formed part of barrages built across estuaries to prevent flooding from rising sea levels.

35.   The UK has abundant wind energy distributed across much of its landmass. The surrounding seas offer an even larger wind resource, and very large quantities of energy in the form of waves and strong tidal currents. All should be harnessed for our needs. Despite frequently overcast skies, solar energy could also make a substantial contribution to UK energy needs – through electricity-generating photovoltaic panels, solar panels which heat water for use in buildings directly and building designs which enable sunshine to warm and light interiors.

NON-FOSSIL FUELS

36.   Alternative fuels to coal, oil and gas can also make a contribution to reducing the UK's overall carbon dioxide emissions. The combustion of agricultural and forestry wastes, methane from waste in landfill sites and household rubbish could play a limited but worthwhile role. The growing of energy crops such as coppice willow, which are then burned or gasified and combusted to generate electricity and supply heat, could make a much larger contribution to the UK's long-term climate change strategy. They might also contribute to increasing

biodiversity and improving farmland landscapes. But this cannot be achieved without major changes to agricultural support systems. We propose that energy crops should receive the same level of support as other crops, but with improved environmental safeguards.

37.   Some of the technologies needed to harness these renewable energy resources are now well established. Their total contribution is still minor, but the number of installations has been growing fast. Onshore wind turbines are an example. Wave power devices and undersea turbines turned by tidal streams have great potential but are still at the earliest stages of development with relatively little government support.

SUPPORTING RENEWABLE ENERGY

38.   The UK's supply of energy from these non-fossil fuel, non-nuclear sources has more than doubled in the past decade, a welcome increase. But considering the enormous potential of UK renewable energy resources, it has been slow to make progress; several other European nations have achieved more. Irrespective of global warming, renewable energy resources will have a growing role to play around the world and there are likely to be major export opportunities which the UK will be unable to take advantage of unless its domestic renewables industry expands from its current small size.

39.   We welcome the government's recent commitments on expanding renewable energy, but this sector needs further support. There cannot, however, be some central master plan for new energy sources. It is impossible to predict 50, or even 15, years ahead how each area of technology will develop, and how competitive it will become in cost and in other terms. Policies should continue to be based on facilitating and stimulating the emergence of new technologies and reducing their environmental impacts. A carbon tax would help, by enabling renewable energy sources to compete with fossil fuels.

40.   It makes sense to provide guarantees or subsidies for those technologies which are proven and closest to providing energy at open market prices. Experience has shown that the resulting mass deployment makes them more competitive still. But there is also a strong need for direct government support for research and development on some of the least developed technologies which offer great potential but are some way from being competitive, such as wave power, tidal stream turbines and photovoltaic cells. In coming decades the government will need carefully to monitor novel energy technologies which can reduce carbon dioxide emissions, supporting further research and development in those that are most relevant to the UK's circumstances.

41.   Because renewable energy installations tend to be relatively small, there will need to be more of them and they are likely to be more dispersed. Plans to construct wind farms in scenic upland areas have run into serious, and understandable, opposition. More effective use must be made of the land use planning system to help the deployment of such energy systems whilst respecting people's legitimate wishes to protect cherished landscapes and wildlife. A more strategic approach to selecting sites is required, at national and regional levels, in development plans and offshore. This process would be assisted if programmes to develop renewable energy systems were subject to strategic environmental assessment. Every community should review its impact on the environment in terms of demands for energy, and the ways in which they can be met. Promoters of schemes should establish a dialogue with the local community at an early stage.

COMBINED HEAT AND POWER

42.   For far too long, policies have favoured the generation of electricity in ways that waste vast quantities of heat – heat that could be used to warm buildings. The more recent promotion of renewable energy sources has focussed almost entirely on electricity rather than heat output.

43.   Regulatory and planning policies should encourage the widest possible adoption of combined heat and power (CHP) technology in urban locations to supply heat. Local communities should be encouraged to establish heating networks serving entire estates or urban districts, supplied by CHP. Gas-fired CHP plant will reduce carbon dioxide emissions by making more efficient use of energy, even though it will for the time being reinforce the role in the UK energy system of a fossil fuel. The expansion of CHP generating heat for district heating systems could provide a growing market for renewable fuels such as energy crops. Electrically powered heat pumps, which can utilise the abundant low-grade heat in surface and ground waters and in municipal wastewater can also provide warmth and hot water for buildings via heat networks, substantially reducing carbon dioxide emissions.

CHANGING THE GRID

44.   The relatively small size of renewable energy plants generating electricity and local CHP plants does not fit easily with an electricity distribution and transmission network based on massive generators and highly centralised control. The national grid and the regional distribution systems need to become more favourable to small and very small environmentally friendly generators which sometimes need to import electricity. Regulatory policies will need to promote, and must not inhibit, this development. The government and the electricity supply industry must together devise a system which can handle a growing quantity of this embedded generation securely and efficiently.

45.   As the proportion of electricity supplied by wind, waves, tides and sunshine increases, the intermittency of these sources will pose growing problems in matching supply with demand. Electricity cannot currently be stored in very large quantities. If the UK is to rely heavily on these intermittent resources to reduce emissions, then it will either need massive but little used reserve generating capacity (consisting of fossil fuel or renewable fuel plant), or large new energy stores or novel energy carriers. Hydrogen produced using electricity and then consumed in power-generating fuel cells is one possible carrier. The costs and complexities associated with these approaches could form a substantial barrier to the major deployment of intermittent renewables. Government must stimulate research into solving the problems that large-scale intermittency and embedded generation would pose to the electricity supply system as a matter of urgency.

ALTERNATIVE SCENARIOS

46.   We have drawn up four scenarios for energy supply and demand in the UK, on the assumption that carbon dioxide emissions from fossil fuel combustion must be reduced by 60% from their 1998 level in 2050. We have developed these scenarios in numerical terms, because figures impose some discipline even though they are only as good as the assumptions on which they are based. The scenarios assume various degrees of reduction in energy demand, all of them substantial, and various mixes and levels of renewable energy resources. Two of the scenarios assume a large contribution from nuclear power or an equivalent electrical output from large, fossil fuel-burning power stations with carbon dioxide capture and isolation in geological strata. The other two have neither nuclear power nor carbon dioxide capture and isolation.

47.   The conclusion that emerges is that, unless energy demand is curbed to a significant degree, making substantial reductions in UK emissions would require a massive and environmentally intrusive contribution from renewable sources augmented either by nuclear power or by fossil fuel power stations with large-scale capture and isolation of carbon dioxide.

ACTION NOW

48.   Energy policies of the kind we are seeking will not emerge unless there is a thoroughgoing change of approach and change of culture within government. Some aspects of present energy policies are in conflict with the reduction of carbon dioxide emissions, and current policies aimed at reducing emissions seem likely to fall short of the goal of reducing annual carbon dioxide emissions by 20% between 1990 and 2010. The government's current arrangements for making and implementing energy and environment policy are inadequate for the task which lies ahead. We propose that a Sustainable Energy Agency should be set up to provide impetus for the improvements in energy efficiency required and the necessary development and expansion of renewable energy resources.

49.   There is little public awareness or acceptance of the measures needed to accomplish sustained, deep reductions in greenhouse gas emissions. The government needs to secure active support by industry, commerce, local authorities and society in general. People and organisations should be made aware of the way in which their use of fossil fuels is contributing to climate change and then be encouraged to take responsibility for their own reductions in fossil fuel consumption. But the framework in which energy and environment policies are devised must enable people to feel that if they are 'doing their bit' then so are others – including local and central government, large corporations and institutions.

50.   Concerted policies for changing the UK's energy system and reducing carbon dioxide emissions need to be sustained through successive Parliaments. We propose that challenging national targets should be set for improving energy efficiency and developing new energy sources. These will need to extend beyond the timescale of current obligations on the UK under the UN's Framework Convention on Climate Change.

51.   In this report we illustrate ways in which the UK could cut its carbon dioxide emissions by 60% by 2050. Achieving this will require vision, leadership, and action which begins now. Governments are seldom asked to look and to plan so far into the future; the quickening pace of change and the shrinking power of the nation state may make it increasingly difficult to do so. We emphasise that an even greater reduction in carbon dioxide emissions is likely to be required by the end of the century.

52.   The enormous challenge posed by humanity's intervention in the Earth's climate, threatening generations to come, demands action on this scale. If the UK does not show it is serious about doing its part, it cannot expect other nations – least of all those which are much poorer – to do theirs.

ENERGY: DEFINITIONS AND UNITS

FORMS OF ENERGY

With the exception of nuclear reactions which convert matter to energy, energy can be neither created nor destroyed. There are, however, different forms of energy:

heat - energy which makes a body hotter, or causes it to melt or evaporate

work - energy which moves a body or changes its shape or volume

chemical energy - energy stored in the chemical bonds of a substance which can be released by a chemical reaction (such as burning a fuel).

Energy can be transformed from one form to another, but the forms are not completely interchangeable. Work can be dissipated as heat, but heat cannot be transformed completely to work (see box 3A). Electrical energy is effectively a form of work.

UNITS FOR ENERGY

The **joule** is the *Système Internationale*[1] unit for energy, defined as the energy of one kilogram moving at one metre per second. One **watt** is equivalent to one joule supplied each second. The following standard prefixes are used for joules and watts:

K = kilo = thousand = 10^3	M = mega = million = 10^6
G = giga = billion = 10^9	T = tera = trillion = 10^{12}

The two most commonly employed measures of quantities of energy supplied or used, at national and global levels, are millions of tonnes of oil equivalent (MTOE) for fossil fuels and terawatt hours (TWh) for electricity. We have departed from convention; neither of those measures features in this report. Rather than *quantities*, our numerical discussion of energy concerns *rates* of energy supply or use, usually averaged over a year. For clarity and simplicity, we refer to energy use and supply in terms of gigawatts (GW); one GW is a billion (thousand million) watts. This allows easy numerical comparisons between different primary sources of energy (fossil fuels, nuclear power, renewable sources), between different forms of energy, and between the different stages of energy supply and use.

Dispensing with MTOE and TWh as measures of energy also simplifies discussion of the capacity and average output of energy sources. The *maximum rate* of energy supply from a plant which generates electricity is referred to as its *capacity*, commonly expressed in GW or MW. Where we refer to the capacity of a plant, we follow the same convention. But most plants do not operate at maximum capacity over extended periods of time, so their *average output* is less. We express this actual output in terms of the average rate of supply in GW over a year. The *load factor* of a generating plant is its average output divided by its capacity; thus a power station of 1 GW capacity with an average output of 0.5 GW over a year would have a load factor of 0.5.

For purposes of comparison with the more conventional measures, one MTOE is the amount of energy released when one million tonnes of crude oil is burnt. (One million tonnes of gas would release rather more than one MTOE of energy when burnt, one million tonnes of coal rather less.) One MTOE is equivalent to an average rate of energy supply of 1.33 GW over a period of one year and an average rate of energy supply of one GW over one year is equivalent to 0.754 MTOE.

One TWh is the quantity of energy supplied when one trillion watts of electrical power is generated continuously for one hour (or one billion watts for 1,000 hours). One TWh supplied over one year (1 TWh/year) is equivalent to an average rate of energy supply of 0.114 GW and an average rate of energy supply of one GW is equivalent to 8.78 TWh/year.

Part I

The Global Context

Chapter 1

THE RADICAL CHALLENGE

Human use of energy has grown enormously, based overwhelmingly on burning fossil fuels. This is causing a significant change in the composition of the atmosphere which, unless halted, is likely to have very serious consequences

1.1   Energy, both as heat and work, has played a central part in the development of human societies throughout the world. Early communities depended on heat from burning wood, dung or agricultural residues and on work performed by human and animal muscles. Many millions of people in rural areas of developing countries still do. But as societies have become industrialised, other sources of energy have been harnessed on an increasing scale. For centuries, wind and water have driven pumps and mills. The industrial revolution was made possible by the invention of steam engines that could obtain work from heat, using coal as fuel.

1.2   During the 20th century, the rate of worldwide energy use has increased ninefold. As figure I-1[1] shows (red curve), nearly all the increase has occurred since 1945. From then until the early 1970s the rate at which primary energy was being used grew at almost 5% a year; growth slowed to around 2% a year following the sharp increase in oil prices in 1973-74, but quickened again in the 1980s. Expressed as an average per person (black curve), energy use has not increased significantly in recent years, but total energy use worldwide continues to rise.

1.3   The most rapid growth in demand has been for electricity and mobility. Between 1971 and 1995, final demand for electricity increased by 147% and final energy demand for mobility by 82%. These two sectors now account respectively for 25% and 17% of global final energy consumption.[2] Worldwide demand in all sectors will inevitably grow further as lower-income countries develop.[3]

1.4   There have been accompanying changes in energy sources. In 1930 over three-quarters of the energy being used worldwide came from fossil fuels, among which coal predominated.[4] By 1971 97% of the energy being used came from fossil fuels, but half was from oil. Following the oil crises of the 1970s, however, the relative importance of oil declined, while gas, nuclear and hydro power all increased rapidly in importance. In 1995, about 90% of world primary energy supply came from fossil fuels (about 40% from oil, 28% from solid fuels, 22% from gas), 7% came from nuclear, 3% from hydro power and 0.4% from other renewable sources.[5]

1.5   The benefits provided by energy – warmth, light, and the power used in industry and transport – are easy to identify. But it has long been apparent that the extraction, processing, movement and use of all kinds of fuel brings risks not only to workers in the relevant industries but also to the population at large, and plant and animal life, through the environmental damage that some of these activities cause.

1.6   Adverse effects associated with use of fossil fuels prompted some preventive actions. In Britain, the premature deaths caused by days of heavy smoke and sulphur dioxide pollution in urban areas in the 1950s led not only to domestic smoke controls, but also to a new generation of large power stations in rural areas, with tall stacks to ensure dilution of the emitted gases.

Recognition that this did not prevent the deposition of acid sulphate and nitrate – and indeed favoured their international dispersion to fall as acid rain thousands of kilometres from source – led to demands for fuels with a lower sulphur content, flue gas desulphurisation and low-nitrogen oxide burners. Alarm over the oxidant smogs produced largely by pollutants reacting in sunlight, and the effects these have on human health and sensitive crops (first voiced in California), focused attention on emissions from vehicles, which like industrial emissions are subject to increasingly stringent limits.

1.7 Even so, current levels of air pollution are judged to have both acute and chronic effects on human health. In Britain exposures over short periods to small particles, sulphur dioxide, nitrogen dioxide and ozone have been estimated to contribute to 24,000 deaths and 24,000 hospital admissions each year.[6] The deaths are labelled as 'brought forward' because the exposures are thought to precipitate death in people with pre-existing illness; there is no reliable estimate to indicate by how much they are brought forward. In addition, longer-term exposure to air pollution may have effects on initiation of disease, but estimates of the size of such effects in the UK are not available.

1.8 While these risks associated with using fossil fuels can hopefully be controlled more effectively by applying reasonably well-established technology, the issues raised by nuclear power have proved to be less tractable. The initial enthusiasm in the 1950s for what was hailed as a clean and potentially limitless source of electricity became muted when it emerged that some of the wastes from that industry, and some of its disused installations, would inevitably contain very long-lived radioisotopes requiring isolation for many millennia. Accidental releases of radioisotopes, especially in the disaster at Chernobyl in Ukraine in 1986, together with concerns about the safety and costs of disposal of nuclear wastes and the decommissioning of plants, halted the construction of new nuclear stations in many countries, and led to commitments in Sweden and Germany to phase out nuclear power.

1.9 Building the installations required to obtain and transport energy has also caused controversy. Debates over the siting of power stations and large hydro power schemes – and the acceptability of their impact on landscape, amenity, local human communities and wildlife – have been impassioned. Visual intrusion caused by wind farms is now also the subject of heated arguments in the UK and other countries.

1.10 These experiences emphasise that there is no energy source without its environmental problems.

1.11 During the last decade a new concern about the environmental effects of energy use has become dominant. It arises because burning fossil fuels converts the carbon present in all such fuels into the gas carbon dioxide. The concentration of carbon dioxide in the Earth's atmosphere is rising steadily. The effects are likely to be significant warming of the world's climate, a rise in sea level, changes in weather patterns, and according to most studies a greater frequency of extreme events. The environmental and social consequences of such changes are potentially catastrophic.

1.12 The world community is confronted with a radical challenge of a totally new kind. Modern civilisation currently depends heavily on the use of fossil fuels. That situation cannot easily or quickly be modified. Yet continuing use of fossil fuels on anything like the present scale may make the whole process of development unsustainable: it may (using the words of the Brundtland Commission) 'meet the needs of the present' but compromise 'the ability of future generations to meet their own needs'.[7]

enhancement in the greenhouse effect.[11] The role of individual sources is uncertain. A large proportion of methane emissions are the result of land use, including those from wetlands, paddy fields and termites. About 28% are thought to be associated with fossil fuel extraction (through leakage from coal mines, gas pipelines and oil wells); 7-8% come from landfill sites and comparable amounts from sewage treatment and from animal wastes.[12] The significance for global warming of greenhouse gases other than carbon dioxide is considered further in boxes 2B and 2C below.

2.9   Figure 2-II shows the relative magnitudes of some natural energy flows, various forms of electricity generation, and human consumption of primary energy both in the UK and globally. It shows why enhancement of the greenhouse effect (in red type) is a matter of such concern. The rate at which primary energy is consumed worldwide by human activity is 10,000 times less than the rate at which energy reaches the Earth from the sun. It is about 1,000 times less than the rate at which the atmosphere and oceans transfer energy from low to high latitudes (for example through the northward movement of warm water in the North Atlantic). The waste heat passing into the atmosphere as a result of human energy consumption can therefore be regarded as having a negligible direct effect on the global climate system. The increase in the

Figure 2-II
Global and UK energy sources and consumption

annual average rate of energy use or supply in watts - logarithmic scale

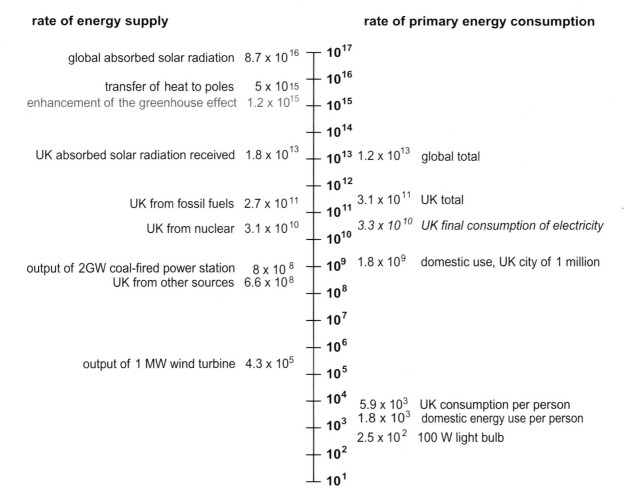

concentration of greenhouse gases, on the other hand, is much more significant in its potential impact. If the same quantities of gases had suddenly been added to the atmosphere, the result would have been a massive imbalance in the rates at which energy is received and lost by the Earth; the magnitude of that imbalance is only four times smaller than the rate at which energy is transferred naturally towards the poles, and is therefore very significant in terms of the climate system. Further large enhancements of the greenhouse effect are in prospect if carbon dioxide emissions continue to rise.

THE GLOBAL CARBON CYCLE

2.10   In the absence of human intervention, the concentration of carbon dioxide in the atmosphere is the outcome of a natural cycle, illustrated in figure 2-III.[13] Assessing the effects of burning fossil fuels involves understanding how that cycle operates. The gross flows (green arrows) are much larger than the net flows (red arrows). Rocks, organic material and the oceans continuously release carbon into the atmosphere in the form of carbon dioxide and continuously re-absorb it. If the rate of re-absorption balances the rate of release, a dynamic equilibrium is maintained and the concentration of carbon dioxide in the atmosphere remains approximately constant. That was the situation for 10,000 years prior to industrialisation.

2.11   Figure 2-III also indicates the sizes of the various natural pools of carbon; figure 2-IV compares these with the amounts of carbon represented by specified concentrations of carbon dioxide in the atmosphere. Worldwide, vegetation is estimated to contain 600 gigatonnes of carbon (GtC), which is also roughly the amount that was in the atmosphere before

Figure 2-III
Global carbon cycle

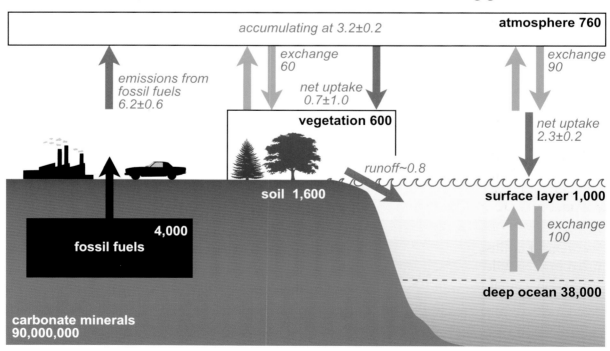

figures in **bold** type show estimated size of pools
figures in *italics* show estimated average annual flows

Figure 2-IV
Amounts of carbon in atmosphere and pools

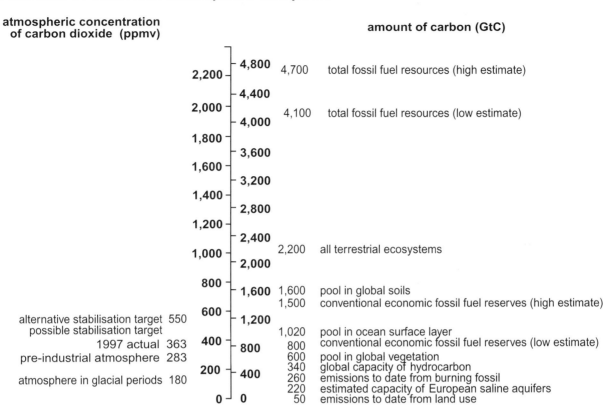

atmospheric concentration
of carbon dioxide (ppmv)

amount of carbon (GtC)

Following common practice, amounts of both carbon and carbon dioxide are expressed in this report in terms of tonnes of carbon. The left-hand scale shows, for the amounts of carbon indicated on the right-hand side of the diagram, what they would represent as an addition to the concentration of carbon dioxide in the atmosphere if they were to be released into the atmosphere instantaneously in the form of carbon dioxide.

industrialisation began. The organic matter in soils represents a larger pool of carbon (1600 GtC), much of it in peats or in forest or wetland soils (see table 3.1). Enormous quantities of carbon are locked up in carbonate minerals. Otherwise the largest pool of carbon is in the oceans, an estimated 1000 GtC in the surface layer and 38,000 GtC in deeper waters.

2.12   The natural carbon cycle operates on different time-scales. Over years and decades, respiration by animals and plants and the natural burning and decay of vegetation release carbon dioxide into the atmosphere, while growth of vegetation removes it. The residence time of carbon dioxide dissolved in the surface layer of the oceans and taken up by living organisms can also be short. Carbon may remain in soils for a century, and in peat deposits for millennia. Over tens of millions of years, the dead remains of organisms which have taken up carbon are buried in accumulating sediments, mostly in the oceans; carbonate rocks are formed; and the carbon they contain is eventually released by erosion.

2.13   Over the last 250 years the mining and burning of fossil fuels has removed 260 GtC from the slow part of the natural cycle and transferred it rapidly to the atmosphere.[14] Carbon has not been removed from the atmosphere at a correspondingly rapid rate because the natural pools, or *sinks,* have not been able to absorb it in such quantities over such a relatively short period.

The oceans are estimated to have absorbed 140 GtC;[15] but terrestrial ecosystems have been the source of a further 50 GtC, mainly as a result of forest clearance and other changes in land use. The net addition since 1750 to the amount of carbon dioxide in the atmosphere is therefore estimated to have been 170 GtC.[16]

NATURAL VARIATIONS

2.14   Figure 2-V shows variations in the carbon cycle that have occurred naturally over the last 400,000 years (in black) and how these related to changes in temperature (in red); box 2A describes the nature of the evidence, which comes from the Greenland and Antarctic ice sheets. During relatively warm periods (similar to the climate over the last 10,000 years) the concentration of carbon dioxide in the atmosphere was, as in the pre-industrial period, about 270-280 ppmv; during the coldest parts of glacial periods it was significantly lower, about 180-190 ppmv.

Figure 2-V

Carbon dioxide concentration and temperature: evidence from ice cores

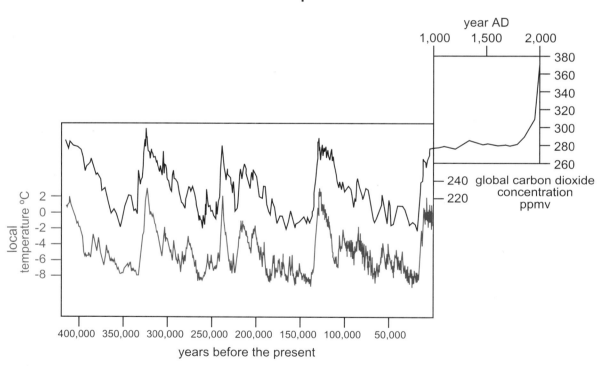

2.15   The shifts between these two concentrations reflect changes in the carbon pools shown in figure 2-IV. The oceans and terrestrial ecosystems can act either as net sources of carbon or net sinks. During periods when the Earth is cooling, cold water upwelling in the equatorial oceans absorbs carbon dioxide from the atmosphere; its concentration in the atmosphere therefore falls. During periods when the Earth is heating up, the reverse effect occurs: the equatorial oceans become a net source of carbon and the concentration in the atmosphere increases. During these cycles of cooling and warming, the amounts of carbon stored in terrestrial ecosystems also increase and decrease, but there is no consensus as yet on when terrestrial ecosystems act as a sink and when as a source (see appendix D, D.26-D.29).

2.16   All the significant changes in temperature shown in figure 2-V were associated with a significant change in the concentration of carbon dioxide in the atmosphere. The precise causation is more difficult to determine. The current view is that small cyclical changes in the solar radiation reaching the Earth are amplified by positive feedback between surface temperature and carbon dioxide concentration (see box 2A).

BOX 2A	EVIDENCE OF NATURAL VARIATIONS

The centres of the Greenland and Antarctic ice sheets are stratified layers providing a continuous record over half a million years. For at least the last 30,000 years annual layers can be identified. The isotopic composition of the ice enables a reliable estimate to be made of the air temperature in that area at the time when precipitation caused the ice to form. Gas bubbles within the ice are thought to provide a reliable record of the concentration of carbon dioxide in the global atmosphere shortly after the ice formed.

Figure 2-V shows the record in cores taken from the Vostok ice sheet in Antarctica of carbon dioxide concentration (in black) and temperature (in red) over the last 400,000 years.[17] The inset shows the concentration of carbon dioxide in the global atmosphere over the last 1,000 years; it is based on analysis of gas bubbles in stratified layers in glaciers, and for more recent years on direct measurements.

Changes in the carbon dioxide concentration in the atmosphere have been closely correlated with changes in temperature. Does a rise in temperature cause carbon dioxide to be released from the oceans, thus increasing the concentration in the atmosphere, or does an increased concentration of carbon dioxide cause temperature to rise? It is known that both processes occur. Equally, it is known that warm tropical oceans release carbon dioxide, whilst cold, polar oceans absorb carbon dioxide. The correlation shown in figure 2-V is probably forced ultimately by changes in the distribution of the solar radiation received, especially by the polar regions, caused by cyclical changes in the Earth's orbit. If changes in solar radiation raise the temperature of the Earth's surface, there is a net release of carbon dioxide from the oceans, the concentration in the atmosphere increases, and further warming occurs because of the greenhouse effect; that in turn releases more carbon dioxide, and so on in a positive feedback. The reverse process occurs if changes in solar radiation result in a cooling of the Earth's surface. Complicating factors include the expansion and contraction of ice sheets (which absorb less solar radiation) and the factors governing the rate at which carbon moves into and out of the deep oceans (3.12, 3.24).

2.17   The present concentration of carbon dioxide in the atmosphere, about 370 ppmv,[18] is well outside the range recorded over the last half million years. To find anything comparable means going back 3 million years to the Pliocene period. The concentration is thought to have been higher than now (around 500 ppmv, double the pre-industrial level) in the Eocene period, between 35 and 57 million years ago. Modelling suggests that concentrations of 1,000 ppmv were last present some 70 million years ago, in the Late Cretaceous period, towards the end of the age of the dinosaurs.[19] At that time, global mean surface temperature is thought to have been some 6°C higher than today.

2.18   The present concentration of carbon dioxide in the atmosphere is bound to increase further because emissions are continuing to rise, and because carbon dioxide remains in the atmosphere for 50-200 years.[20] As we show below, models indicate that that this change in concentration will lead to significant changes in climate. There is no precedent in recent geological history to help us understand precisely what consequences will follow. Nor can we use analogies from the more distant past to show what changes in climate will result, for two reasons. Many other conditions, such as the strength of the sun and the positions of the continents, were radically different at that time; and the speed at which the carbon dioxide concentration is changing appears to be unparalleled in geological history.

POSSIBLE SCENARIOS

2.19   Assessing the seriousness of the challenge posed by climate change involves several stages. First, projections have to be made of the amounts of greenhouse gases that will be emitted into the atmosphere in future. For carbon dioxide those projections have to take into account, not only emissions from burning fossil fuels, but also any other increased amounts entering the atmosphere as a result of human activities (for example forest clearance). To determine what effects emissions will have on the concentrations in the atmosphere, estimates have to be made of the amounts that will be removed by the global carbon cycle and other natural chemical cycles. Next, the likely consequences for the climate have to be predicted. Finally, the impacts of the changing climate have to be assessed. Each stage uses mathematical models. Predicting changes in climate involves constructing and running complex models, requiring use of the largest and fastest computers, in order to represent the behaviour of the atmosphere, oceans and land surface and the relevant interactions between them.

2.20   Some of the main scenarios for future emissions used by IPCC are described in box 2B. Figure 2-VI shows some of those included in its Second Assessment in 1995. Scenario IS92a (the black line in figure 2-VI) was regarded as 'a reasonable central case projection for global emissions';[21] it assumes there will be a considerable improvement globally in the efficiency of energy use and a very big increase in the amounts of energy obtained from sources other than fossil fuels,[22] but that carbon dioxide emissions will nevertheless increase rapidly. On this scenario, the carbon dioxide concentration in the atmosphere in 2100 would be more than 700 ppmv, roughly double the present level and more than two and a half times the pre-industrial concentration. Models run by the Hadley Centre for Climate Prediction and Research (part of the Meteorological Office) indicate that the outcome by 2100 would be a global mean surface temperature $4.3°C$ above the pre-industrial level.[23]

2.21   Even if emissions from burning of fossil fuels had simply continued at the 1990 level, the concentration of carbon dioxide in the atmosphere would have increased to 500 ppmv by 2100,[24] with further increases thereafter. All the scenarios described in box 2B assume that the continuing growth in emissions cannot immediately be halted and they will continue rising for some years. The other scenarios in figure 2-VI were included in IPCC's 1995 assessment to show how hypothetical reductions in emissions might eventually stabilise the carbon dioxide concentration at 450 ppmv (green), 550 ppmv (blue) or 750 ppmv (red). These stabilisation scenarios provide an important basis for considering what form the world community's response to the problem of climate change should take, the issue we consider in chapter 4. Modelling indicates that the increase in global mean surface temperature by 2100 would be limited to $2.8°C$ under the 750 ppmv scenario and $2.3°C$ under the 550 ppmv scenario. The temperature increases in 2200 would be $3.9°C$ and $2.9°C$ respectively, with only small increases after that date.[25] The three solid lines in figure 2-VI assumed adjustment would begin in the mid-1990s. The relevant scenarios now therefore are the broken lines, which show adjustment beginning from later dates and emissions dropping more quickly.

2.22   In its Third Assessment IPCC is examining a range of scenarios for emissions up to 2100, based on alternative storylines for the world economy, population growth, development and application of technology, and social and political behaviour. The graphs in figure 2-VII show four scenarios for carbon dioxide emissions from burning fossil fuels, extended from 2100 to 2300 on the basis described in box 2B. Also shown are the consequences the projected emissions would have for carbon dioxide concentration, according to a simplified model developed at the

Hadley Centre. To highlight the main features of these new scenarios, as extended for the purposes of this report, we call them 'total exhaustion' (that is, exhaustion of the total resource base of fossil fuels), 'partial exhaustion', 'late adjustment' and 'earlier adjustment'.

2.23   In the *total exhaustion scenario* (red in figure 2-VII) there is a continuing large growth in emissions from burning fossil fuels. By 2100 use of fossil fuels on this scale would exhaust conventional economic reserves of such fuels, even at the higher end of the range of estimates of such reserves (appendix D, D.5); by 2200 the total resource base of such fuels would be exhausted on current estimates. By 2100 the concentration of carbon dioxide in the atmosphere would be about three times, and by 2200 about six times, the pre-industrial level. It would peak towards the end of the 23rd century at about 2,100 ppmv. In the *partial exhaustion scenario* (blue) the growth in carbon dioxide emissions is much less rapid (and less rapid than in the previous IS92a scenario); but, because it continues unchecked throughout the 21st century, conventional economic fossil fuel reserves would run out by about 2100 at the middle of the range of estimates. As in the previous scenario, the concentration of carbon dioxide in the atmosphere would peak in the latter part of the 23rd century, but would be about half as high, at more than three and a half times the pre-industrial level.

2.24   The other two scenarios shown in figure 2-VII both envisage that emissions from burning fossil fuels will be on a downward path well before the end of the 21st century, but differ in the timing and nature of the adjustment. In the *late adjustment scenario* (orange) global emissions over the next 50 years are close to those in the total exhaustion scenario, but then decrease rapidly until 2200. By that time the carbon dioxide concentration has become nearly constant at about 800 ppmv, nearly three times the pre-industrial level. In the *earlier adjustment scenario* (green) the rise in carbon dioxide emissions slows much more quickly. At their peak in 2060 global emissions are two-thirds as high again as today. The concentration in the atmosphere rises to nearly double the pre-industrial level by 2100 and then becomes nearly constant at about 600 ppmv.

2.25   The alternative policies implied by the four scenarios exert their effects over a very long period (see the lower two graphs in figure 2-VII; these predictions for temperature and sea level include a contribution from other greenhouse gases, as explained in box 2C). In 2100 the increases in global mean surface temperature above the pre-industrial level range from 4.5°C under the total exhaustion scenario to 3.2°C under the earlier adjustment scenario; taking today as the starting point, the predicted increases are about 1°C smaller. By 2200 the range is much wider, from 7.7°C to 4°C. There are considerable time-lags in the climate system: temperatures continue to rise long after emissions have started to decline, mainly because of the slowness of natural cycles (2.12, 2.13). Thus, although emissions in the late adjustment scenario drop below those in the partial exhaustion scenario by 2100, it is not until 60 years later that the increase in temperature is less; under both adjustment scenarios global mean surface temperature is still rising slowly in 2300, by which time it is about 4.9°C and 4.2°C, respectively, above the pre-industrial level.

2.26   Assessments of climate change have not usually taken into account interactions between the different stages in the calculations (2.19), for example how changes in climate would affect the rate at which greenhouse gases are removed from the atmosphere by natural processes. Recent work at the Hadley Centre has, for the first time, coupled a model of the land and ocean carbon cycle into a full climate model in order to make predictions for the next 100 years. Preliminary results suggest that in the second half of the century the carbon dioxide concentration in the atmosphere will rise more rapidly than in standard climate predictions, partly because some tropical rain forests will be reduced in area and partly because higher

Figure 2-VI
IPCC 1995 stabilisation scenarios

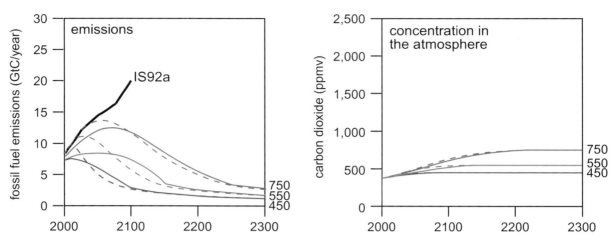

Figure 2-VII
Four scenarios for carbon dioxide emissions and their effects

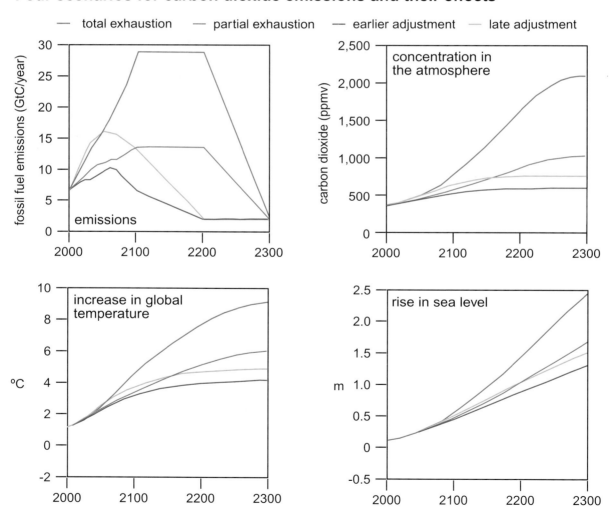

BOX 2B	SCENARIOS FOR EMISSIONS

Emission scenarios are projections of anthropogenic emissions of greenhouse gases based on assumptions about future trends in key determinants such as population, economic growth, energy supplies, technological change, land use and emission control policies. In 1992 IPCC developed a set of six emission scenarios. Emissions of greenhouse gases other than carbon dioxide were taken into account, but it was thought likely that increased concentrations of those gases would be approximately balanced at global level by the cooling effect of an increase in small particles in the atmosphere, also due to human activities. Future quantities of small particles and their cooling effect are now thought to have been over-estimated.

One of IPCC's 1992 scenarios, IS92a, which has been much used subsequently and is shown in figure 2-VI, is usually referred to as 'business-as-usual', although that name is somewhat misleading (2.20). Also shown are three pairs of scenarios constructed by IPCC in 1995, in which carbon dioxide emissions increase initially but then fall rapidly. According to the model used then, these pairs of scenarios would stabilise the concentration of carbon dioxide in the atmosphere at 450, 550 and 750 ppmv, respectively. They have been used extensively in policy discussions. To a first approximation, the eventual concentration in the atmosphere depends on cumulative emissions rather than the exact path followed. These stabilisation scenarios should therefore be viewed as examples of families of curves that would achieve almost the same results.

In 1996 IPCC decided to develop a new set of emission scenarios, using four storylines for world economic, social, political and technological development up to 2100. Figure 2-VII shows four emission scenarios for carbon dioxide representative of these storylines, with simple extensions to 2300 which we have made in order to analyse longer-term implications for climate and sea level.

In the two *adjustment scenarios* (2.24) emissions are assumed to fall by 2200 to a sufficiently low level that the concentration of carbon dioxide in the atmosphere would be roughly stabilised. A main factor taken into account in extending the other two scenarios (2.23) is estimates of fossil fuel resources. In the *exhaustion scenarios* emissions are assumed to continue at a constant rate from 2100 to 2200. In the *total exhaustion scenario* the total fossil fuel resource base (excluding methane hydrates) would have been used up by 2200, even at the upper bound of estimates (appendix D, D.5). In the *partial exhaustion scenario* burning of fossil fuels up to 2200 would have used up half that resource base, on the lower bound of estimates. In both scenarios, for simplicity, emissions fall linearly to a very low level by 2300; if they were reduced directly to this low level at 2200, the effects on temperature and sea level would be little different to those shown in figure 2-VII.

temperatures may increase emissions from soils. Thus the predictions shown in figure 2-VII, made with uncoupled models, may well be under-estimates.

NATURE AND CONSEQUENCES OF CLIMATE CHANGE

2.27   Apart from increases in global mean surface temperature, it is predictions about rises in sea level that can be made with most confidence. As the water in the oceans becomes warmer, it expands. It takes a very long time, however, for warming of the ocean surface to be transmitted in full to the deep ocean: emissions of carbon dioxide over coming decades will produce rises in sea level for many centuries.

2.28   In the 20th century the rise in sea level indicated by Hadley Centre models, about 0.13 m, is within the range of observed changes. Calculations based on IPCC's 1995 scenarios predict a future rise in sea level of about 0.7 m a century (IS92a), 0.4 m (stabilisation at 750 ppmv) or 0.3 m (stabilisation at 550 ppmv). This is broadly consistent with the predictions of the new scenarios shown in figure 2-VII. By 2200 sea level has risen by 0.9-1.4 m. In the 23rd century it

---

BOX 2C   **OTHER GREENHOUSE GASES**

The United Nations Framework Convention on Climate Change defines greenhouse gases as 'those gaseous constituents of the atmosphere, both natural and anthropogenic, that absorb and re-emit infrared radiation'.[26] Carbon dioxide is estimated to have contributed two-thirds of the current enhancement in the greenhouse effect (2.7), but other greenhouse gases directly affected by human activities make a larger contribution to the greenhouse effect in relation to the amounts in which they are present in the atmosphere. Some of them exist naturally but are now present at higher concentrations, such as nitrous oxide and ozone (in the lower part of the atmosphere). Others are synthetic, for example halocarbons such as chlorofluorocarbons (CFCs), hydrofluorocarbons (HFCs) and related bromine compounds.

The other greenhouse gases covered by the Kyoto Protocol (4.8) are methane, nitrous oxide, HFCs, perfluorocarbons and sulphur hexafluoride.

The use of CFCs is being phased out because of another effect they have, which is to deplete the ozone layer in the stratosphere (4.57); unfortunately HFCs, which were introduced as substitutes, are themselves extremely powerful greenhouse gases, with a global warming potential many thousands of times larger than the same mass of carbon dioxide.

The concentration of other greenhouse gases in the atmosphere is sometimes expressed as the concentration of carbon dioxide that would have a similar effect globally (the equivalent quantity varies according to the concentration of carbon dioxide present). Until recently, most climate models and many scenarios have used this approach to provide a single measure of the effects of all greenhouse gases directly affected by human activities.

In the four scenarios shown in figure 2-VII emissions of greenhouse gases other than carbon dioxide increase in accordance with IPCC's storylines up to 2100, and are then assumed to continue at a constant rate until 2300.

---

rises by a further 0.4-1.0 m, even though emissions under all four scenarios are by then falling to a very low level. The new scenarios therefore predict a further rise in sea level between now and 2300 ranging from 1.2 m (earlier adjustment) to 2.3 m (total exhaustion).

2.29   A rise in sea level on that scale would submerge much of the territory of some island nations. It would accelerate the erosion of coasts made of soft rocks and threaten many low-lying hinterlands which are protected at present by coral reefs or mangroves. Deltas such as those of the Nile and the Ganges/Brahmaputra in Bangladesh would be especially at risk. So would coral atolls; the rates at which sea level is predicted to rise may outstrip the growth capacity of corals and they are liable to be damaged by the higher temperature of the sea.[27] The rise in sea level predicted under the IPCC IS92a scenario has been estimated to increase the number of people in the world affected by coastal flooding from 13 million each year to 94 million each year by the 2080s, unless there were to be large-scale migration away from threatened areas. Four-fifths of the people affected would be in south and south-east Asia.[28]

2.30   One possibility frequently discussed is that over several hundred years sea level might rise by an additional 5-8 m because of the collapse of the West Antarctic ice sheet. This ice sheet is grounded on islands slightly below sea level and it has been suggested that it may become unstable as a result of increases in temperatures and sea level. The balance of opinion appears to be against that occurring, but it remains a possibility.[29] If it occurred, the rapidity and extent of the rise in sea level would indeed be catastrophic.

2.31   Climate models show the average surface temperature on land increasing half as fast again as the global mean, and twice as fast in northern high latitudes.[30] Thus, by 2100, an increase in the pre-industrial global mean surface temperature ranging from 2.3°C (550 ppmv stabilisation scenario) to 4.5°C (total exhaustion scenario) implies an increase on land in northern high latitudes of the order of 4-9°C. For precipitation, most models predict increases globally, but especially in winter in high latitudes. They also predict more frequent and intense floods and droughts, because the hydrological cycle will become more intense.

2.32   Beyond these very broad statements, it is difficult to make confident predictions about the changes in regional climates, or about the occurrence of extreme events such as storms. Most impacts of climate change, apart from sea level rise, will be dependent on such local detail. The difficulties of prediction stem partly from current limitations in understanding, partly from limits on computational power, and partly from the inherent variability of weather and climate. There is less confidence as the region of interest becomes smaller and the time period becomes shorter. Precipitation is more difficult to predict than temperature. Despite the problems of making predictions for relatively small areas, attempts have been made to assess the likely impacts on the UK, and the conclusions are summarised in box 2D.

2.33   A change in the average surface temperature in northern high latitudes which would be of the order of 9°C by 2100 at the upper end of the range is more dramatic than it may look at first sight. It is comparable with the temperature difference on the northern continents between the coldest part of the last glacial period, 18,000 years ago, and the beginning of the interglacial period, 10,000 years ago. That historic change in temperature, which was associated with enormous changes in the environment, took place over a long period. The temperature changes indicated by the emission scenarios are of a similar magnitude but take place at ten to fifty times the speed. Recent studies suggest that smaller changes in climate have sometimes occurred rapidly, over centuries or decades. But this combination of magnitude and rate of change would exceed anything species and ecosystems have experienced in the last half million years.

2.34   There are also uncertainties about whether abrupt changes in climate might occur. For example some models predict that the North Atlantic ocean circulation system, which transports heat from the sub-tropics towards Europe, might shut down. The result would be that western Europe would not warm up so much, and might even become cooler than now. Abrupt changes are typical of non-linear systems, and climate models may not be very accurate in predicting them.

2.35   Despite the uncertainties about effects at regional level, an attempt has been made to assess the effects the IS92a emission scenario shown in figure 2-VI would have on agriculture and natural ecosystems.[35] The change in climate and the higher concentration of carbon dioxide might increase cereal yields at high and mid latitudes. On the other hand yields would be reduced in Africa, the Middle East and India. There could be a similar disparity in the case of natural ecosystems: there might be considerable additional forest growth in North America, northern Asia and China, but a large-scale die-back of tropical forests and increasing desertification, especially in South America and southern Africa. Other nations and communities will face changes in the environment that will force them to make drastic alterations in their ways of life and in land use and other practices. In some parts of the world millions of people might become environmental refugees, with widespread suffering, economic disruption, and consequent social and political instability.

BOX 2D IMPACTS OF CLIMATE CHANGE ON THE UK

Current global climate models cannot reliably predict changes in the climate of the UK or any other individual country.

One change that can be predicted with confidence, because it will be worldwide, is the rise in sea level. Rises of the magnitude shown in figure 2-VII will have a significant effect on coastal areas of the UK. Erosion will become more severe, especially on the long stretches of the south and east coasts composed of chalk, clay and other soft rocks. On the east coast sea level is already rising because of slow sinking of the Earth's crust. More than half the grade 1 agricultural land in the UK lies beneath the 5 m contour, and much of it lies behind vulnerable eastern coasts. Areas closest to the sea may become contaminated with salt through underground intrusion of sea water; unless such land is protected, its productivity will decrease drastically.[31] Major cities, notably London, lie on east coast estuaries and are already at risk of being flooded by tidal surges. A combination of new estuarine and coastal defences, including tidal barriers, and managed retreat (abandoning some land to the sea) is likely to be necessary.

Assessments of other effects must be regarded, in general, as illustrative scenarios.[32] On the assumption that the rate of warming in the UK will be similar to the global rate, a medium to high projection of climate change implies that by the 2080s nearly every year will be warmer than 1997, which was the third warmest year ever recorded in the UK and 1.1°C warmer than the average between 1961 and 1990.

Increased frequency of climate extremes, such as droughts and floods, would have some of the most noticeable impacts. Summer rainfall 50% below the current average is likely to occur once a decade, as against once a century under the present climate.[33] If, as some models suggest, very heavy precipitation becomes more frequent, flash floods would become more prevalent, with an increased threat to towns and villages built on flood plains.

Predictions about what will happen in different parts of the UK are subject to even greater uncertainty. A study for Scotland has suggested that rainfall and severe gales would increase, with an increased risk of flooding.[34] One scenario suggests that the south east of England could experience the greatest warming and significantly drier summers. If this were to happen, water supplies would come under stress, not least because lower summer rainfall would increase the demand for farm irrigation.

Warming would tend to increase agricultural and forestry yields, but also favour some pests and diseases. Changes in temperature and rainfall would alter the distribution of wild species; a 1°C rise in average temperature displaces the limits of tolerance of a species 300 km northwards, or 150 m vertically. There would be losses and gains: the species lost would be likely to include arctic-alpine plants and birds that maintain small populations on the highest hills, while the gains would be especially in the south east (assuming suitable habitats exist). An increased frequency of climate extremes would be significant for plant and animal species, which may survive one season, but not a sequence of extreme events. In addition to the damage to coastal nature reserves from the rise in sea level, some small inland nature reserves might cease to provide habitats for the species for which they were created.

Although the speculative dimension of scenarios makes planning difficult, the potential impact of climate change needs to be taken into account in long-term strategies for land use planning, water resource management, coastal and flood defences, agriculture, forestry, countryside recreation and nature conservation.

FACING THE ISSUES

2.36 We received a few submissions,[36] including one from a major oil company, arguing that the scientific evidence about climate change[37] is too uncertain to provide an adequate basis for changes in policies. By signing and ratifying the United Nations Framework Convention on Climate Change (UNFCCC), governments have signalled their rejection of such views (4.5).

There is a broad consensus among leading climate scientists that emissions from human activities are enhancing the natural greenhouse effect, that this is already having a discernible effect on climate, and that the ultimate effect will be much larger. Predictions of changes in global mean surface temperature, and in sea level, can be made with some confidence. Considerable uncertainties remain about the nature and extent of other effects, but that is an inescapable feature of environmental science.[38] By the time the effects of human activities on the global climate are clear and unambiguous it would be too late to take preventive measures. There is a very strong likelihood that the overall impact will be seriously damaging. There is also the possibility that abrupt changes in the climate system might be triggered and have even more dramatic impacts.

2.37   Countering the threat of climate change means controlling the combined effect from increases in the concentrations of all greenhouse gases. Although carbon dioxide is the most important greenhouse gas in terms of human impact on the atmosphere, increases since industrialisation in the concentrations of other greenhouse gases are currently equivalent in effect to a further increase of 50 ppmv in the concentration of carbon dioxide (see box 2C). Moreover the exploration of alternative scenarios has to take into account further increases that may occur in emissions of those gases. The four new scenarios for carbon dioxide emissions shown in figure 2-VII assume emissions of other gases will also increase. In terms of predicted effects therefore IPCC's 1995 scenario for stabilisation at 750 ppmv of carbon dioxide shown in figure 2-VI (based on the view that there would not be any further net addition to the greenhouse effect from other gases) is broadly equivalent to the earlier adjustment scenario shown in figure 2-VII, which eventually results in a nearly constant carbon dioxide concentration of about 600 ppmv. In terms of temperature, both eventually achieve equilibrium at a global mean surface temperature about 4 $^{\circ}$C above the pre-industrial level.[39] Similarly, because it did not include any addition from other greenhouse gases, IPCC's 1995 scenario for stabilisation at 550 ppmv is equivalent, in terms of current modelling, to a scenario that would eventually result in a nearly constant carbon dioxide concentration of 450-500 ppmv. Both eventually produce a global mean surface temperature about 3 $^{\circ}$C above the pre-industrial level.

2.38   In this report we address the environmental impact of energy use and concentrate on carbon dioxide. Not only has it made the greatest contribution to the current enhancement of the greenhouse effect, it is by far the most important greenhouse gas in the long run because of the large, and increasing amounts being emitted, and because it is chemically stable and remains in the atmosphere for a long time. However, measures to control emissions of all greenhouse gases are also of great importance, and UNFCCC makes provision for that. Also very important are measures to limit carbon dioxide emissions that result from changes in land use rather than burning of fossil fuels, an aspect to which we return in later chapters.

2.39   Nothing the world community can now do will prevent climate change occurring on a substantially greater scale than has happened already. But measures to limit the increase in the carbon dioxide concentration in the atmosphere could bring major benefits. In addition to any benefits from reducing the concentration eventually reached, such measures could have major effects in spreading changes over longer periods. Under the 750 ppmv scenario, for example, an increase of 2 $^{\circ}$C in the present global mean surface temperature would be deferred for 50 years (from the 2050s to the 2100s), and by 100 years under the 550 ppmv scenario. A rise in sea level of 0.4 m would be deferred from the 2080s by about 25 years under the 750 ppmv scenario and by 40 years under the 550 ppmv scenario. A slowing in the rate of change would be a major benefit because it would reduce the urgency and magnitude of the adaptations human communities will have to make and increase the possibility that wildlife communities can adapt.

In the 2080s the number of people it is estimated would be affected each year by coastal flooding (2.29) would be reduced from 94 million (under IS92a) to 34 million (750 ppmv) or 19 million (550 ppmv). Although the 750 ppmv scenario brings little benefit in terms of the number of people who would be affected by water shortages in the 2080s, under the 550 ppmv scenario the number might be reduced from 3 billion to 1 billion.[40]

2.40   Greenhouse warming has the potential to cause very serious environmental damage and social upheaval. It appears to us reasonable that governments should take action to slow the rate of change and limit the concentration of carbon dioxide in the atmosphere to levels well below those that would result if past trends continue.

2.41   UNFCCC provides a mechanism for global action. In the next chapter we review the full range of possible measures to limit the concentration of carbon dioxide in the atmosphere and make an assessment of their practical potential. In chapter 4 we consider what kind of global response is appropriate to the scale and nature of the challenge, how far international action to counter climate change needs to go beyond what has already been agreed, and how such an agreement might be achieved. We consider what position the UK should adopt in international negotiations. Then, in part II of our report, we consider the implications for the UK's own policies as they affect future emissions of carbon dioxide from the burning of fossil fuels.

The concentration of carbon dioxide in the atmosphere is already higher than for possibly 3 million years. This is having a discernible effect on climate. The prospect is of much larger increases in carbon dioxide concentration, temperatures and sea level, and the impacts would be seriously damaging. Limiting the amount of carbon dioxide in the atmosphere would have a worthwhile effect in slowing down that process

Chapter 3

POSSIBLE PREVENTIVE MEASURES

What actions can the world community take to limit the increase in the amount of carbon dioxide in the atmosphere?

3.1   In chapter 2 we explored the possible consequences of the enhancement in the greenhouse effect brought about by the increased concentration of greenhouse gases in the atmosphere. We reached the conclusion that governments should take action to prevent the concentration of carbon dioxide rising to the levels that will be reached if emissions from burning fossil fuels continue to increase, or even continue for the next 100 years at their present rate. In this chapter we identify and discuss different types of measure that could be taken to achieve that result.

3.2   Although the main focus for debate has been reducing the amounts of carbon dioxide emitted as a result of burning fossil fuels, there has also been considerable interest in other approaches that could in theory be used. We look first at three approaches which seek to solve the problem by managing other aspects of the global carbon cycle, and involve respectively:

> preventing the carbon dioxide produced when fossil fuels are burnt from reaching the atmosphere (3.4-3.14)

> increasing the amounts of carbon dioxide removed from the atmosphere by growing vegetation (3.15-3.23)

> increasing the rate at which carbon dioxide is taken up by the surface layer of the oceans and transferred to the deep ocean (3.24-3.26).

3.3   We then look at the scope for responding to the problem by changing the ways in which the world obtains and uses energy. Changes that would reduce carbon dioxide emissions can be categorised under three headings:

> reductions in the use of energy (3.28-3.34)

> greater efficiency in the use of fossil fuels (3.35-3.43)

> substitution of other energy sources for fossil fuels (3.44-3.52).

The challenge is so huge that an effective response to the threat of climate change will certainly require different types of measure to be used simultaneously and on a very large scale.

MANAGING ASPECTS OF THE CARBON CYCLE

PREVENTING CARBON DIOXIDE FROM REACHING THE ATMOSPHERE

3.4   The traditional 'end-of-pipe' solution to a pollution problem is to fit equipment to a chimney or outlet and remove the polluting substance at that point so that it can be disposed of in some other way.[1] It is technically possible to do this with the carbon dioxide produced when fossil fuels are burnt. It would then have to be disposed of as a waste under conditions which ensure that it will not reach the atmosphere. Possible additional uses for carbon dioxide in the chemical and food industries are on a small scale relative to the quantities that are being produced, and in any case would not prevent it from entering the atmosphere eventually.

3.5   The carbon dioxide recovered could be disposed of by injecting it into deep geological strata, which naturally contain enormous quantities of carbon (figure 2-III). The most suitable geological settings are depleted oil and gas fields, deep underground formations containing saline water, or coal formations which are too deep to mine.[2] The pore spaces in such strata are large enough to contain a significant fraction of the carbon dioxide produced globally by burning fossil fuels for many decades to come. The oil industry has practical experience of injecting carbon dioxide in two contexts: as a technique to extract a higher proportion of the oil in a field and, more recently, to dispose of carbon dioxide after its removal as a natural constituent of gas from certain fields (appendix D, box D).

3.6   Technologies for recovering carbon dioxide are well developed, and could be incorporated in new combustion plants or retro-fitted to existing plants. Two approaches are available:

> capturing carbon dioxide from the mixture of flue gases leaving the plant, by applying technologies developed to remove it from natural gas (appendix D, D.15-D.18);

> operating the combustion process with oxygen rather than air so as to produce a flue gas which is up to 95% carbon dioxide. Some of the carbon dioxide has to be recycled in order to moderate the boiler temperature.[3]

Calculations have shown that the second approach may be among the least energy-intensive processes for recovering carbon dioxide.[4]

3.7   The loss of efficiency in generating electricity has to be taken into account alongside the costs of installation and operation. Using the first approach is estimated to increase the cost of generating electricity by between 51% and 66% for gas-fired plant and between 20% and 86% for coal-fired plant; and to give costs for emissions avoided of £34-35/tonne carbon and £18-70/tonne carbon, respectively. The second approach (in which the cost of capturing carbon dioxide is replaced by the cost of separating oxygen from air) is estimated to increase the cost of electricity generation by 85% for gas-fired plant and 27% for coal-fired plant; and to give costs for emissions avoided of £13-57/tonne carbon.[5]

3.8   These technologies are suitable only for very large installations. To achieve a comparable result for dispersed energy uses in transport or the home, it would be necessary to decarbonise fossil fuels at a central point and distribute energy in the form of hydrogen. That would involve large energy losses. The possibility of using hydrogen as an energy carrier is discussed later in this report (8.61).

3.9   The carbon dioxide recovered would be transported to the disposal site by pipeline in liquid or supercritical[6] form. The estimates quoted above do not include the cost of that, or of injection, but these would be small by comparison: £1.6-2.3/tonne carbon/100 km for transport by pipeline, and £0.8/tonne carbon or £1.4/tonne carbon for injection into, respectively, saline aquifers and depleted gas fields.[7] Further information about disposal into deep underground strata is in appendix D (D.19-D.25).

3.10   On the assumption that the carbon dioxide would be in supercritical form, provisional estimates are that the total capacity of suitable geological strata in Europe is about 200 gigatonnes of carbon (GtC), equivalent at the present rate to 770 years of emissions from European power stations. Of that capacity, 89% is in the form of saline aquifers in the territorial waters of the UK and Norway. In some aquifers horizontal movement of the injected carbon dioxide would be prevented by natural seals. Simulations over 1,000 years suggest that in other aquifers the carbon dioxide would migrate less than 4 km before dissolving completely in the groundwater, with some becoming permanently fixed through reactions with host minerals;[8] monitoring of injection already taking place taking place under the North Sea supports that conclusion.[9]

3.11   The engineering of a system for carbon dioxide disposal would have to be of a high standard to limit the risk of any large-scale leak that would pose a threat to human or animal life, for example through fracture of a pipeline. If injection was into deep underground strata on land, there would be a risk, even if it could be shown to be infinitesimally small, that slow seepage could lead to a build-up of carbon dioxide in a confined space, for example beneath housing. The gain in safety therefore points towards use of geological strata beneath the seabed, some of which in the North Sea are more than 200 km from shore. These also have a far greater capacity.

3.12   An alternative way of trying to isolate the recovered carbon dioxide from the atmosphere would be to dispose of it in the deep oceans. These represent a very large natural pool of carbon (see figure 2-III), and the intention would be to bypass the constraints which limit the rate at which carbon moves into this pool under natural conditions (3.24). Rather than using pipes to inject carbon dioxide at great depths, it has been suggested that a dense enough plume of carbon dioxide-enriched seawater created at shallow depth would sink to much greater depth if the slope of the seabed is favourable and the water column is not highly stratified. Alternatively, carbon dioxide might be injected into the ocean at shallow depth at locations where natural currents will carry it to greater depth; a research project is being funded by the US, Japanese and Norwegian governments.[10] Information is needed about the possibility of environmental damage, especially the effects on marine organisms from increased carbon dioxide concentrations and increased acidity. In any event, there is considerable uncertainty whether disposal into the oceans would achieve the aim of long-term isolation, in that carbon dioxide disposed of into seawater at a depth of 3,000 m might be returned to the atmosphere within the relatively short time of 250 to 550 years.[11]

3.13   It is open to interpretation whether disposal of carbon dioxide into the ocean or under the sea-bed would be permissible under current international law. Greenpeace contends[12] that either practice would violate the London Convention on the prevention of marine pollution by dumping of wastes and other matter.[13]

3.14   In our view, injection of recovered carbon dioxide into oil and gas fields (possibly to enhance oil recovery) or into saline aquifers beneath the sea-bed would be more effective and easier to monitor, and would have less environmental impact, than disposing of it in the deep oceans.

INCREASING TAKE UP OF CARBON BY VEGETATION

3.15   Another aspect of the global carbon cycle open to further human intervention is the exchange of carbon between the atmosphere and terrestrial ecosystems (figure 2-III). The limits on carbon dioxide emissions imposed under the United Nations Framework Convention on Climate Change include a country's net emissions from this source. Most of the carbon in terrestrial ecosystems is in forests, mainly in the soils in forests. Most of the remainder is in wetland soils, including peats. Table 3.1 shows how carbon is distributed between forests in different latitudes, and between the vegetation and the soils in those forests.

3.16   Most of the movement of carbon from the atmosphere into forests occurs when trees are growing to maturity (appendix D, D.26-D.27). When vegetation dies some of the carbon it contains passes into the soil, and the rest is released to the atmosphere in the form of carbon dioxide. Once the trees in a forest have reached maturity it will no longer remove a substantial net amount of carbon from the atmosphere, but nor should it become a net source. When trees die and rot, or are burnt, there should not be any net emission of carbon dioxide into the atmosphere in the medium term if new trees grow up in their place, either naturally or through human intervention. If, on the other hand, that does not happen, and the soil is cultivated or otherwise disturbed, not only will the carbon formerly contained in the trees enter the atmosphere, but a substantial part of the carbon in the soil may be released into the atmosphere in the form of carbon dioxide.

3.17   Deforestation and changes in land use have contributed to the enhancement of the greenhouse effect that has already occurred (2.7). Rapid deforestation is taking place now in many developing countries. Between 1990 and 1995 the area of forest in developed countries increased by 9 million hectares but the forest area in developing countries was reduced by about 65 million hectares. The drivers have been conversion to cultivation to support increasing human populations and unsustainable commercial logging.[14] Any consideration of the potential for increasing the take-up of carbon by vegetation as a way of countering climate change has to take into account the economic and social conditions that are currently shaping land management.

3.18   To have any significant effect on the amount of carbon taken up globally by vegetation it would be necessary to plant very large areas with trees or allow very large deforested areas to regenerate through natural succession. As it is only trees growing to maturity which take up carbon dioxide rapidly, the impact of a programme of tree-planting would depend on the length of time for which it could be maintained. To remove the amount of carbon projected to be emitted globally over the next half century from burning fossil fuels would require afforestation of an area as big as Europe from the Atlantic to the Urals.[15] The Intergovernmental Panel on Climate Change (IPCC) estimated in 1995 that a global programme up to 2050 consisting of reduced deforestation, enhanced natural regeneration in tropical countries and worldwide afforestation could take up 60-87 GtC,[16] equivalent to 12-15% of projected emissions from burning fossil fuels over that period.[17]

3.19   IPCC estimated the cost of the programme it considered as £8-13 per tonne of carbon removed from the atmosphere, depending on the region, with no discount rate applied.[18] A study of the Mexican state of Chiapas has produced much higher estimates: £30/tonne carbon with a 5% discount rate and £40/tonne carbon with a 10% discount rate.[19] Large programmes of afforestation or reforestation in themselves need careful appraisal and extensive public consultation if severe political, social and environmental problems are to be avoided. Monoculture plantations, for instance, reduce biodiversity. And afforestation in the dry tropics can lower the water tables and river flows on which people depend.

Table 3.1

Carbon pool in forests and forest soils (1987-1990)[20]

	total carbon in forests and forest soils		proportion of carbon in soils
	GtC	%	%
boreal forest (high latitudes)	559	30.0	84
temperate forest (mid latitudes)	159	8.5	63
tropical forest (low latitudes)	1,146	61.5	50
all forests	1,864	100.0	61
all terrestrial ecosystems	2,200		73

3.20   A crucial consideration is the impact that the higher concentration of carbon dioxide in the atmosphere and changes in climate will in themselves have on the take-up of carbon dioxide by vegetation. There is considerable uncertainty about that (appendix D, D.28), and the effects may vary between regions. In some regions of the world climate change may stimulate forest growth. Because of a large reduction in the area covered by tropical rain forest the overall effect is likely to be a reduction in the capacity of terrestrial ecosystems to take up and store carbon (2.35). The predictions of one computer model[21] which simulates the global distribution of natural vegetation as it responds to changing atmospheric carbon dioxide concentrations suggest that terrestrial ecosystems can be expected to remove 2-3 GtC a year from the atmosphere over the next half century; but thereafter increasing aridity and dieback of vegetation may convert them into a net source of some 2 GtC a year.[22]

3.21   Preserving and expanding the existing carbon storage capacity of terrestrial ecosystems can contribute to limiting the concentration of carbon dioxide in the atmosphere. Achieving that aim globally would involve a reversal of current trends, and in the long term climate change may seriously constrain the extent to which it can be achieved. In some countries which are largely forested, for example Finland,[23] forest management could largely offset emissions from burning fossil fuels. It would be unrealistic however to base policies on the assumption that this could happen globally.

3.22   The greater part of the carbon in terrestrial ecosystems is in soils rather than vegetation. Because most carbon in soils comes from vegetation, there are no measures available to produce direct increases in the amounts of carbon stored there. Because of the very large amounts of carbon dioxide and methane that could be released from soils however, the effects on soil carbon are a very important consideration in assessing the effects of land management practices on carbon dioxide emissions.

3.23   Rather than attempt to offset carbon dioxide emissions from fossil fuels by planting trees, a more robust policy may be to grow trees, shrubs or fast growing grasses in managed systems to provide a substitute for fossil fuels. If the vegetation harvested to supply energy is always replaced by new growth, the quantity of carbon dioxide taken up from the atmosphere will almost compensate for the quantity emitted when the preceding crop is burnt, and this closed cycle can continue indefinitely (3.47).

INCREASING TAKE UP OF CARBON BY THE OCEAN SURFACE

3.24   Through the exchanges between the atmosphere and the oceans in the global carbon cycle (see figure 2-III) there is a net movement of carbon into the oceans, which have absorbed about 40% of the extra carbon dioxide emitted since industrialisation began (2.13). Under natural conditions the rate at which carbon moves into this pool is determined by the solubility of carbon dioxide in the surface layer of the oceans, the amount of carbon contributed by biological productivity in the surface layer, and the rate of mixing between the surface layer and deep oceanic water. Increasing the biological productivity of the surface layer can increase the amount of carbon transferred to the deep oceans and, as a result, increase the amount of carbon dioxide absorbed by the ocean surface (appendix D, D.6-D.12). For one-fifth of the oceans, in particular the Southern Ocean, the limiting factor in biological productivity is thought to be the amount of iron available. Elsewhere the limiting factor is thought to be the availability of nitrogen.

3.25   Experiments have confirmed that sprinkling iron on the ocean surface can increase productivity and the transfer of carbon from the surface layer to greater depth,[24] although it has yet to be demonstrated that the technique can be scaled up and successfully repeated. It is estimated however that, in order to reduce the atmospheric concentration of carbon dioxide by 50 parts per million by volume (ppmv), very large quantities of iron would have to be sprinkled continuously on a quarter of the world's ocean surface.[25] This could be very expensive: estimates in two studies range from £30 to £120 per tonne of carbon removed from the atmosphere.[26]

3.26   Exploitation of the biological resources of the Southern Antarctic Ocean that threatens to impair ecosystem functions is prohibited by the Convention on the Conservation of Antarctic Marine Living Resources.[27] Modelling studies suggest that artificial fertilisation of the oceans could have severe ecological consequences.[28] It is likely to reduce oxygen concentrations significantly in certain zones. As well as reducing biomass and biodiversity, that is likely to increase the amounts of other greenhouse gases such as methane and nitrous oxide released from the oceans, possibly to the point where the exercise becomes self-defeating. Although research into artificial fertilisation of oceans is expanding, particularly in the USA, we concur with IPCC's conclusion that it is not a viable method of increasing carbon uptake from the atmosphere.[29]

CHANGING THE WAYS IN WHICH ENERGY IS OBTAINED AND USED

3.27   The scenarios discussed in chapter 2 indicate the scale of reduction in emissions from burning fossil fuels that would be necessary to stabilise the concentration of carbon dioxide in the atmosphere. To achieve stabilisation at 550 ppmv (about twice the pre-industrial level) global emissions would eventually have to be reduced to about 70% below their present level (see figure 2-VI). Although increased uptake of carbon by vegetation could in principle offset a proportion of the emissions from burning fossil fuels, there is equally the possibility that terrestrial ecosystems may be the source of further net emissions of carbon dioxide in future (3.20, 3.22). Even allowing for the possibility that carbon dioxide produced in large combustion plants might be recovered and disposed of to prevent it reaching the atmosphere, limiting the concentration of carbon dioxide in the atmosphere will clearly require more fundamental modifications in the ways the human race obtains and uses energy. We review first the scope for reducing the amounts of energy used, then the possibility of making more efficient use of fossil fuels, and finally the availability of other sources of energy that can be substituted for fossil fuels.

REDUCTIONS IN ENERGY USE

3.28   The rise in carbon dioxide emissions reflects the enormous increase in energy use over the last half century (see figure 1-I). This has been the result partly of the growth in world population and partly of higher standards of living. As human societies become wealthier, an increasing variety and volume of products and services are manufactured and provided, and people travel more.[30] Electrification brings a sharp rise in energy consumption because it enables households to use a wide variety of appliances. With greater affluence, people want higher levels of illumination. They want their homes and workplaces to be warmer in winter and cooler in summer. Many coveted activities and possessions are linked to high levels of energy consumption, for example long-haul air travel and large cars.[31]

3.29   To the extent that the increase in world energy use has been driven by population growth, it could be expected to continue for much of the 21st century, even though the average energy use per person globally has come close to stabilising since the oil crisis of the 1970s (see figure 1-I). Continuing economic growth could also be expected to boost energy use. As economic growth proceeds, it becomes less energy-intensive;[32] the energy intensity of the global economy is falling.[33] IPCC's key 1995 scenario (2.20) assumed that it will continue to decline by 1% a year over the next half century. Nevertheless there continues to be a strongly positive association between economic growth and energy use.

3.30   Countries at an earlier stage of economic development (for example, China and India) still have energy intensities well above the global mean.[34] The hopes of developing countries for attaining living standards and life expectancies that became common in the developed world decades ago seem to depend on very large increases in energy consumption. Some part of the increase may be only apparent, if it involves substituting commercial supplies of energy for local sources not usually recorded in the statistics, such as dung, firewood and charcoal; but that is a declining part of the picture. The 2 billion people who still do not have electricity in their homes, including two-thirds of the rural populations of Africa, Latin America and Asia outside the former Soviet Union,[35] are being deprived of such basic necessities as refrigeration and adequate lighting. Even in wealthy countries there may be significant proportions of the population who are deprived of some of the key benefits energy brings, as illustrated by the concern about inadequate home heating for vulnerable groups in the UK (6.5-6.6).

3.31   Despite the greatly increased global demand for energy it has remained abundant and cheap. This is one of the factors that has made such rapid economic growth possible. Industries which use large amounts of energy have faced pressures to cut costs by using energy and materials more efficiently. For most firms however, and for most individuals in developed countries, the cost of energy represents a very small part of their expenditure. Like any cheap and abundant commodity, it is often used wastefully.

3.32   There are therefore cultural and attitudinal barriers to improvements in energy efficiency; we discuss in chapter 6 what effect these have in the UK. Moreover, increases in the efficiency of energy use do not automatically result in less energy being used. Some of the energy savings which could be obtained by efficiency increases will not be realised because consumers respond by making more use of the relevant service or device. For instance, if houses become better insulated, people may choose to maintain higher temperatures rather than reduce their energy consumption. Car engines have become more efficient, but that did not necessarily lead to reductions in fuel consumption because cars tended to become larger and heavier, with a much wider range of equipment.[36] Another reason why it has been argued that increased efficiency will not lead to less use of energy is that the cash savings made available as a result of increased efficiency will be spent elsewhere in the economy, raising energy demand.[37]

3.33   Nevertheless, there is very great potential for increasing the efficiency of energy use through smarter use of technology, especially in the heating and cooling of buildings and in propelling cars and other vehicles. While some of the benefits from such improvements will be taken in other ways, we do not accept the pessimistic view that they will be ineffectual or self-defeating in reducing energy use. There is also very large scope, as we illustrate below and discuss in chapter 8, for reducing the losses that occur within the energy system. These losses represent the difference between *final consumption* of energy by consumers at the end of supply chains and the considerably larger *consumption of primary energy* at or near the beginning of supply chains. To the extent that such losses within the system can be eliminated by better use of technology, energy use can be reduced without any adverse implications for human wellbeing.

3.34   It would not be realistic to base policies for reducing energy use on exhorting people to forgo the benefits of using energy, nor would it be acceptable to deny them access to essential energy services. Nonetheless, changes in behaviour, within an appropriate social, institutional and economic framework, will be a necessary component of the transition to a more sustainable energy economy. The market prices of energy sources do not necessarily reflect their substantial external effects, in particular the enhancement of the greenhouse effect in the case of fossil fuels. If the prices paid by users can begin to reflect such external costs, that can have a significant effect on their decisions. They will have a greater incentive to use energy more efficiently and to select those sources of energy that cause less environmental damage. We discuss the appropriate use of economic instruments, in a UK context, later in this report (6.149-6.169).

USING FOSSIL FUELS MORE EFFICIENTLY

3.35   Another approach to reducing carbon dioxide emissions is to obtain more energy from fossil fuels in relation to the amounts of carbon dioxide produced. One way of doing that is to use a fossil fuel which has a lower carbon content in relation to its energy content, the other way is to utilise that energy content more efficiently.

3.36   Gas has a lower carbon content in relation to its energy content (14.6 kilograms per gigajoule) than oil (carbon content 18.6 kg/GJ), which in turn contains less carbon than coal (carbon content 24.1 kg/GJ).[38] Supplies of gas have expanded greatly in recent decades, and it is now being used on a rapidly increasing scale globally to generate electricity. Some experts believe that global production of oil will peak between 2010 and 2030, and then decline slowly (appendix D, D.3). Gas reserves are expected to last longer: it has been suggested that global production will not peak until 2090.[39] However it is the fossil fuel with the highest carbon content, coal, which is in the most plentiful supply. Identified global reserves of coal are sufficient for several hundred years at present rates of use. Several major countries, notably China and India, have relatively little oil or gas available in their territories but large reserves of coal.

3.37   In the short and medium term there is scope for making greater use of gas, in preference to other fossil fuels, as a way of reducing carbon dioxide emissions. However even complete substitution of gas in the processes in which coal is used at present would reduce carbon dioxide emissions from those processes by only about 40% (other things being equal), and would not in itself represent a solution to the problem of limiting carbon dioxide emissions. Moreover, in the absence of other major changes in the way the world obtains and uses energy, it would be necessary to return to the use of coal at a later date. Switching from other fossil fuels to gas could nevertheless have a useful part to play in the transition to a new energy economy.

3.38   Improvements in technology have increased the efficiency of fossil fuel generating plants. A new coal-fired generating plant typically has an efficiency of 40% in converting the energy content of the coal to electricity. A new combined cycle gas turbine typically has an efficiency of 52%. Coal can be used as fuel in a combined cycle plant if it is first gasified: plants of that type, which are not yet available commercially, are expected to have a typical efficiency of 42%.[40]

3.39   When fossil fuels are burned to generate electricity or drive internal combustion engines or gas turbines however, the efficiency with which the heat energy they produce can be converted into work is subject to a severe and fundamental physical limitation, as explained in

BOX 3A	EFFICIENCY OF ENERGY CONVERSION

Heat engines

Although the first law of thermodynamics states that energy can be neither created nor destroyed (see the definitions at the beginning of this report), the different forms of energy are not simply interchangeable. Converting heat to work involves using some form of heat engine in which heat enters continuously at a high temperature (T_1) and leaves at a low temperature (T_2). The maximum fraction of the heat entering which can be converted to work is

$$\eta_{max} = 1 - (T_2/T_1) = (T_1 - T_2)/T_1$$

The fraction of the heat not converted to work leaves the engine as *low-grade heat* at the lower temperature. The maximum possible efficiency of conversion of heat to work is sometimes termed the Carnot efficiency. This relationship is a statement of the second law of thermodynamics.

A common form of heat engine is the steam cycle, commonly used to generate electricity from fossil fuels in power stations. Heat from the burning fuel is used to produce high-temperature, high-pressure steam. The steam drives a turbine, producing work, which drives an electricity generating set. The low-grade heat is rejected, usually to cooling water, by condensing the steam to water, which is recycled within the power station and heated back to steam. Internal combustion engines and gas turbines are other types of heat engine.

The *efficiency* of the process is measured as the ratio of useful energy output (as electricity in the case of a power station) to thermal input obtained from releasing chemical energy by burning the fuel.

Combined heat and power plants

Combined heat and power (CHP) plants provide a way to use more of the energy released by burning a fuel. They are designed to produce energy in the two forms of electricity and low-grade heat. The latter is typically used for space heating (in buildings) or drying (in industrial applications). The overall efficiency of a CHP plant is defined as the ratio of electrical plus thermal energy output to fuel energy input.

Heat pumps

A heat pump is the converse of a heat engine. It uses mechanical work to 'pump' heat from a source at low temperature (T_2) to a higher temperature (T_1). The minimum ratio of work input to heat delivered to the higher temperature is given by the Carnot equation set out above. In the case of a heat pump

$$(\text{Work in} / \text{Heat out})_{min} = 1 - (T_2/T_1) = (T_1 - T_2)/T_1$$

The closer these two temperatures are to each other, the less work is required. Thus heat pumps are useful where relatively low grade heat is needed, at temperatures 10-20°C above that of the heat source, usually for space or water heating. In these circumstances the ratio of electrical energy consumed by a heat pump to the useful heat it delivers to a building is typically 1:3.

Heat is drawn in at the lower temperature (T_2) to evaporate a circulating fluid with an appropriately low boiling point. The vapour passes through a compressor which raises its pressure so that it condenses, giving up heat at the higher temperature (T_1). The condensed liquid passes through an expansion valve, back to the lower pressure, cooler part of the cycle. The work input to the compressor represents the work input to the heat pump.

Chemicals which are powerful greenhouse gases and/or which deplete the stratospheric ozone layer - CFCs, HCFCs and HFCs - have been used as the circulating fluid. If the use of heat pumps is to expand, then less environmentally damaging alternatives will have to be deployed.

The possible scale of operation ranges from relatively large devices contributing to heat distribution networks or industrial installations down to domestic refrigerators (in which heat is pumped from inside to the air outside). Some designs of heat pump can be operated in either direction, for example to provide heating in winter and cooling in summer. The heat source (or heat sink, when the device is used in cooling mode) can be a water stream (such as a river, or municipal wastewater), air, groundwater or soil.

Fuel cells

A fuel cell converts chemical energy directly to work (in the form of electrical energy) without using a heat engine. They are not subject to the Carnot efficiency limit.

box 3A. A very substantial proportion of their energy content is commonly wasted as low-grade heat. That is all the more significant for the level of carbon dioxide emissions because the most rapid growth in global demand for energy has been for electricity and mobility (1.3). Transmission and distribution of electricity involves further energy losses.

3.40   Beyond a certain point the efficiency with which the energy content of fossil fuels is utilised cannot be further improved unless the low-grade heat produced is put to use. A *combined heat and power plant* (CHP) achieves this, in that it supplies energy in both forms, heat and work. The overall conversion efficiency of such a plant varies according to the ratio of heat to power in its output, but can be as high as 70-80%.[41]

3.41   CHP plants can be sized to produce the heat and electricity required for a single building, such as an hospital or hotel, or for a manufacturing process. Prototypes have been designed that are small enough for a single house. A large CHP plant serving a number of buildings requires a *heat distribution network*, as well as an electricity distribution network. Scandinavian experience shows that a heat distribution network can extend economically for some tens of kilometres and reach tens of thousands of homes and other premises (box 8A). The heat is usually conveyed by hot water at high pressure. It is supplied to users via heat exchangers which transfer heat from the main circuit to a local medium, for example the water circulated at lower pressure through a building's central heating system.

3.42   There are some alternative technologies which are very efficient in energy terms. Fuel cells provide a method of converting chemical energy to electricity which is not subject to the thermodynamic limitation that applies to heat engines. A hydrogen fuel cell can achieve a conversion efficiency of almost 60% in generating electricity, and can also be used as a CHP plant. We discuss the potential role of fuel cells later in this report (8.62).

3.43   Another technology which is a highly efficient way of using electricity for space and water heating is the *heat pump*. This can pick up heat from a lower temperature source, generally outside a building, and deliver it at a higher temperature inside the building, thus making it possible to harness the abundant quantities of heat available from rivers, streams, wastewater, groundwater, soil and air. For reasons explained in box 3A, a heat pump typically delivers, as useful heat, 2.5 to 4 times the rate of energy it consumes in electrical power. The heat distribution network described in box 8A uses heat pumps as a major source of heat, and they can also be used to supply heat to individual buildings. We discuss later in this report, in a UK context, the need to develop a comprehensive strategy for the supply and use of heat as a vital component in policies for reducing carbon dioxide emissions (8.4-8.16).

SUBSTITUTING OTHER ENERGY SOURCES FOR FOSSIL FUELS

3.44   As well as reducing carbon dioxide emissions, there are other motivations for seeking sources of energy that can provide alternatives to fossil fuels. It was always understood that reserves of fossil fuels are finite. Most countries do not have significant supplies of their own. The price increases and shortages during the oil crisis of the 1970s led many countries to take an active interest in developing more diverse sources of energy. A further motivation has been concern over the effects of other substances emitted when fossil fuels are burned (1.6-1.7). Although programmes to develop alternatives date back half a century, realisation of the threat posed by climate change has given the task much greater impetus.

3.45   The ways in which energy can be obtained without producing carbon dioxide are:

from the sun as heat, or by converting sunlight directly to electricity

from the sun indirectly, by utilising the winds caused by differences in temperature between different parts of the Earth's surface, or the wave energy arising from interaction between winds and oceans, or the water power made available inland as a result of rainfall

from gravitational forces between moon, sun and Earth, by exploiting tidal flows in estuaries or elsewhere in the oceans

from heat in the Earth's core (most easily from aquifers in which the water is at a high temperature)

by splitting atoms (nuclear fission).

3.46   In principle energy could be obtained by fusing hydrogen atoms (nuclear fusion, the process by which the sun obtains energy). Despite extensive research programmes this technology is unlikely to become available in the next half century (7.16).

3.47   There are other ways of obtaining energy which can also be beneficial in limiting the greenhouse effect, even though they give rise to emissions of carbon dioxide. Energy from the sun enables green plants to use carbon dioxide to form organic compounds (the process known as photosynthesis). The chemical bonds in these compounds represent a store of energy. The carbon dioxide which growing plants take up from the atmosphere can compensate for much of the carbon dioxide released into the atmosphere if materials derived from plants are used as a source of energy in place of fossil fuels (7.55). Although energy crops are not carbon-neutral, net emissions from their combustion represent only 5-10% of those from fossil fuels.[42]

3.48   Burning methane obtained from biological material gives rise to emissions of carbon dioxide, but does not add to the greenhouse effect if the material would otherwise have emitted carbon dioxide by decaying aerobically. The benefit is much greater if the material would otherwise have decayed anaerobically, for example in a landfill site, and emitted methane into the atmosphere, because methane is a more powerful greenhouse gas (7.57).

3.49   A rigorous comparison between the implications which different energy sources have for the greenhouse effect involves analysing not simply the processes from which energy is obtained, but whole supply chains. Before any energy source can be exploited, energy has to be used in constructing or manufacturing and installing the necessary equipment. The *energy payback period* is the length of time before the energy obtained from a source exceeds the energy that had to be used in order to exploit it. The costs of constructing an energy installation often provide a broad indication of the energy required to do so. Energy may also be used in mining fuels, in processing them (for example, in enriching uranium) or in transporting them to a generating plant (especially significant for fuels, such as crops, which have a low energy density); in transporting, treating and disposing of any wastes produced; or in decommissioning power stations or other equipment. The extent to which energy use elsewhere in a supply chain gives rise to carbon dioxide emissions depends on the sources from which that energy is obtained. If fossil fuels become progressively less important as an energy source for electricity generation, for example, energy use elsewhere in supply chains will become less important as a contributor to carbon dioxide emissions.

3.50   Comparative analyses of entire life cycles of energy sources, based on current patterns of energy supply, confirm that the carbon dioxide emissions attributable to electricity generation using some key renewable sources are an order of magnitude, sometimes two orders of magnitude, lower than the emissions attributable to electricity generation at a modern fossil fuel plant.[43] The margin of difference is smaller for photovoltaic cells because of the amounts of energy used in their manufacture.[44] The carbon dioxide emissions attributable to electricity generation at a nuclear power station are also far lower than in the case of a modern fossil fuel plant.[45]

3.51   Countries differ in their endowments of renewable energy sources. The UK has less solar power available than many other countries, and much less inland water power than some. On the other hand it has very large resources of wind and wave power, and substantial power available in tides. Countries also differ in the extent to which they are committed to using nuclear power.

3.52   There is general agreement that the large-scale development of alternatives to fossil fuels must be a central part of the response to the challenge of climate change. A key scenario in IPCC's 1995 assessment assumed that the amount of power obtained from 'carbon-emission-free' sources in 2050 will be equivalent to all current energy sources combined (2.20). There are strong disagreements however about whether the emphasis should be on renewable energy sources or on nuclear power. Some have contended that 10% of the world's electricity could be provided from wind power by 2020.[46] What is clear is that providing alternatives to fossil fuels, while at the same time keeping pace with an increasing global demand for energy, will require very large programmes of investment and construction, both in developed and in developing countries. Some of the technologies involved are complex or at an early stage of development. That points to a need to ensure there are adequate programmes of research and development. Many developing countries will also require considerable technical and financial assistance if they are to develop their energy systems in the ways that will cause least damage to the environment.

CONCLUSION

3.53   Climate change is the outcome of processes that operate globally, and can be countered only through concerted international action. This review of possible preventive measures has confirmed that the measures required to limit the concentration of carbon dioxide in the atmosphere will in all probability be taken by national governments. It is unlikely that international agreements will prescribe the detailed form of such measures, as distinct from the results they are required to achieve in reducing emissions. Consideration of their potential and practicability is nevertheless an essential basis for discussing, in chapter 4, how a general international agreement to counter climate change might be reached and the position the UK should adopt in negotiations.

3.54   Any measure for limiting the concentration in the atmosphere of carbon dioxide or any other greenhouse gas will have to be safe, legal under national and international law, cost-effective, and politically and socially acceptable. Of the approaches considered in this chapter, we do not consider that attempting to increase the take-up of carbon dioxide by the ocean surface is worth pursuing (3.24-3.26). Nor would we support disposal of recovered carbon dioxide into the deep oceans (3.12). Given the extent to which the human race has already modified the global carbon cycle over the last two centuries, further interventions in the cycle designed to reverse or halt those effects can be justified only if there are grounds for confidence that they will not in themselves have major, unintended environmental impacts.

3.55   Naive suggestions are often made that climate change can be countered by planting more trees. Managing land use so as to preserve and expand the carbon storage capacity of terrestrial ecosystems is a necessary element in policies to limit the concentration of carbon dioxide in the atmosphere. In practice however there may be significant overall losses globally, in the medium term as a result of social and economic pressures (3.17), and in the long term through some of the effects of climate change (3.20). At best, human management of this pool could never offset the current level of global emissions from burning fossil fuels. And in the event what happens to it may exacerbate the effect of those emissions.

3.56   Recovering carbon dioxide produced when fossil fuels are burnt and disposing of it in deep underground strata has promise. Familiar technologies can be used, and for north-west Europe the strata used would probably be under the sea-bed. There is good reason to believe that carbon dioxide injected into offshore aquifers would remain isolated from the atmosphere and not pose a threat to terrestrial or marine organisms (3.10). Although recovering and disposing of carbon dioxide would add considerably to the cost of generating electricity from fossil fuels, it could still be cheaper than using plant material to generate electricity.[47] Whether disposal of the recovered carbon dioxide under the sea-bed would constitute waste disposal and contravene current international law has been discussed by the parties to the London Convention, and no decision has been taken (3.13). It remains to be seen whether such an approach would be socially acceptable.

3.57   The major limitation of the approach discussed in the previous paragraph is that it is not suitable for small installations or dispersed energy uses. Even if it proves to be socially and legally acceptable therefore it could never be a complete answer to the problem of limiting the concentration of carbon dioxide in the atmosphere. The primary methods for doing so must be more fundamental modifications in the ways the human race obtains and uses energy. The themes introduced in the second half of this chapter are explored in much greater detail in the examination of UK policies in part II of our report. The scope for reducing energy use is discussed in chapter 6, the scope for substituting other energy sources for fossil fuels in chapter 7, and the scope for increasing the overall efficiency of the energy system in chapter 8. In chapter 9 we consider the respective contributions these approaches might make to reducing the UK's carbon dioxide emissions.

The core of a global response to the threat of climate change must be the most effective and reliable forms of action, those which reduce the amounts of carbon dioxide produced by burning fossil fuels. Some contribution might be made by recovering some of that carbon dioxide and disposing of it in underground strata. The more the carbon storage capacity of terrestrial ecosystems can be preserved, and if possible expanded, the less daunting the challenge of reducing carbon dioxide emissions will be

Chapter 4

PROSPECTS FOR AN EFFECTIVE GLOBAL RESPONSE

What has the world community done so far to counter the threat of climate change? What would be an appropriate global strategy? What approach should the UK adopt in international negotiations? What are the implications for its own future emissions of greenhouse gases?

4.1   Human-induced climate change appears to have begun (2.4), it will continue (2.25) and, once in train, it can only be reversed after centuries have elapsed. Unless an effective response is mounted to this challenge, there will be serious, and possibly catastrophic, damage to people and ecosystems (2.27-2.35). In order to reduce both the extent of climate change and the rate at which it will happen (2.39-2.40), the crucial contribution must come from reductions in global emissions of carbon dioxide from the burning of fossil fuels, as chapter 3 showed. It will also be necessary to protect natural sinks by controlling land use changes.

4.2   We now consider the adequacy of the response by the world community to date (4.3-4.9) and what further response is required at global level now and in the coming decades (4.10-4.20). In particular, we consider the role of economic appraisal in determining the optimum level of response (4.21-4.28), what concentration of carbon dioxide ought not to be exceeded (4.29-4.34), the timing of measures to reduce emissions (4.35-4.39) and how the effort should be shared between different nations (4.40-4.54). Finally we discuss the implications for the UK (4.55-4.70), thus paving the way for Part II of this report.

A DECADE OF CLIMATE DIPLOMACY

4.3   There has now been more than a decade of climate diplomacy involving nearly all the world's nations. The two major achievements have been the United Nations Framework Convention on Climate Change (UNFCCC), signed by the overwhelming majority of world leaders at the 1992 Earth Summit in Rio de Janeiro, and the Kyoto Protocol, signed at the Third Conference of the Parties to UNFCCC in Japan in 1997.

4.4   These international agreements took a great deal of time and effort to negotiate, involving the highest levels of governments. Yet they are modest achievements when considered against the scale of the task that appears to lie ahead.

4.5   UNFCCC sets out a legal framework for controlling emissions of greenhouse gases. In article 2 the contracting parties pledge themselves

> to achieve stabilisation of greenhouse gas concentrations in the atmosphere at a level that would prevent dangerous anthropogenic interference with the climate system. Such a level should be achieved within a time frame sufficient to allow ecosystems to adapt naturally to climate change, to ensure that food production is not threatened, and to enable economic development to proceed in a sustainable manner.

Article 3.3 states that

> Where there are threats of serious or irreversible damage, lack of full scientific certainty should not be used as a reason for postponing [precautionary] measures, taking into account that policies and measures to deal with climate change should be cost effective so as to ensure global benefits at the lowest possible cost.

4.6   There is already therefore a commitment in international law to the principle of co-operating to slow and eventually halt the rise in concentrations of greenhouse gases. It is binding on the UK and over 180 other nations, containing more than 98% of the world's population, which have ratified UNFCCC. But there is not as yet any agreement on what the maximum tolerable concentrations might be, nor on how the effort required to prevent them being exceeded should be distributed amongst nations.

4.7   UNFCCC also placed an obligation on developed nations to aim to reduce their annual emissions of greenhouse gases to the 1990 level by 2000. Very few of them are expected to achieve that goal. The UK will have done so; but, as we show later (5.48-5.50), this is largely fortuitous, rather than the consequence of policies devised with that objective in mind.

4.8   Developed nations took matters further at Kyoto. They agreed that by 2008 to 2012 they would reduce their annual emissions of a basket of six greenhouse gases (see box 2C) by amounts that in aggregate represent a reduction of 5.2% from the 1990 level. The European Union (EU) undertook to reduce its emissions by 8%, and the Council of Ministers subsequently agreed what contribution each Member State should make to that. The Kyoto Protocol however will not enter into force until at least 55 parties to UNFCCC have ratified it, including nations which contributed at least 55% of the total greenhouse gas emissions by developed nations in 1990. At the time of finalising this report no developed nations had ratified the protocol. There is strong political resistance to doing so in some countries, notably the USA. Keeping the developed nations to what they agreed at Kyoto depends on the completion of further complex and difficult negotiations. These largely concern mechanisms, such as trading, which would allow reductions in one nation's greenhouse gas emissions, over and above its legal obligations, to be credited and/or sold to another nation (box 4A).

4.9   The direct benefit from the Kyoto Protocol will be modest. It sets emission limits only for the developed nations. The reductions they are pledged to make are expected to be outweighed by the increase in developing nations' emissions between 1990 and 2012, and global emissions will therefore continue to rise. The protocol's effect in reducing the carbon dioxide concentration in the atmosphere below what it would otherwise have been is calculated to be only 10 parts per million by volume (ppmv) in the middle of the 21st century (equivalent to 5% of the increase that has already occurred, 2.7) and 20 ppmv at the end of the century.[2] Much more needs to be done.

THE NEED FOR INTERNATIONAL AGREEMENT TO LIMIT CLIMATE CHANGE

4.10   Each nation will make its own assessment of how much damage various degrees of climate change would impose on it in terms of harmful impacts and costly adaptations. A few may even anticipate an overall benefit from climate change, for example through increases in crop yields and opportunities to grow new crops. Given the current uncertainties about the regional impacts of climate change (2.32), and the possibility that shifts in climate may be more abrupt than currently envisaged (2.34), it would be foolish for any government to count on such a benefit.

BOX 4A	FLEXIBILITY UNDER THE KYOTO PROTOCOL

The Kyoto Protocol allows the industrialised nations of the Organization for Economic Co-operation and Development (OECD) and the former Warsaw Pact to meet some of their emission limitation commitments by actions outside their own borders. There are three ways in which this can be done:

Emissions Trading enables a nation to purchase the credit for greenhouse gas emissions reductions made in another nation and count them as its own. A nation which sells emissions reductions it has made at home cannot then count them as a contribution towards meeting its own commitment. This direct trading in emissions, or rather in *assigned amounts* of greenhouse gas quota, is only allowed between developed nations. It is envisaged that nations which find it relatively easy to meet their Kyoto commitment, particularly the Russian Federation, will sell quota at a negotiated price to those which find it more difficult, such as the USA.

Joint Implementation, which also involves only developed nations, is based on specific projects which reduce emissions, the idea being that nations work jointly to meet commitments under the protocol. One nation funds a project in another country, such as a non-fossil fuel power station which substitutes for fossil fuel electricity generation. The donor state then claims the credit for the resulting reductions in emissions. Joint implementation could facilitate investment by OECD nations in major energy efficiency improvements in the former Soviet bloc nations. It can apply not only to reductions in emissions but to enhancement of carbon dioxide sinks.

The **Clean Development Mechanism** (CDM) is similar to joint implementation, but involves emission reduction projects in a developing country financed by a developed nation. The latter will receive *certified emission reductions* which it can count towards its Kyoto commitment. Thus to receive the credit for the reduction the donor nation will have to demonstrate that the project will lead to the recipient's emissions being lower than they would otherwise have been, a difficult concept at a time when developing nations' emissions are rising and are not subject to any limitations. The protocol calls for organisations to be established, including an executive board for the CDM, to ensure genuine reductions are achieved, and audited and verified. An unspecified proportion of the funds flowing from developed to developing nations under the mechanism will be used to cover administrative expenses and 'to assist developing country parties that are particularly vulnerable to the adverse effects of climate change to meet the costs of adaptation' (article 12).

The main purpose of these three 'flexibility mechanisms' is to reduce the overall costs of curbing emissions by concentrating reductions in sectors and regions where they can be made most cheaply. The protocol stipulates that emission reductions which developed nations make outside their borders should be regarded as supplementary to those they make at home. However, no specific limits have been set on the proportion of reductions that they can achieve through the flexibility mechanisms, and that remains the subject of international debate. Projects and trading can be carried out by companies and other organisations. But it is nation states and their governments which must take ultimate responsibility for ensuring they meet their national commitments.

The detailed and potentially complex rules required for these three mechanisms to begin operating have yet to be drawn up. However, several nations have already pioneered joint implementation-type projects. Some have made it clear that they will rely heavily on these flexibility mechanisms to meet a substantial part of their commitments under the protocol. The government of the Netherlands, for instance, has said it will make half its 6% cut in greenhouse gas emissions in this way.[1]

4.11   While any country or community can make its own attempts to adapt to climate change, there is little scope for any nation to act alone to reduce the accumulation of greenhouse gases. The UK's emissions are about 2% of the global total; whatever the UK does to limit its own emissions will have a minute impact on its own future climate and those of other countries. Nations must act together, even though there will be intense and prolonged debate over how the burden should be shared among them.

4.12   The appropriate mix of measures to reduce carbon dioxide emissions, and their costs, will vary from country to country according to stage of development, the availability of particular energy sources and the scope for management of terrestrial ecosystems. Some countries, including the UK, are potentially rich in renewable energy sources such as wind, wave and tidal power. In others solar energy is abundant. A few may be able to offset emissions from burning fossil fuels by planting large areas of fast growing forests (3.21). Still others, such as the oil-rich nations of the Middle East, are anxious to sell fossil fuels from the abundant reserves that are the mainstay of their economies. Some developing nations, notably India and China, have immense coal reserves which they may wish to use as a cheap, indigenous fuel source.

FRAMING A RESPONSE

4.13   The analysis in chapter 2 showed what the aim of stabilising greenhouse gas concentrations implies in terms of reducing emissions from burning fossil fuels. Because reductions on that scale will necessitate very substantial changes in the way energy is obtained and used, some consumers or industries or nations will resist change, fearing it will seriously harm their interests. This has been seen already in the demands of some major oil-exporting nations to be compensated for any large reductions in fossil fuel use, in the extensive advertising and lobbying against the Kyoto Protocol organised by some US industries, and in the UK in the strong resistance to the road fuel duty escalator (6.117).

4.14   However, important benefits may flow from the reduced dependence on fossil fuels that will accompany substantial reductions in carbon dioxide emissions. The most obvious is an improvement in public health due to reductions in the air pollution associated with burning fossil fuels. There will be other important gains: emissions from fossil fuels are the major contributor to acid deposition and photochemical smogs which damage buildings and ecosystems and can reduce crop growth.

4.15   Policies aimed at reducing carbon dioxide emissions from transport can be integrated with policies for reducing the congestion, noise and environmental degradation associated with increasing road traffic. This was the subject of the Commission's 18th and 20th reports. A shift away from largely oil-based economies would reduce the risks of oil spills such as those which gravely damaged wildlife and fisheries along the coasts of south-west Wales in 1996 and Brittany earlier this year.

4.16   Policies for enhancing natural carbon sinks could reduce the rate of deforestation in tropical countries and increase the UK's forested area. These outcomes could bring benefits additional to climate change abatement, such as conserving biodiversity, preventing soil erosion and landslides, and increasing people's enjoyment of the countryside.

4.17   While there may be coincidental benefits from reducing carbon dioxide emissions, any attempt to make radical changes in current energy systems is bound to face resistance. The complaints of those who are certain they will be harmed by a change of direction tend to drown out the approval of those who believe they might gain. Given such resistance, the global debate about the appropriate response to climate change becomes chiefly one about equity between generations. How much effort is the current generation prepared to undertake, how much change will it contemplate, in order to reduce the impacts and risks of climate change through this century and the next?

4.18   There is a moral imperative to act now. If this generation took no measures to curb rising emissions, it would be condemning our children, grandchildren and generations beyond them to considerable dangers (2.27-2.35). In the light of where the harshest impacts are likely to fall, that would perpetrate an enormous global injustice. The developed nations are responsible for by far the largest part of the current enhancement in the greenhouse effect, even though they contain only a fifth of the world's population.[3] Yet most studies have concluded that the developing nations in the tropics and sub-tropics will suffer more harm from climate change that the developed countries in higher latitudes.

4.19   This is partly because of what are likely to be major regional differences in the effects of climate change (2.29, 2.35), but also because many developing nations lack the income and capacity to mount an adequate adaptive response to significant shifts in temperature and rainfall and rising sea levels. Their populations may include large numbers of nomads or subsistence farmers and fishermen whose livelihoods will be particularly threatened by climate change. An adaptation such as raising the height of flood defences on coasts and river banks which might cost the UK a very small proportion of its gross domestic product would impose a very much heavier strain on a country such as Bangladesh. The wide gap in incomes, educational attainment and life expectancies between the richest and poorest nations is likely to be widened still further by climate change. Rising sea levels may eventually cause some of the world's small island nations to disappear entirely.

4.20   While there could be seen to be a moral duty for all nations, especially developed nations, to act now in order to reduce the dangers of climate change, action should not of itself cause even greater injustices. In responding, nations should not burden the weakest and most vulnerable among their own citizens. The response to the threat should not be disproportionate. If society were to take excessively costly action in order to reduce emissions, that would harm the prospects both of this generation and of future generations that will build on its achievements. Resources which might have been devoted to healthcare, food production, clean water and sanitation would be diverted into reducing emissions to an unjustifiable extent, given the benefit in reduced risks.

ECONOMIC APPRAISAL

4.21   We have considered the extent to which economic appraisal might help in deciding the level of an appropriate response. Climate change will impose costs on future generations, either directly or through adaptations they have to make. But reducing emissions in order to limit climate change becomes increasingly costly, the greater the desired impact. Somewhere between a policy of no action and the allocation of a significant proportion of the total available resources is a range of policies consistent with the attempt to find a level of preventive action at which the overall costs to the global economy of climate change and its limitation are minimised.

4.22   One leading economist seeking an acceptable response to climate change has summarised the problems in estimating the likely costs of unabated climate change thus:

> It must be emphasised that attempts to estimate the impacts of climate change continue to be highly speculative. Outside of agriculture and sea-level rise for a small number of countries, the number of scholarly studies of the economic impacts of climate change remains vanishingly small. Estimates of the regional climatic impacts of global warming are still inconsistent across different climate models, and economic studies have made little progress in estimating impacts, particularly in the low-income countries.[4]

4.23   Identifying and assessing the global costs of reducing emissions of greenhouse gases may be somewhat easier than assessing the costs imposed by climate change, because more of the former involve resources that are traded in markets. Even so, there are currently no reliable estimates even for the costs of reducing greenhouse gas emissions to any given percentage of their 1990 level by a given year in the future. The long time-lags which underlie climate change mean that preventive measures have to be carried out several decades, and even centuries, before the harm they seek to avert. Economic analysis of such a process involves discounting future events. Other things being equal, the discounting would be at a positive rate, so that events taking place today are given more weight in decision-taking than those expected to take place in the future. The discount rate used should take into account the combination of a rising standard of living and the declining value of a marginal addition to income as people become richer, or the increasing pain attaching to marginal cuts in income should people become poorer – perhaps as a result of severe climate change. If an acceptable policy for responding to the threat of climate change has a substantial effect on economic growth, that will impinge on the discount rate appropriate for use in the economic analysis.

4.24   It has been suggested that changing discount rates should be used, applying a conventional rate for the short term, and then a very low or zero rate after that, or possibly even a negative discount rate if climate change threatened to make continuing positive growth of material consumption unlikely or unsustainable.[5,6] These risks, too, should be taken into account. If there is the possibility of a major disruption to society, such as would arise from extreme shifts in climate, then this should be incorporated into the analysis.

4.25   In addition, the analysis should take account of expected changes in people's relative willingness to pay for environmental benefits. If the climate does not change so fast as to threaten the growth in material consumption, that growth is likely to reduce the acceptability of any associated environmental degradation.

4.26   Several studies have set out to explore the implications of a range of possible responses to the threat of climate change using computer models that integrate the global economy, emissions, the carbon cycle and the climate system. Most conclude that some measures to reduce emissions from burning fossil fuels or enhance sinks are now justified, usually in the shape of an internationally agreed carbon tax (which penalises the burning of fossil fuels according to how much carbon dioxide is emitted) or international trading in permits to emit specified quantities of greenhouse gases.

4.27   Some of these studies have concluded that the Kyoto Protocol cannot be justified on economic or social grounds, because the costs which will fall on the developed nations in the next decade as they reduce their emissions are not justified by the effects of the resulting, very small reductions in climate change.[7] They advocate rather low corrective carbon taxes. However, other studies using similar integrated models have concluded that a stronger response and much higher taxes are justified. The gap is largely explained by differences in the discount rates employed, the projected price of replacement energy sources and the size of the ancillary benefits which flow from reducing fossil fuel consumption.

4.28   We have argued that there is a moral imperative to act now (4.18-4.20). That argument and economic appraisal both point towards similar actions for the short to medium term – reductions in greenhouse gas emissions from their current rising trend, led by the developed nations, and adaptation where impacts are already inevitable.

A PRAGMATIC APPROACH

4.29   We are concerned about the longer term. The principle that concentrations of greenhouse gases should be prevented from rising to a dangerously high level is enshrined in international law (4.5). Deciding on an appropriate long-term response to the threat of climate

4.48   A system of *per capita* quotas could not be expected to enter into force immediately. At the same time as entitling developing nations to use substantially more fossil fuels than at present (which they might not be able to afford), it would require developed nations to make drastic and immediate cuts in their use of fossil fuels, causing serious damage to their economies.

4.49   A combination of two approaches could avoid this politically and diplomatically unacceptable situation, while enabling a *per capita* basis to be adhered to. The first approach is to require nations' emission quotas to follow a *contraction and convergence* trajectory. Over the coming decades each nation's allocation would gradually shift from its current level of emissions towards a level set on a uniform *per capita* basis. By this means 'grandfather rights' would gradually be removed: the quotas of developed nations would fall, year by year, while those of the poorest developing nations would rise, until all nations had an entitlement to emit an equal quantity of greenhouse gases per head *(convergence)*. From then on, the quotas of all nations would decline together at the same rate *(contraction)*. The combined global total of emissions would follow a profile through the 21st and 22nd centuries which kept the atmospheric concentration of greenhouse gases below a specified limit.

4.50   The upper limit on the concentration of greenhouse gases would be determined by international negotiations, as would the date by which all nations would converge on a uniform *per capita* basis for their emission quotas, and the intermediate steps towards that. It would probably also be necessary to set a cut-off date for national populations: beyond that date, further changes in the size of a country's population would not lead to any increase or decrease in its emission quota.

4.51   In table 4.1[17] we have applied the contraction and convergence approach to carbon dioxide emissions, and calculated what the UK's emissions quotas would be in 2050 and 2100 for four alternative upper limits on atmospheric concentration. We have assumed for this purpose that 2050 would be both the date by which nations would converge on a uniform *per capita* emissions figure and the cut-off date for national populations.[18] If 550 ppmv is selected as the upper limit, UK carbon dioxide emissions would have to be reduced by almost 60% from their current level by mid-century, and by almost 80% by 2100. Even stabilisation at a very high level of 1,000 ppmv would require the UK to cut emissions by some 40% by 2050.

Table 4.1

Contraction and convergence: implications for UK carbon dioxide emissions

maximum atmospheric concentration ppmv	permissible UK emissions in 2050 % of 1997 level	permissible UK emissions in 2100 % of 1997 level
450	21	11
550	42	23
750	56	47
1,000	58	61

4.52   The UK-based Global Commons Institute has taken the lead in promoting contraction and convergence, and has developed a computer model which specifies emission allocations under a range of scenarios.[19] The concept has been supported by several national governments and legislators. Some developed nations are very wary of it because it implies drastic reductions in their emissions, but at least one minister in a European government has supported it.[20] Commentators on climate diplomacy have identified contraction and convergence as a leading contender among the various proposals for allocating emission quotas to nations in the long term.[21]

4.53   The other ingredient which would make an agreement based on *per capita* allocations of quotas more feasible is flexibility of the kind already provided in outline in the Kyoto Protocol (4.42 and box 4A). Nations most anxious to emit greenhouse gases in excess of their allocation over a given period will be able and willing to purchase unused quota at prices which incline other countries to emit less than their quota, to the benefit of both parties. The clean development mechanism, which allows developed nations to claim emission reductions by sponsoring projects which reduce emissions in developing nations to levels lower than they would otherwise have been, can also be seen as a form of trading.

4.54   In the longer term trading by companies in emission permits, drawn from national emission quotas determined on the basis of a contraction and convergence agreement, could make a valuable contribution to reducing the global costs of stabilising greenhouse gas concentrations while transferring resources from wealthy nations to poorer ones. Trading needs to be transparent, monitored and regulated, and backed by penalties on nations which emit more than they are entitled to. If it became merely a means of enabling wealthy nations to buy up the emission entitlements of poor countries on the cheap, thereby evading taking any action at home, trading would not serve the cause of climate protection. Nor would it if developing countries which had sold quota heavily went on to emit in excess of their revised entitlements.

UK POLICY IN A GLOBAL CONTEXT

4.55   It will take several years, possibly decades, before agreement is reached on a climate change protocol which commits the majority of nations, developed and developing, to quantified limits on their emissions of greenhouse gases. Meanwhile there remains a great deal of negotiating to be done on the detailed mechanisms of the Kyoto Protocol. There is a risk that the number of ratifications needed to bring it into force (4.8) will not be reached in time to affect emissions in 2008-2012 (or, if it has not been ratified, that too few binding commitments will have been made voluntarily). If the USA, the world's largest emitter of greenhouse gases, were neither to ratify nor make the agreed reductions voluntarily, that would be likely to nullify the protocol. We conclude this chapter by considering what stance the UK should take amid this continued diplomatic uncertainty.

4.56   There is a dismal but real possibility of very limited progress in climate negotiations over the next decade, with the Kyoto reductions not being delivered and further commitments being modest or non-existent. Climate change would then continue unabated. It would become a case of *sauve qui peut*, with the peoples of some of the world's poorest nations suffering most. Alternatively, the Kyoto reductions may prove to be but a first step in progress towards concerted and effective global action. Over the next 50 years greenhouse gas reduction targets would then become progressively more demanding in order to prevent prudent maximum atmospheric concentrations from being exceeded.

4.57   The 1985 Vienna Convention on the Protection of the Ozone Layer offers a reasonably encouraging precedent. Over the decade following its adoption, as the severity of the threat to the Earth's protective ozone layer grew, and as the threat became better understood, a series of agreements were reached, commencing with the 1987 Montreal Protocol, which accelerated the phasing out of ozone-depleting chemicals. Reducing emissions of greenhouse gases will, however, require vastly greater effort.

4.58   There are three reasons why the UK should strive, at home and abroad, to ensure that an effective international response to the threat of climate change is mounted, beginning now and extending far into the future. First, there is the moral imperative outlined above (4.18-4.19) which requires developed nations to take the lead in addressing the threat (as does UNFCCC, which the UK has ratified). Second, the more nations there are which hesitate, the less chance there is of concerted global action. Even if only a minority of nations adopt a 'wait and see' stance, this could jeopardise progress in future negotiations. Third, the UK is very likely to be harmed by climate change. Although the direct impacts of climate change within the UK are generally difficult to predict (see box 2D), adaptation to them is likely to be costly, and would become more costly if climate change is allowed to proceed further and faster. Adding the burden of climate change and necessary adaptation to the already complex set of parameters involved in development planning in this country will intensify the existing problems of delivering acceptable levels of environmental quality and protection. The UK would not, furthermore, be able to shut itself off from the economic, social and political disruption that climate change might cause elsewhere in the world, leading to mass migrations and international conflicts over scarce resources.

4.59   We have considered what the UK could do to help bring about international agreement on further effective action. To date it has been a leader in advocating early action to reduce the threat of climate change. Compared to other developed nations it is already obliged to make relatively large reductions in greenhouse gas emissions between 1990 and 2012; only four other nations, all EU Member States, are obliged to make larger reductions under the Kyoto Protocol. The government has set the further goal of reducing carbon dioxide emissions in 2010 to 20% below the 1990 level. In its evidence to us the Foreign and Commonwealth Office said:

> The most effective role the UK can play [in influencing the development of international climate policies] is practical leadership. Many countries will be watching to see how the UK achieves its proposed 20% reduction in carbon dioxide emissions. Measures we use to help meet that aim will be the strongest influence we can provide to influence the policies of others.

The government's draft programme for achieving the 20% goal is discussed in the next chapter (5.46-5.60).

4.60   The question the UK now has to confront is what further action to take in advance of commitments by other countries and what further reductions it should be planning for the years after 2012. Our view is that nations which advocate strong preventive action should demonstrate their good intentions and commitment by taking measures which not only meet current obligations but also put them on a path to achieve the much more demanding targets which will be necessary if the threat of climate change is to be adequately addressed. They will then carry more weight in international negotiations on a future climate change agreement, especially if there are more than a small number of such nations and they include major economies. If the UK is to be effective in urging long-term, global action it must have, as well as some like-minded allies, a credible policy for reducing its own emissions over several decades, in particular emissions of carbon dioxide.

4.61   If, as we hope, there emerges a sustained global drive to reduce greenhouse gas emissions, to improve existing non-carbon energy sources and develop new ones, and to raise the energy efficiency of manufacturing and commerce substantially, there may be an economic advantage for nations whose industries take a lead in developing and deploying the necessary new technologies. Irrespective of the threat of climate change, there is an expectation that the global market for non-fossil fuel energy sources will expand rapidly through this century in order to meet the growing demand for energy as conventional oil and, later, conventional gas reserves come under pressure. But while there are examples of 'first mover' status bringing economic success to some national industries, such as Denmark's wind turbine industry, that has not always been the case.

4.62   The issue for the UK however is, not so much whether to be a first mover as whether to catch up. While it has taken a lead in promoting international agreement on climate change, and has made early reductions in emissions, the UK trails several other European states in its development of renewable energy sources, the energy efficiency of its housing stock and the willingness of equipment and appliance manufacturers to improve energy efficiency. It will face real difficulties in maintaining emission reductions after 2012; we discuss this in the next chapter. High risks of losing existing markets, and failing to enter new ones, arise from being a laggard when energy production and energy efficiency technologies are changing rapidly in the UK's major competitors.

4.63   The privatisation of energy industries and the liberalisation of energy markets which the UK has pioneered (5.14) could create a good basis for encouraging new technologies if these changes bring a culture of innovation. We discuss in general terms in the next chapter (5.18-5.28), and in more specific contexts in later chapters, what forms of intervention can best be used to encourage energy companies operating in liberalised markets to move in directions that are environmentally desirable.

4.64   The development of an international market for trading greenhouse gas emission permits will help reductions to be made cost-effectively and could enable some nations to buy time to allow the technological options to be deployed. There is considerable interest in the UK in such trading, as shown by the work of the UK Emissions Trading Group and the encouragement the government has given.[22] Two major energy corporations, BP Amoco and Royal Dutch Shell, have set up internal trading schemes. **We urge government to facilitate and encourage the creation of a national trading scheme, to help position the City of London – which has the necessary skills and capacity – as the world centre for international trading in emission permits when that emerges from the negotiations on implementing the Kyoto Protocol.**

4.65   The UK has already had some success as a broker of global deals on climate change, working on its own and as a member of the EU. Its commitment to make substantial early reductions in emissions has contributed to this success, even if its ability to do so has been largely fortuitous (5.48-5.49). The EU has proved to be a formidable force in climate negotiations, because of its importance to global trade and its demands for substantial emission reductions on the part of the developed nations.

4.66   We believe the UK, working within the EU, can strengthen its position as a broker of climate agreements if it develops a long-term strategy for reducing greenhouse gas emissions. Its EU and Commonwealth memberships and its links to the USA all favour this role. The UK will not be alone in urging action; several other European nations also appear willing to adopt this stance.

4.67   As the impacts of climate change become clearer, large developing nations which are major greenhouse gas emitters, such as China and India, may begin to change their current position of holding back from commitments to specific emission limitations. They may look to make common cause with the UK, the EU and others in putting pressure on nations with very high *per capita* emission levels which currently seem prepared to do little to abate climate change. If, as seems possible, this issue comes to dominate international relations in the first quarter of the 21st century the political and diplomatic advantages to the UK of a leading position on climate change could be considerable.

4.68   We recommend that the UK should continue to play a forceful leading role in international negotiations to combat climate change, both in its own right and through the European Union. The government should press for further reductions in the greenhouse gas emissions of developed nations after 2012, and controls on the emissions of developing nations.

4.69   The government should press for a future global climate agreement based on the contraction and convergence approach (4.47-4.50), combined with international trading in emission permits (4.53-4.54). Together, these offer the best long-term prospect of securing equity, economy and international consensus.

4.70   To demonstrate its willingness to accept and implement an agreement based on the contraction and convergence approach, the UK needs to adopt a strategy now for making major reductions in greenhouse gas emissions in the period after 2012. In doing this, it will not only be anticipating the global climate agreement that will probably be concluded during the next two decades, but will also be improving the chances that negotiations will be able to bring about the large reductions that are needed in global emissions. The core of the strategy will have to be very large reductions in carbon dioxide emissions from the burning of fossil fuels. In part II of this report we consider UK energy policies in that perspective, in order to determine what the nature and content of a long-term strategy for carbon dioxide emissions should be.

Given current knowledge about humanity's impact on climate and IPCC's findings, we support 550 ppmv as an upper limit on the carbon dioxide concentration in the atmosphere. Major reductions in global emissions are necessary to prevent that limit being exceeded. The UK should be prepared to accept the contraction and convergence principle as the basis for international agreement on reducing greenhouse gas emissions, and should adopt a long-term strategy for reducing its own emissions

Part II

The United Kingdom's response

Part II of this report considers the implications for internal policies in the UK of the conclusions reached in **part I** about the urgent need for an effective global response to the threat of climate change and the most credible form for that response.

The key conclusion reached was that, as the corollary of accepting 550 ppmv as an upper limit on the carbon dioxide concentration in the atmosphere, and the contraction and convergence principle as the basis for global agreement, the UK should adopt now a long-term strategy for reducing its emissions of greenhouse gases. The core of that strategy must be very large reductions in carbon dioxide emissions from burning fossil fuels.

Chapter 5 briefly characterises the UK's present energy situation, summarises key trends over recent decades and official projections for the next two decades, and analyses the draft Climate Change Programme.

Chapter 6 discusses the current trends in energy use in the UK by consumers, the potentials for greater efficiency, and the prospects for reducing the amounts of energy used in different consumption sectors. We consider what instruments government should use in order to achieve that.

Chapter 7 discusses the alternatives to using fossil fuels as sources of energy in the UK. This involves analysing the scales on which alternative sources are available, their environmental impacts if they were developed on a large scale and their costs relative to the costs of fossil fuels. It also involves considering what the barriers would be to their rapid development.

Chapter 8 discusses the scope for making fundamental changes in the UK's energy system. We consider the different forms in which energy is required and the most efficient ways of providing it in those forms. Discussion of policy options has often focused on meeting the demand for electricity and disregarded the larger amounts of energy used in other forms. The most difficult uses of fossil fuels to replace will be providing heat and providing power for transport. We identify the problems posed by the intermittency, unpredictability and location of several of the renewable sources of energy, and conclude that reappraisal and some reconfiguration of the current grid system of electricity distribution will be required if they are to deployed on a large scale.

Chapter 9 sets out four illustrative scenarios in which a 60% reduction in UK carbon dioxide emissions is achieved by 2050 through different combinations of reductions in energy demand and development of alternative sources.

Chapter 10 discusses what changes are now needed in policies and institutions to put the UK on a path to making the substantial, long-term reductions in carbon dioxide emissions which are necessary. It also brings together our **key recommendations**, and is followed by a complete list of **our recommendations**.

Chapter 5

THE UK'S PRESENT SITUATION AND POLICIES

What is the UK's present energy situation? What have been the effects of policies followed by successive governments? What has happened to energy supply and use, and to carbon dioxide emissions? What is likely to happen over the next 20 years? Is there a coherent relationship between energy policies and environmental objectives?

5.1   This chapter sets the scene for the remainder of our report by outlining how the UK obtains and uses energy, the key features of present government policies, and the current prospects for the next two decades. We summarise the main trends in energy supply and use over recent decades and the latest official projections for the next 20 years (5.2-5.11). We briefly consider the main features and objectives of UK energy policies (5.12-5.17) and discuss the environmental implications of the privatisation of formerly state-owned industries and the liberalisation of energy markets (5.18-5.28). We review the ways in which environmental regulation and policies have impinged on the energy system up to now (5.29-5.45) and assess the draft Climate Change Programme for the UK (5.46-5.60). Finally we discuss government funding of research and development into new energy technologies (5.61-5.66).

THE OVERALL ENERGY SITUATION

5.2   Since 1965 (figure 5-1)[1] energy consumption by final users in the UK has increased by 16%[2] and consumption of primary energy by 24%.[3] Projections published by the Department of Trade and Industry (DTI) in March 2000 (also included in figure 5-I and other figures in this chapter) show energy use continuing to grow steadily.[4]

5.3   Primary energy is being used in the UK at an average rate of about 300 GW (for our use of units, see the box on page 10).[5] Almost 90% of it comes from fossil fuels. In 1998 the UK was also exporting fossil fuels at a net rate of 53 GW. The other main source of primary energy is nuclear power using imported uranium. Most of the remainder comes from electricity imported from France (0.4%); and from direct flow hydro and wind power (0.2%).[6]

5.4   Major changes have occurred in the sources of primary energy (figure 5-II), as the result of a complex interplay of forces in which government policies have been only one element. Perhaps the biggest influence has been the prices of fossil fuels, relative to each other and to other goods and services. Movements in prices have been largely determined by events outside the UK. Discoveries of new reserves, and technological advances that enabled oil and gas to be obtained from increasingly remote and difficult locations, expanded supplies and tended to keep prices down. But the cartel formed by the Organization of Petroleum Exporting Countries (OPEC) has from time to time been able to restrict oil supplies and push prices up. Oil is traded so widely, and in such large quantities, that large fluctuations in its market price have influenced the prices of other energy sources and global economic growth. It retains an almost complete dominance as the energy source for transport, and provides 33% of UK primary energy.[7]

Figure 5-I
Rate of UK energy use 1965-2020

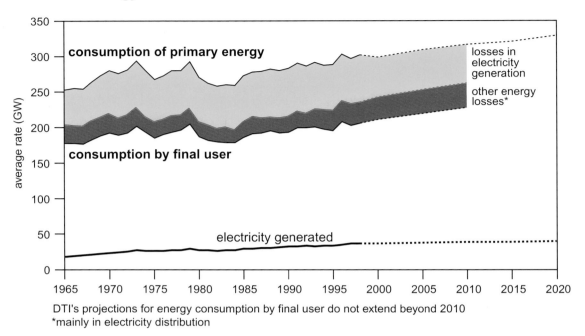

DTI's projections for energy consumption by final user do not extend beyond 2010
*mainly in electricity distribution

Figure 5-II
UK primary energy sources 1965-2020

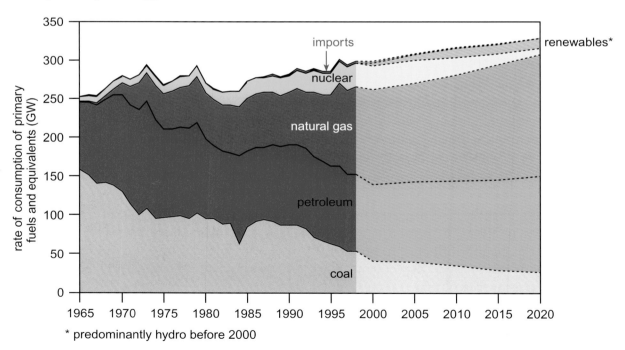

* predominantly hydro before 2000

5.5   The proportion of energy provided by gas has been rising, in line with the global trend (1.4). Following the discovery of large reserves in the North Sea, its share of UK primary energy rose from zero in 1960 to 37% in 1998, the largest share of any fuel.[8] Over the same period, coal's share fell from 74% to 18%. The shift occurred because gas is more convenient and less polluting than coal and because it costs less, both for space heating and for electricity generation.

5.6   About a third of primary energy use in the UK is to generate electricity.[9] Electricity's share of consumption by final users has increased from 7% in 1960 to 17% in 1998.[10] This reflects its convenience as a form of energy and the growing range of electrically powered equipment available to households and other users. We discuss below changes in the mix of fuels used to generate electricity and their implications.

5.7   Whereas the average rate of primary energy use in the UK is about 300 GW, the average rate of final consumption is only about 210 GW.[11] The difference represents losses within the energy system. The largest component, as figure 5-I shows, is energy losses in the course of electricity generation. This is in one sense a matter of thermodynamics (see box 3A), in another sense it reflects the lack of any commercial or institutional structure for using the low-grade heat produced in generating electricity. The gap between primary energy use and final consumption increased by 28% between 1965 and 1998 but remained at about 31% of primary energy demand.[12] The main reason has been the increasing demand for electricity. Figure 5-I does not show all the energy losses attributable to thermodynamics: not included are the substantial losses for that reason at point of use, in particular in vehicle engines.

5.8   By sector, transport is the largest component in final use of energy (34%), followed by households (30%), manufacturing industry (22%), and commercial and public services (14%). The official energy projections, based on analysis of 12 economic sectors, shows transport's share rising to 37% in 2010 and households' falling to 26%.

5.9   Figure 5-III[13] shows what has happened, and is projected to happen, to the *energy intensity* of the UK economy (in red), defined as the ratio of inland consumption of primary energy to gross domestic product (GDP). Consumption of primary energy has grown less rapidly than the economy: as a result energy intensity fell from 0.72 W/£ GDP in 1960 to 0.4 W/£ GDP in 1998.[14] We discuss later in the report the extent to which this reduction in energy intensity was the result of improved efficiency, rather than structural changes in the economy (6.7, 6.13).

5.10   The most direct comparison for the UK is with other Member States of the European Union (EU), which for the most part have broadly similar population densities and levels of income. In 1998 the UK economy had a higher energy intensity than 9 of the other 14 states, and a higher energy intensity for transport than 11 other states. All the other Member States obtained a greater proportion of their total energy from renewable sources; and 10 of them made more use of combined heat and power (CHP) plants (3.40). The *carbon intensity* of the UK economy (the ratio of carbon dioxide emissions to gross domestic product) is also high in relation to other industrialised nations.[15]

5.11   The official energy projections show energy intensity falling more rapidly than in the past: by 1.8% a year between 1995 and 2010 compared with 1.5% a year between 1985 and 1995. They also show primary energy use growing more slowly to 2010 (about 0.6% a year) than final

Figure 5-III

Energy intensity of the UK economy 1965-2020

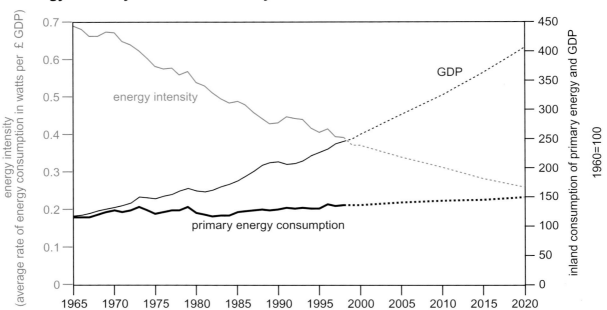

energy use (about 0.9% a year): there is further growth in use of electricity, but a significant improvement in the efficiency with which it is generated. These projections are based on the assumption that there will be increased use of CHP plants, and take into account the estimated effect of the climate change levy to be introduced in April 2001 (6.19) and other measures aimed at reducing energy use. The major trends of the 1990s continue. We discuss the implications for carbon dioxide emissions later in this chapter (5.53). The comparisons with other EU Member States suggest there is significant potential, given appropriate policies, to reduce both energy use and carbon dioxide emissions without any adverse effect on the standard of living. We now consider the current nature of UK energy policies.

UK ENERGY POLICIES

5.12   UK governments have never pursued an integrated and coherent energy policy.[16] Policies have been separate and sometimes conflicting: to promote the development of North Sea oil and gas, to sustain the coal industry, to maintain gas as a premium fuel, to use the non-fossil fuel obligation to shelter the nuclear industry and promote the development of renewable sources, to privatise electricity generation and distribution, to liberalise energy markets and promote competition. The most basic aim has been to obtain energy supplies at low prices in order to help promote economic growth and meet social needs. This has been pursued within constraints relating to health and safety, environmental protection and land use, some of them stemming from European legislation or international conventions.

5.13   The nearest approach to an energy policy the UK has had, with some attention to conserving energy and to security through diversity of supply, was stimulated by the abrupt increases in oil prices in 1973 and 1980, when the actions of the OPEC cartel caused concern about national vulnerability to unilateral actions elsewhere. The overall objective the government has now formulated for energy policy is: 'Ensuring secure, diverse and sustainable supplies of energy at competitive prices'.[17] This objective is regarded as including the government's concern 'to achieve environmental improvements as a key component of the overall goal of sustainable development'.[18] The pursuit of energy efficiency has been treated as a separate issue.[19]

5.14   For the last two decades the most significant, and far-reaching, component of government policy has been privatisation of nationalised energy industries followed by liberalisation of markets for gas and electricity. In 1980 the state owned the gas, coal, nuclear and electricity industries, as well as having a major stake in the oil industry. By 2000, it owned nothing except part of the nuclear industry. The purpose of the changes has been to bring into energy supply and distribution the benefits of competition, private sector management skills and private sector investment. All fuels are now supplied on a competitive basis. Coal and oil have been open retail markets for many years; retail gas and retail electricity have been opened more recently, down to the level of domestic customers. Policies intended to remove remaining barriers to the operation of competitive forces have continued under the present government.

5.15   The present structure of the electricity and gas industries in the UK is summarised in box 5A. Enabling consumers to choose their supplier of gas or electricity has been seen as the most effective way of keeping down costs. Operation of distribution systems and bulk transmission networks, on the other hand, are natural monopolies. A regulator (the Office of Gas Supply and the Office of Electricity Regulation, now combined in the Office of Gas and Electricity Markets[20]) was established to prevent abuse of monopoly power and push down prices charged to other companies for use of such networks to the lowest practical level. In those parts of the industries which are not monopolies, the regulator's main role has been to promote effective competition and seek to prevent anti-competitive behaviour. The future nature of the regulator's role is discussed later in the report (10.38-10.42).

5.16   Governments have ceased to see it as their responsibility to plan how the demand for energy will be met. The partial exceptions that have been made in practice have been prompted by the effects which the operation of market forces have had, or threatened to have, on the coal industry. Under the resulting political pressures, both the Conservative government in its 1992 White Paper and the present government in its 1998 White Paper[21] found it necessary to take a comprehensive look at the electricity supply industry and its key sources of fuel, although these reviews did not make a substantial difference to the subsequent course of events.[22]

5.17   In privatising energy industries and liberalising markets the UK has been in the lead internationally. The European Commission has sought to open up electricity and gas markets across Europe in accordance with the general aim of creating a single market. Progress has been slow, and the European legislation in place or in prospect[23] lags far behind the pace of liberalisation in the UK. This legislation nevertheless constrains the UK government's freedom of action in certain directions, for example in the extent of the support that can be given to renewable sources.

ACHIEVING ENVIRONMENTAL OBJECTIVES IN LIBERALISED ENERGY MARKETS

5.18   Our concern is with the achievement of environmental objectives, in particular with the prospects for reducing energy use, substituting alternative energy sources for fossil fuels and transforming the UK's energy system in the light of the aim of making very large reductions in carbon dioxide emissions over the next half century. We have looked in more detail, from this point of view, at the way liberalised energy markets have operated, and can be expected to operate in future.

BOX 5A   **STRUCTURE OF ELECTRICITY AND GAS INDUSTRIES**[24]

Gas

Transco (a subsidiary of BG plc, formerly British Gas plc) *transports and stores* gas and provides the network of pipelines linking gas terminals to end users. Its 'network code' sets out terms for the use of this network. In some areas low pressure spur networks are being constructed by competing companies to transport gas to new, mainly domestic customers.

The *supply* of gas is undertaken by over 60 companies active in the contract market and by 26 companies licensed to supply domestic customers. Centrica plc (trading as British Gas, but demerged in 1997) has less than a fifth of the industrial and commercial market, but over three-quarters of the domestic market.

Electricity

Over 30 UK companies, categorised as 'major power producers', have as their prime purpose the *generation* of electricity and account for 94% of electricity generated and the same proportion of gross electricity supplied. Five companies have 73% of the market in England and Wales; and Electricité de France and the two Scottish generators have a further 9%. The National Grid Co plc owns and operates the *bulk transmission network* in England and Wales, and operates the Electricity Pool through which generators and suppliers trade electricity. The Pool is regulated by its members, which include generating companies. The Pool is being reformed to prevent the largest generators using their market power to keep the wholesale price high.[25]

The *supply* of electricity is undertaken by 14 'public electricity suppliers' (the 12 regional electricity companies (RECs) in England and Wales and the two Scottish companies) and by a further 26 companies which like them hold licences as 'second tier suppliers'. Since June 1999 all domestic customers in Britain have been free to choose their supplier. Larger customers have had that freedom for some years: of sites in England and Wales with a maximum demand of 1 MW and above, 37% are supplied by the REC for that area and a further 33% by a REC as second tier supplier; of sites with a maximum demand of 100kW-1MW, 59% are supplied by the REC for that area and a further 32% by a REC as second tier supplier.

Public electricity suppliers also owned and operated the *distribution network.* Distribution businesses are obliged to facilitate the development of competition and must be kept completely separate from supply businesses, just as companies which both supply and generate have already been required to maintain a separation between the two businesses. Some of the original public electricity suppliers are selling their supply businesses and retaining their distribution businesses.

Larger customers have had freedom since 1994 to select which company should *meter* their supply, and there are now 18 registered meter operators; this freedom will be extended to all customers in the course of 2000.

In Northern Ireland, Northern Ireland Electricity plc is responsible for power procurement, transmission, distribution and supply. The major power stations are owned by three companies. Of sites with a maximum demand of 100kW and above 2% are supplied by second tier suppliers.

SUPPLY OF GAS AND ELECTRICITY

5.19   As electricity suppliers compete with each other in a high volume activity with low margins, they shave the unit price in order to increase the amount of electricity they sell, so spreading their overhead costs over a larger volume and minimising their costs per unit supplied. Gas suppliers have a similar incentive. The market for the supply of gas to small users, including households, was opened to competition throughout Britain in 1998 and the market for supply of electricity to small users in 1999. The last few years have seen aggressive marketing to sign up new customers, or in the case of the previous monopoly suppliers to retain existing customers, often on the basis of supplying both gas and electricity. To prevent the scales being unduly weighted against new suppliers entering the market, the regulator stipulates that any supply agreement must be terminable at not more than 28 days notice.

5.20   The supply of gas and electricity to large users has been open to competition for some years. Suppliers have in some cases been able to persuade large users to focus on their overall energy bill, rather than the unit price of energy, and accept packages of energy efficiency measures which substantially reduce their total energy consumption. For the customer, the incentive is to reduce total expenditure on energy. For the supplier, the incentive comes in retaining some of these cost savings, thereby making the investment in improving the customer's energy efficiency profitable. In these circumstances the supplier is seeking to win or retain customers by offering a more competitive energy service rather than a more competitive unit price for energy. A major contribution to reducing the cost of energy services by raising efficiencies has often been installation of a CHP plant fuelled by gas.

5.21   In general however competition for customers has been on the basis of unit price. The government and the regulator have also seen it as a primary objective to reduce the unit cost to consumers of gas and electricity. Since 1985 the situation has been one of declining prices in real terms for both domestic and industrial users (figure 5-IV) and growth in primary and final energy consumption (figure 5-I). Low world energy prices have played an important part in bringing prices down, as well as competition leading to cost reductions by electricity and gas suppliers. Although there have been improvements in the technical efficiency of electricity generation, that is the area in which competition has so far had least effect in reducing prices.

Figure 5-IV
UK energy prices 1970-1998

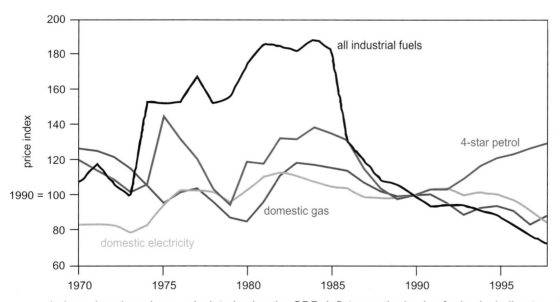

Index values have been calculated using the GDP deflator on the basis of price including tax

5.22   At present therefore the operation of the retail gas and electricity markets does not encourage efficiency in the use of energy. In the USA electricity companies that were at risk of failing in their obligation to meet demand because of shortage of generating capacity have sometimes taken steps to reduce energy use by customers generally, by such methods as supplying or subsidising high-efficiency appliances or improving insulation. They were however monopolies regulated on the basis of rate of return on capital, as distinct from the price cap applied in the UK: limiting energy use was the least cost method of ensuring supply met demand. The Merseyside and North Wales Electricity Board adopted a similar approach on Holyhead Island in North Wales in order to avoid the cost of expanding the capacity of the link from Anglesey; but in general electricity suppliers in the UK have not been faced with capacity shortages. In the USA least cost planning is regarded as having achieved only a qualified success and it was being abandoned even before the present move to liberalisation of retail markets.

5.23   There has been much debate about the possibility that, following the model already well established for large users, energy suppliers might evolve into suppliers of energy services to domestic users and small businesses.[26] There is no sign of that happening as yet. There would be considerable legal and administrative complexities in drawing up and fulfilling energy service contracts with large numbers of small users, and in avoiding loss to the supplier if a customer exercised her or his right to terminate the supply contract at 28 days notice. There are also doubts whether standards of service could be specified satisfactorily, or could be achieved consistently and profitably without what might be an unacceptable degree of interference in the way households live their lives. Moreover, the industry's perception is that the unit price of energy is the first priority for customers. These difficulties have dissuaded electricity and gas suppliers from trying to go down this path. The expansion of the Energy Efficiency Standards of Performance Scheme,[27] which we discuss in the next chapter (6.62–6.69) will, however, require electricity and gas suppliers to spend more on enabling households to raise energy efficiency.

ELECTRICITY GENERATION, TRANSMISSION AND DISTRIBUTION

5.24   In a liberalised market suppliers seek to obtain electricity from generators at the lowest price. Generators seek to bring down the cost at which they can provide electricity by using a fuel which they expect to continue to be available at a low cost and by building generating plants which have a low capital cost, are quick to construct and use well-tried technology, preferably available in modular form. Gas-fired generation has rapidly become the technology of choice for generators. Some companies have sought to use other low cost fuels to generate electricity, in the form of orimulsion or heavy oils, but public resistance based on the potential for environmental harm associated with such fuels has prevented their adoption on any significant scale. In contrast, the use of gas for electricity generation has expanded very rapidly (figure 5-V); this has been the 'dash to gas'.

5.25   At present, gas-fired plants produce electricity at a lower unit price than almost all renewable energy sources in the UK. Electricity from the more expensive renewables exceeds the price of electricity from all types of fossil fuel plant and nuclear power stations. Some renewables are also less attractive to suppliers because they operate intermittently. Construction of renewable energy plants and sale of their output has therefore been almost entirely dependent on support from the non-fossil fuel obligation and the Scottish and Northern Ireland Renewables Orders, which we discuss below (5.38–5.42).

Figure 5-V
Fuel input for UK electricity generation 1965-2020

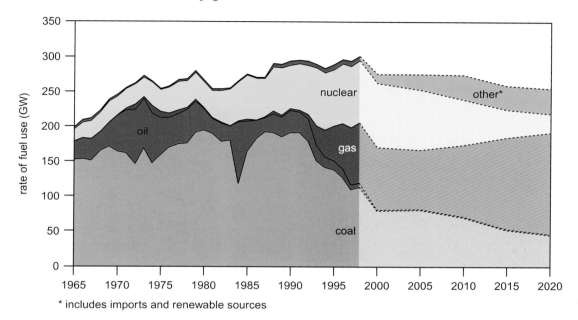

* includes imports and renewable sources

5.26   Transmission and distribution companies remain as monopolies and have their prices controlled by the regulator. In the absence of any special provision by the regulator to cover the additional costs of such activity, they have no incentive to operate in a way that would be beneficial or encouraging to small embedded and/or intermittent generating plants nor to decentralise the control of their networks.

IMPLICATIONS FOR ENVIRONMENTAL OBJECTIVES

5.27   Privatisation and liberalisation of energy industries and markets need not make the achievement of environmental objectives harder. Liberalising markets has brought some incidental environmental benefit in the short and medium term. Gas produces about 40% less carbon dioxide per unit of energy than coal (3.36), and also (for UK supplies) much less sulphur dioxide. Widespread concern about the decline of the UK coal industry has not prevented the expansion of gas-fired generation and, because of this 'dash to gas', emissions of both gases are now substantially less than they would otherwise have been (5.35, 5.49). But, in general, solving the environmental problems associated with energy requires some form of intervention, by government in setting the statutory and fiscal framework for the energy industries or by a regulator in putting government policies into effect.

5.28   To the extent that inefficiency in energy use has been encouraged by low and falling prices, the appropriate form of intervention is likely to be to levy corrective taxes designed to reflect the environmental damage caused by different types of fuel. This would encourage customers to increase the efficiency with which they use energy and favour the use of less environmentally damaging fuels (3.34).

ENVIRONMENTAL REGULATION AND POLICIES

5.29   As we emphasised at the beginning of this report (1.10), obtaining energy from any source has impacts on the environment. There has long since been, and continues to be, regulation of the energy industries intended to protect people, and more recently plant and animal life, from the adverse effects of their activities. There are also certain energy policies which have been pursued, at least in part, on environmental grounds, even before climate change become an issue. We review the most relevant aspects briefly before discussing the draft Climate Change Programme for the UK published by the government in March of this year. Bearing in mind that the emphasis of this report is on the possibility of reducing considerably the use of fossil fuels, we have not described here the statutory controls which apply to their extraction (for example, from open cast coal mines or offshore oil or gas fields).

CONSENT FOR NEW ENERGY INSTALLATIONS

5.30 Plants to generate electricity may require various forms of statutory consent. *Combustion plants* with a net rated thermal input of 50 MW or more are subject to integrated pollution control and require authorisation from the Environment Agencies.[28] An authorisation requires the operator to use the best available techniques not entailing excessive cost to reduce emissions of prescribed substances and places limits on such emissions. Carbon dioxide has not been treated as a controlled substance under the UK legislation on integrated pollution control. That is in the course of being replaced by the EC Directive on Integrated Pollution Prevention and Control,[29] which we discuss in the next chapter (6.25-6.26). At smaller combustion plants, emissions to air are regulated by local authorities in England and Wales and by the Scottish Environment Protection Agency in Scotland; and liquid emissions and disposals of waste materials are regulated by the Environment Agencies.

5.31 *Nuclear power stations* require a licence from the Nuclear Installations Inspectorate of the Health and Safety Executive in order to operate. Their emissions and disposal of their wastes are regulated by the Environment Agencies.

5.32 *Generating plants of any type* which have a capacity of 50 MW or more require consent from the Secretary of State for Trade and Industry in England and Wales or the Secretary of State for Scotland under the Electricity Act 1989. The same Ministers give approval for overhead transmission lines. Before taking a decision in either context, the Minister consults local planning authorities; if the local planning authority objects or the Minister considers it appropriate, a public inquiry may be held. If consent or approval is given under the 1989 Act, the Minister also directs that planning permission is deemed to be granted.[30]

5.33 For energy installations on land which are not covered by the procedures described in the previous paragraph, planning permission has to be obtained in the same way as for any other development, and application is normally made to the local planning authority. If the application is refused, the applicant may appeal to the Environment Minister. The Minister will then appoint an inspector to consider the appeal;[31] in cases of significant public interest or controversy a public inquiry will normally be held. If a case appears to raise issues of national importance, the Minister may call it in for his/her own decision, following a public inquiry. A planning permission will carry various conditions; in the case of an energy installation these are now likely to include its decommissioning and removal after it ceases to be used.

REDUCING AIR POLLUTION

5.34 The health effects, and other local and regional effects, of pollutants released from the burning of fossil fuels have long been a major concern (1.6). The standards applied to emissions are now much more stringent, but the overall quantity of fossil fuels used has greatly increased.

Current levels of air pollution in the UK are judged to have both acute and chronic effects on human health (1.7). Standards are set at EU and national levels for concentrations of pollutants in the atmosphere, and the government has recently published the UK's second Air Quality Strategy under the 1995 Environment Act to indicate how those standards will be achieved.[32]

5.35   Power stations now generally have a relatively small influence on air quality in the UK. The main driver for reducing their emissions has been international pressure to reduce the effects on the natural environment from acid precipitation across north-west Europe. Progressive reductions in emissions of nitrogen and sulphur oxides have been required under the Convention on Long Range Transboundary Air Pollution of the United Nations Economic Commission for Europe and parallel EU legislation. Emissions of sulphur dioxide have dropped sharply, largely as the outcome of the 'dash to gas' for electricity generation (5.24). A new protocol under the convention requires the UK to make further substantial reductions by 2010 in emissions of sulphur dioxide and nitrogen oxides, and also control emissions of volatile organic compounds and ammonia.[33]

5.36   In most areas of the UK the major determinant of air quality is emissions from use of fossil fuels in vehicles. The most important controls over such emissions are now the mandatory standards in EU legislation for new vehicles and for fuels. Those standards are also being progressively tightened.

5.37   While the focus of this report is the carbon dioxide produced from burning fossil fuels, policies to reduce emissions of other pollutants will continue to be a major factor, both in the UK and across Europe. The small particles present in the lower atmosphere as a result of sulphur dioxide pollution have a cooling effect (see box 2B); reducing sulphur dioxide emissions therefore makes the enhancement in the greenhouse effect rather larger than it would otherwise have been. There are also conflicts which arise at the margin between reducing the local and regional effects of emissions and reducing energy use. Removing sulphur from crude oil in order to reduce sulphur dioxide emissions from vehicles and ships requires refineries to burn more fuel. Flue gas desulphurisation, which removes sulphur dioxide from power station flue gases, also requires more fossil fuel to be burnt. Catalytic converters fitted to vehicles increase fuel consumption, and other conflicts arise in vehicle technology, as we illustrate in chapter 8. In broad terms however reducing the use of fossil fuels will contribute directly to reducing regional and local air pollution.

RENEWABLE ENERGY SOURCES

5.38   Government programmes to develop renewable sources of energy date back to the oil crisis of the 1970s. Initially they took the form of funding research. As part of the arrangements for privatisation of the electricity industry, a non-fossil fuel obligation (NFFO) and a non-fossil fuel levy were established in England and Wales. The primary purpose was to maintain an assured market for electricity generated by nuclear power stations, but they also created an assured market for renewable energy technologies which were regarded as having a chance of being able to 'compete equitably with other energy technologies in a self-sustaining market'.[34] Corresponding arrangements to support the emergence of such technologies were made in Scotland and Northern Ireland. The national policy to promote renewable energy was incorporated in the land use planning system through guidance issued in England, Scotland and Wales; planning authorities must have regard to that guidance in drawing up development plans and exercising their development control responsibilities.[35]

5.39   Decisions on the award of NFFO contracts have not included any consideration of the environmental impact of particular projects. Developers seeking to have their projects included in NFFO submitted bids to supply a specified amount of electricity at a specified price. Over the five rounds of bidding the average price of electricity in successful bids halved, and in the fifth round was only 2.71 p/kWh, marginally above the average pool selling price (see box 5A and 8.43) of 2.60 p/kWh in 1998.[36]

5.40   Although renewable energy sources still supply only a very small proportion of the UK's primary energy or the energy for electricity generation, there has been rapid expansion under the stimulus of NFFO and its Scottish and Northern Ireland counterparts. Between 1990 and 1997 the average rate of energy supplied by renewable sources as heat and electricity rose from 1.57 GW (0.5% of UK primary energy consumption) to 3 GW (1.0%).[37]

5.41   Whereas the previous contribution from renewable energy sources had come predominantly from large-scale inland water power schemes, the new projects commissioned with NFFO support have predominantly involved burning municipal or agricultural wastes or landfill gas. These sources accounted for more than 90% of the increase in output from renewable sources between 1990 and 1998. In the final bidding round for NFFO municipal and industrial waste projects accounted for 41% of the electrical capacity contracted for, large wind farms for 29% and landfill gas for 27%.[38] These three dominant sources have had very different success rates in terms of gaining planning permission and achieving actual implementation. By the end of 1998, 95% of landfill gas schemes accepted in the first three rounds had been commissioned but only a quarter of the waste-to-energy projects; the proportion for wind farms was 39%, but had declined with time.[39]

5.42   As figures 5-II and 5-V show, the output from renewable energy sources is projected to increase very rapidly over the next 20 years. The government's proposed target is that the proportion of UK electricity requirements met from renewables should be increased from 2.5% now to 5% by the end of 2003 and 10% by 2010. The target for 2010 carries the proviso that the cost to consumers must be acceptable; the government is undertaking consultations with the industry and consumer groups on that aspect.[40] To achieve the target for 2010 there will be a new system of support: legal requirements will be placed on electricity suppliers to purchase specified proportions of electricity from renewable sources. In the light of the pattern of development of renewable sources so far, there must be some doubt whether these short-term targets will be achieved. The three dominant technologies mentioned above account for 74-83% of the contribution of new schemes to the 10% target in three scenarios drawn up by the Energy Technology Support Unit (ETSU), the government's consultants on renewable energy.[41] We discuss in chapter 7 the prospects for renewable energy generally and for particular sources, and assess the support that will now be available for them.

PROMOTING ENERGY EFFICIENCY

5.43   Government has promoted energy efficiency with subsidies, advice and publicity campaigns during recent decades. The motive has mainly been to increase economic efficiency, although governments have also used policies and campaigns aimed at reducing overall consumption during transient energy crises caused by coal mining strikes and oil embargoes. During the 1990s, the reduction of fuel poverty and the need to limit greenhouse gas emissions from burning fossil fuels have become the main driving forces behind the government's energy efficiency programmes.

5.44   Current arrangements for England are summarised in figure 5-VI, and are discussed further in chapter 6. The Department of the Environment, Transport and the Regions (DETR) has lead responsibility for energy efficiency issues and oversees energy efficiency in England at the point of end use; the devolved administrations have many of these responsibilities in other parts of the UK. The way DETR exercises its responsibilities for building control, integrated pollution control and transport also has important implications for energy efficiency. It has no direct oversight of the efficiency of energy production, distribution and supply. These are matters for DTI, which is also responsible for security of energy supplies, regulation of energy markets and government-funded energy research and development.

Figure 5-VI
Energy efficiency: current responsibilities and points of action

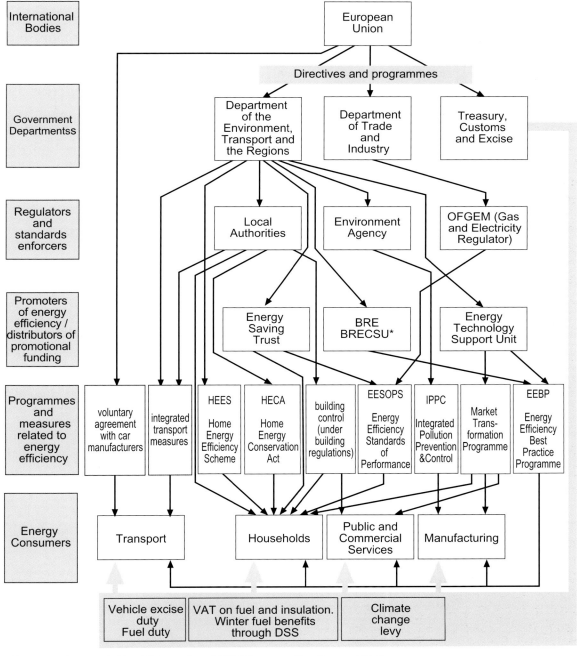

* Buildings Research Establishment and BRE Conservation Support Unit
To simplify, the responsibilities shown in this diagram are those that apply in England

5.45   The government has recognised that combined heat and power (CHP) schemes (3.40) are one of the most important means of saving energy. At the end of 1998 there were just under 1,400 such schemes in the UK with a total electricity generating capacity of almost 4 GW. The great majority of this capacity was in schemes serving manufacturing industry but there were some 1,000 plants providing heat and electricity to buildings including hotels, hospitals and blocks of flats. The government believes it is broadly on course to meet its immediate target of increasing capacity to 5 GW by 2000/01.[42] It is due to set out a new strategy for CHP that would include a target of at least 10 GW of electricity generating capacity by 2010. The main instrument that has encouraged CHP schemes is an exemption from DTI's policy of restricting construction of new gas-fired generating plants. For the future, the fuel input to CHP plants, their heat output and some of their electricity output will be exempt from the climate change levy (see 6.19). Turbines and engines in CHP schemes will also be exempt from non-domestic rates.

CARBON DIOXIDE EMISSIONS – THE UK CLIMATE CHANGE PROGRAMME

5.46   Once ratification of the Kyoto Protocol (4.8) has been completed and an EU legal instrument is in place, the UK will be legally bound to reduce its annual emissions of a basket of six greenhouse gases in 2008-2012 to 12.5% below the 1990 level. This is its agreed share of the 8% reduction for the EU as a whole. The government has also set a goal (deriving from a manifesto commitment in the 1997 general election) to reduce the UK's annual carbon dioxide emissions in 2010 to 20% below their 1990 level. The UK had previously accepted the non-binding proposition under the United Nations Framework Convention on Climate Change (UNFCCC, 4.3-4.7) that developed countries should prevent emissions of greenhouse gases in 2000 from exceeding their 1990 level.

5.47   UK governments have published two climate change programmes, in 1994[43] and (in draft) in March 2000.[44] These have reported on changes in greenhouse gas emissions since 1990; given projections for future emissions (in the case of carbon dioxide, based on DTI's projections of energy use (5.2) and current energy policies); and put forward proposals for new measures to bring emissions below the projected levels.

5.48   In the event the UK has had no difficulty in bringing emissions in 2000 below the 1990 level. Carbon dioxide emissions fell from 168 million tonnes of carbon (MtC) in 1990 to 158 MtC in 1998, a fall of 10 MtC or almost 6% (figure 5-VII). The government's projection is that in 2000 they will have fallen further, to 152 MtC. Emissions of the other greenhouse gases have also fallen.

5.49   By far the largest contribution to this big reduction in carbon dioxide emissions has come from electricity generation; between 1990 and 2000 this industry's emissions are estimated to fall by some 14 MtC, a quarter of its total emissions at the beginning of the period. This very rapid decline was due mainly to the 'dash to gas' (5.24). The entry into service of a large new nuclear power station (Sizewell B) and more efficient operation of existing nuclear power stations also contributed. Thus it was that carbon dioxide emissions fell even as UK energy consumption continued to rise (see figure 5-I).

5.50   Governments deployed a range of measures aimed, at least in part, at reducing carbon dioxide emissions, and these have contributed to keeping emissions below the level they would otherwise have reached. But their aggregate effect was less than that from the substitution of gas and nuclear energy for coal in electricity generation.[45] Most of these measures are still in existence and some have been extended. They included policies aimed at reducing demand for energy (chiefly the increase in road fuel duties; the encouragement of energy efficiency

Figure 5-VII
UK carbon dioxide emissions 1990-2020: effect of government's draft programme

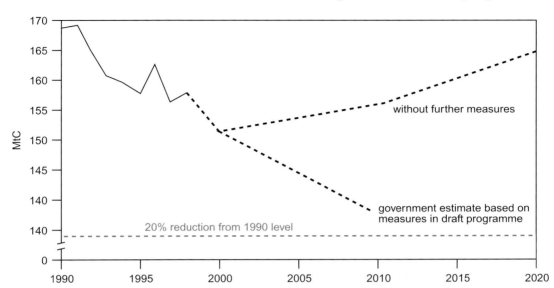

measures by businesses and households through advice, demonstration programmes and subsidies; and the introduction of VAT on household gas and electricity), which we discuss in chapter 6; and policies to reduce carbon dioxide emissions from energy supply by developing renewable sources, which we discuss in chapter 7, and increasing the number of CHP schemes.

5.51   After 2000 carbon dioxide emissions are expected to rise in the absence of further measures, as figure 5-VII shows. In 2010 they are projected to be 156 MtC a year, 7% below the 1990 level; in 2020 they are projected to be 165 MtC, only 2% below. This rising trend reflects expectations that energy use will continue to rise with economic growth and the UK will remain fundamentally dependent on fossil fuels.

5.52   Despite this, the government is confident that the UK can meet its Kyoto Protocol obligation to cut annual emissions of a basket of six greenhouse gases by 12.5% (5.46). This confidence is based on the large reduction in carbon dioxide emissions already achieved, and the even deeper cuts already achieved or in prospect for the other five gases in the basket.[46] Total emissions of all six gases are projected to be 13.5% below the 1990 level in 2010, and 10% below in 2020.

5.53   For carbon dioxide these projections assume, on the one hand, a continuing shift to using gas and, on the other hand, some decline in nuclear power as older plants cease operating. They also take into account the effects of present energy policies and programmes, including three important recent developments. The first is the target of expanding the proportion of UK electricity generated by renewable sources to 10% by 2010 (5.42). The second is the climate change levy which will begin in April 2001 (6.19); as well as bringing about some reduction in demand, this should stimulate investment in renewable energy and in CHP schemes. The third is the government's decision to scale down the road fuel duty escalator (6.117); as a result, some reductions in demand which had been expected will be lost.

5.54   The draft Climate Change Programme published in March sets out significant additional policies ('the core programme'). These are discussed in more detail in chapter 6. The government maintains that, in total, they would deliver a further reduction in carbon dioxide emissions of 17.6 MtC a year in 2010. Carbon dioxide emissions in 2010 would therefore be 17.5%, rather than 7%, below the 1990 level; and emissions of the basket of six greenhouse gases would be 21.5% below the 1990 level.

5.55   Beyond this core programme, the government expresses confidence 'that the large number of measures not yet quantified [in terms of emission reductions] will have a substantial impact and could allow emissions to fall further still, so that the UK's carbon dioxide emissions reach 20% below 1990 levels in 2010.' These unquantified measures include action by the devolved administrations and by local authorities (especially in reducing emissions associated with household energy use), improved management of traffic speed, tree planting and public awareness campaigns.

5.56   We question three of the major elements in the core programme which together are claimed to deliver some 10 MtC of the further 17.6 MtC reduction in annual carbon dioxide emissions. The first is the 4 MtC a year reduction in emissions from cars, most of which is to be achieved through agreements between the European Commission and European, Japanese and Korean manufacturers, and the remainder through changes in company car taxation and vehicle excise duty. The manufacturers have agreed to reduce average carbon dioxide emissions per kilometre from new cars to 25% below the 1998/99 level by 2008 (European manufacturers) or 2009 (Japanese and Korean). There are intermediate targets in 2003 and 2004. Meeting these targets will require a rapid improvement in the fuel consumption of cars, coming after a decade in which there was virtually no improvement.

5.57   The second element we question also relates to transport. The core programme assumes that carbon dioxide emissions will be reduced by up to 2.7 MtC a year as a result of 'very intensive implementation' of the options for reducing pollution and congestion set out in the Transport White Paper.[47] That was one of a range of scenarios for transport policy implementation which DETR has analysed for England. Given the current rate of progress in implementing the policies in the White Paper, and the decision to scale down the fuel duty escalator, it is questionable whether all the necessary measures could be in place by 2010. In DETR's lowest intensity scenario the estimated reduction in emissions is only 0.6 MtC a year. We discuss these scenarios further in the next chapter (6.112, 6.118-6.121).

5.58   The third element in the core programme we question relates to energy use in the home. The government estimates that, if the great majority of households were to take up cost-effective energy-saving options already available, emissions could be reduced by between 2.7 and 3.8 MtC a year by 2010. We show in the next chapter that there are a variety of reasons why such options are generally not taken up. A key instrument intended to change that situation for the future will be obligations on electricity and gas suppliers to carry out energy-saving measures for households, particularly low-income households (6.62-6.67). The latest of these Energy Efficiency Standards of Performance Schemes however, which will run from 2002 to 2005, is estimated to reduce emissions by only 0.8 MtC a year.[48] There will then be only five years left in which to achieve a large and rapid improvement in the efficiency of energy use by households.

5.59   There is, then, something of a hole in the government's climate change programme. The hole is of uncertain size, but there are assumed reductions in annual emissions of several MtC for which either no policies are in place or it is quite possible the measures identified will not deliver. This, we presume, is why the draft Climate Change Programme speaks of 'moving towards' the domestic goal of a 20% cut in carbon dioxide emissions.

5.60   The goal of reducing the UK's annual carbon dioxide emissions by 20% from their 1990 level by 2010 is a major step in the right direction. Such a substantial, early reduction would be significant because it will become more difficult to make further reductions after 2010. **We recommend that this 20% goal become a firm target and the government should produce a climate change programme that will ensure it is achieved.** In this report we recommend policies which could enable this reduction to be made by 2010 or soon afterwards, with further sustained reductions to follow.

RESEARCH AND DEVELOPMENT

5.61   There is a further aspect of the current situation which causes us great concern, the decline in research and development (R&D). Technological and scientific progress have played the central role in expanding energy supplies. They will continue to be crucial, both in developing alternatives to fossil fuels and in increasing the efficiency with which energy is used. Historically governments have played a big part in energy research and development. Government spending on research and development reported by the 24 developed countries which are members of the International Energy Agency peaked in real terms in 1980, after years in which expenditure on non-nuclear energy had risen especially fast. It has been on a declining trend ever since, with nuclear research and development continuing to make up about half the total (figure 5-VIII).[49]

Figure 5-VIII

Government support for energy-related research and development 1974-1997: International Energy Agency countries and the UK

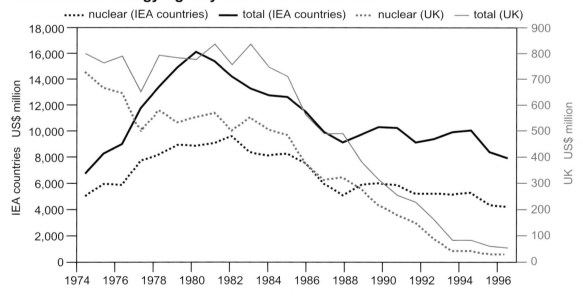

5.62   UK government spending on energy R&D has declined much more rapidly than across the IEA nations as a whole (figure 5-VIII), from £338.5 million in 1987 (at 1998 prices) to £44.4 million in 1998. Spending on renewable energy R&D fell by 81% between 1987 and 1998. Nuclear accounted for the bulk of expenditure until the early 1990s, but has now fallen to about half. By 1997 the UK had the lowest ratio of energy R&D spending to GDP of any IEA country apart from Portugal, Turkey and New Zealand. In proportion to GDP the Japanese government's spending on all forms of energy R&D was 17 times higher than the UK's in 1998, and its spending on non-nuclear R&D 7 times higher than the UK's. US government expenditure on energy-related R&D, expressed as a proportion of GDP, was 5 times higher than the UK's, and 7 times higher for non-nuclear R&D. There is likewise a large gap between the UK expenditure and the average for other EU Member States, although their individual ratios vary considerably.[50] The special circumstances behind the UK's more rapid decline in public expenditure on energy R&D over the past two decades were a general government policy of reducing expenditure on near-market and applied research and the difficulty other technologies had in attracting any significant share of a largely nuclear programme.

5.63   No comprehensive data on private sector spending on energy-related R&D are collected in the UK. However, it appears that, far from compensating for reduced government spending, expenditure by UK industry has either remained flat or fallen over the previous decade, in line with the general trend for private sector R&D spending in the UK.[51] Data for the total R&D spending of groups of companies providing energy services also indicates a decline.

5.64   For the UK-based oil and gas production industry, this fall appears to have been prompted by falling oil prices and receding fears about scarcity. In the nuclear industry, now largely privatised, it has reflected the drying up of the market for new power stations and the ending of the fast-breeder reactor programme. In gas and electricity supply, privatisation of nationalised industries followed by liberalisation of markets has put pressure on companies to cut overheads including R&D. The state-owned electricity industry had several large research and development facilities which have either closed down, scaled back their activities or diversified following privatisation.[52] Figures supplied to us by the DTI showed that spending by the UK gas supply industry fell by 15% between 1994 and 1996 and by 14% for the electricity supply industry.[53] The task of carrying out research and development now falls almost entirely to equipment and plant manufacturers, many of which are not UK-based.

5.65   Later in this report, we discuss the need for major changes in the electricity grid in coming decades to cope with more intermittent and embedded generation. The National Grid Company's R&D expenditure is some 0.5% of the value of its sales.[54] There may need to be substantial increases in R&D spending related to electricity transmission and distribution; the current structure and regulation of the industry will not encourage the private sector to carry this out.

5.66   Over the next few decades very large sums will be spent on replacing existing energy infrastructure which will be reaching the end of its life. The challenge of countering climate change should redirect this investment towards the development and widespread application of innovatory approaches. Large programmes of research and development will be essential to enable this task to be completed successfully and effectively. The inadequacy of present programmes is a major point of concern. We make recommendations on this subject in our concluding chapter.

WHAT KIND OF ENERGY POLICIES?

5.67   The challenge of climate change demands a much greater coherence between policies aimed at ensuring secure, diverse and sustainable energy supplies at competitive prices (5.13) and policies to protect the environment in the long term. There is a widespread view, reflected in the evidence we received[55] and articulated in recent reports from Select Committees, that environmental priorities and energy policies need to be integrated,[56] and in particular that there is a need for an effective energy efficiency strategy. As the House of Commons Environmental Audit Committee put it:

> A new strategy needs to be an integral part of the existing energy policy mantra of 'diversity, security and sustainability' which itself needs definition, each term and the balance to be struck between them.[57]

5.68 Policies are needed which will extend beyond the next decade and achieve the large reductions in demand for energy and the rapid development of non-fossil fuel sources that are essential if there are to be large long-term reductions in carbon dioxide emissions. Those policies are not yet in place. The government has recognised in principle that securing further reductions in carbon dioxide emissions after 2010 is likely to involve significant, far-reaching changes in energy production and use.[58] The scale and nature of these changes are the central themes of this report and are pursued in the following chapters.

The UK has reduced carbon dioxide emissions from burning fossil fuels. But that has been largely fortuitous. It will be difficult to maintain the reductions over the next 20 years. Meanwhile government expenditure on energy research and development has plummeted. Energy policies and environmental policies are not yet integrated

I The UK's most recent nuclear
power station Sizewell B was
commissioned in 1995 with a
capacity of 1.2 GW(7.11)

II The coal-fired Didcot power
station was commissioned in 1972
with a capacity of 2GW

III The Deeside combined cycle gas
turbine (CCGT) power station was
commissioned in 1994 and has a
capacity of 0.5GW

IV This Sainsbury's supermarket (described in box 6A) was designed to use half the electricity of a conventional new food store

V This building at the University of East Anglia (described in box 6A) consumes less than half the energy of an air-conditioned building of comparable size and function

Chapter 6

REDUCING ENERGY USE

What are the main factors that have driven rising demand for energy? What needs and aspirations for energy-related services still remain to be satisfied? What potentials exist for greater efficiency? What are the long-term prospects for reducing the amount of energy used in the UK? What instruments should governments deploy in order to reduce energy use?

6.1   If society could reduce its use of energy, that would reduce the burning of fossil fuels, the threat of climate change and other damaging impacts of energy production and supply. Yet many of the things most closely associated with progress – sustained increases in living standards, rising longevity, large gains in health and welfare, increased opportunities to travel – have been associated with increasing consumption of energy.

6.2   In the UK, energy consumption rose through the 20th century, driven by the rising output of goods and services and growth in population, household numbers, personal travel and freight transport. But while primary energy consumption increased by 24% between 1965 and 1998 and final energy consumption by 16%, the UK's real gross domestic product rose by 147% over the same period (figures 5-I and 5-III).[1] A progressive reduction in energy intensity is a worldwide phenomenon (3.29), and largely a response to the continual pressure to cut costs by reducing the amount of material and energy used to produce services and goods.

6.3   Over and above improvements in the efficiencies with which energy is used by individuals, businesses and public bodies at the stage of final consumption, further very large reductions in the total use of energy, that is use of primary energy (3.33), could be achieved by cutting losses within the energy system (5.7), for example by greater use of combined heat and power plants. We deal with that aspect of the matter in chapter 8.

6.4   In this chapter we consider whether it would be possible to enhance the trend of declining energy intensity to the point where energy use begins a gradual, sustained decline without unacceptable effects on the quality of life, including social equity and cohesion. A distinction must be drawn at the outset between 'energy conservation' and 'energy efficiency'. The former implies reductions in the consumption of energy services. That could be achieved simply by 'making do' with less energy – by turning thermostats down and tolerating lower temperatures, for instance. The latter implies obtaining more useful heat, light or work from each unit of energy supplied, either as a result of technological improvements or by reducing waste; in other words, obtaining the same services with less use of energy. We consider that attempts to protect the environment and prevent climate change based principally on exhorting people to make sacrifices in comfort, pleasure and convenience in order to consume less energy are unlikely to succeed.

6.5   A crucial consideration is that even in a nation as wealthy as the UK, the basic energy-related needs of a significant part of the population are still not being met. The UK experiences about 30,000 more deaths each winter than would be expected given the average death rate for the entire year, the majority among the elderly population.[2] Some nations and regions with much colder climates than the UK's have smaller increases in winter mortality.[3] The difference can be partially attributed to low temperatures in UK dwellings occupied by elderly people on low incomes. Thousands of lives are shortened each year by weeks, months and years in one of the world's richer nations because a substantial proportion of the elderly population cannot afford adequately to warm their homes.

6.6   *Fuel poverty*, as defined by government, is experienced by households needing to spend at least 10% of their income in order to provide adequate warmth in the home. The government estimates that in 1996 there were 4.4 million households – more than a fifth of the total – who suffer fuel poverty in England[4] and the proportions in other parts of the UK are similar. Their low incomes, and the fact that many of them live in homes which are poorly insulated or have highly inefficient heating systems, mean that such households would need to spend this high proportion of their incomes to maintain adequate warmth. Many cannot afford to do so and the elderly, children and chronically ill among them are at risk of a range of cold-related diseases as a consequence. Half of the households in fuel poverty consist of people aged over 60. **Major improvements in the energy efficiency of UK housing are required.** Without them the eradication of fuel poverty would involve substantial increases in energy consumption and in carbon dioxide emissions.

6.7   The gradual long-term reduction in UK energy intensity referred to above (6.2) accelerated in the past quarter century following the first oil price shock in 1973. UK primary energy consumption in 1998 was only 5% higher than in 1973, and final energy consumption only 2% higher, while real GDP rose by 63% over this 25-year period.[5] It is sometimes supposed that a collapse in the most energy-intensive heavy industries has played a dominant role in the decline in energy intensity. It is the case that manufacturing's share of UK output has declined, while that of the less energy-intensive services sector has risen. It is also the case that some of the most energy-intensive industries have contracted. But the Department of Trade and Industry (DTI) has estimated that only one twelfth of the reduction in the UK's overall energy intensity between 1973 and 1995 was due to structural change in the economy.[6]

6.8   Since 1984, however, the rate of decline in UK energy intensity has slowed markedly. Total primary energy consumption rose by 20% between 1984 and 1998 and total final energy consumption by 15% while real gross domestic product rose by 43%.[7] In this more recent period, the trend has been for UK primary energy use to rise by a little over 1% a year. The trend reflects generally low energy prices over this period (although global oil prices have risen markedly in the short interval since early 1999). The government's latest projections for energy trends over the next 20 years are discussed in chapter 5 (5.8-5.11).

6.9   There is a strong economic argument in favour of raising energy efficiency. Repeated analyses have shown that in every sector of the economy large quantities of energy are wasted and that apparently highly cost-effective investments for making energy savings are forgone.[8,9] Improvements in energy efficiency also offer environmental benefits which extend beyond curbing greenhouse gas emissions and other fossil fuel-related pollutants. Nuclear power and renewable energy resources have environmental impacts which can be lessened if energy consumption is reduced. If, furthermore, new energy-saving technologies can be transferred to developing nations this may enable them to raise standards of living while avoiding some of the environmental damage previously associated with industrialisation.

6.10   In this chapter we first review the final energy use of four sectors-manufacturing industry (6.12-6.35), public and commercial services (6.36-6.51), households (6.52-6.106) and transport (6.107-6.131). The changes in their energy consumption since 1965 and the DTI's latest projections for the period to 2010 are shown in figure 6-I. For each, we review recent patterns of energy use and policies, regulation and economic instruments which are currently influencing energy consumption. We consider the short- to medium-term scope for reducing energy demand in each sector, and make some recommendations. We then consider the combined potential for energy savings of all four sectors and the longer-term prospects for reducing energy consumption (6.132-6.148). We consider economic instruments in general (6.149-6.154) before proposing a carbon tax (6.155-6.169). We conclude by considering what kind of changes in regulation and institutional structures might enable the UK to reduce its overall energy use in the long term (6.170-6.174).

Figure 6-I

UK rate of energy consumption by final user, by sector 1965-2010

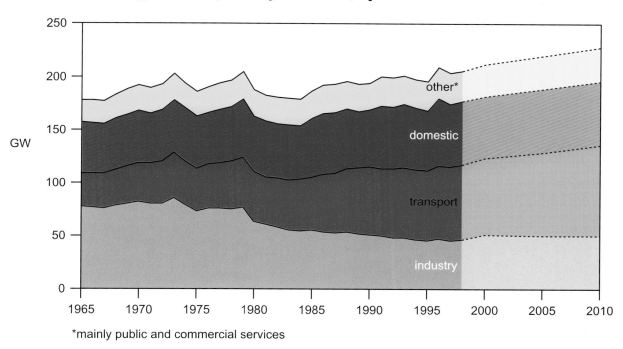

*mainly public and commercial services

6.11   In assessments of the scope for energy savings in the four sectors, a distinction is normally drawn between the technical and the economic potentials for reducing energy consumption. The *technical potential* refers to reductions which could be achieved by the universal application of energy-saving equipment and technologies that are already on the market or proven to the point where they are near market. It is the proportion or quantity of energy which could be saved given current technology and knowledge. The *economic potential* is an estimate of the energy savings that could actually be made with this technology if all improvements and investments in energy-saving equipment which covered their costs were made. In making assessments, both types of potential are considered to be fulfilled over a 10-25 year period as new, higher-efficiency plant and products replace existing ones. The analyses require assumptions to be made about 'business as usual' energy consumption over this period, future energy prices, the discount rates employed in appraising investments and future economic growth. They are illustrative projections, and cannot be regarded as precise estimates of what would actually be saved if the economic or technical potential were fulfilled.

MANUFACTURING INDUSTRY

6.12   The peak year for energy consumption by UK manufacturing industry was 1973, the year of the first oil price shock. Its share of final energy use had been fairly stable for more than a decade before then, hovering close to 42%. But after 1973 it fell away and by 1998 it stood at only 22% of total final energy use. The absolute figure for UK industrial energy consumption also declined by 46% over this same period.[10] Yet industrial output rose by 46% between 1970 and 1996; 59% less energy was required to produce each unit of manufacturing output than was the case in 1970.[11]

6.13   The government considers that efficiency gains were the main reason for this sector's spectacular reduction in energy intensity but the decline in the output of some energy-intensive manufacturing industries such as iron and steel has also played a part. (As was mentioned above (6.7) structural change in industry has played a relatively minor role in the reduction of energy intensity in the economy as a whole.) The chemicals sector, another heavy consumer of energy, more than doubled its output (in terms of total value, adjusted for inflation) between 1970 and 1996 but its use of energy (excluding fuels used as feed stocks) fell by 21%.[12] This was partly due to major gains in efficiency, but also due to restructuring within this sector with the output of higher added value products expanding relative to basic, bulk chemicals.

6.14   Since the late 1980s levels of energy efficiency have improved much more slowly in manufacturing industry than they did in the previous decade. The decline in manufacturing industry's overall energy use appears to have come to a halt. This stagnation is found, to a lesser or greater extent, in all of the major manufacturing sectors and it coincides with a period of low energy prices. In his report for the government on *Economic instruments and the business use of energy* Lord Marshall concluded that there was a causal connection.[13]

6.15   There are three broad approaches to improvement, with some degree of overlap between them. The first is to make existing plant and processes run more efficiently without any major modifications. This is largely a matter of good housekeeping, ensuring that buildings are not overheated and overlit and that equipment is well maintained and never operating unnecessarily or over-performing. To be effective this approach requires management to measure energy consumption widely and frequently, to make and update plans for reductions and to involve staff. In some manufacturing sectors a large proportion of the total energy consumption is devoted simply to heating and lighting buildings. This gives ample scope for housekeeping measures to reduce energy use. According to an analysis by ETSU commissioned by the Department of the Environment, Transport and the Regions (DETR), just under half of the vehicle manufacturing sector's energy use is for heating and lighting.[14]

6.16   The second approach, which also requires investment in management and staff time, is to modify or retrofit existing plant, by replacing individual components such as boilers with higher efficiency alternatives, by installing insulation around pipes and furnaces, and by improving or replacing control systems. The third approach is to invest in larger and more expensive modifications to existing plant or to purchase entirely new plant. There may sometimes be a case for bringing forward the replacement of an entire plant by a few years instead of retrofitting immediately. Major improvements in energy efficiency can often be part of improvements in product quality and productivity.

THE POTENTIAL FOR REDUCING ENERGY CONSUMPTION

6.17   The ETSU analysis (6.15) projected that under a business as usual scenario UK manufacturing industry's energy consumption would rise by 18% between 1995 and 2020.[15] This bottom-up projection, based on trends in output and efficiency improvements in each manufacturing sector, pre-dated the government's proposed climate change levy, and assumed the various sectors continued to make efficiency improvement at the same low rate as they did between 1990 and 1995, at a time of recession and low energy prices. ETSU also projected industrial energy consumption under a scenario in which all cost-effective energy saving measures and technologies were phased in gradually (that is inefficient equipment was not scrapped earlier than usual). This analysis of economic potential assumed industry would only invest if there were fairly short payback periods for the initial investment-just one to two years in the case of retrofit measures and 2-15 years in the case of new plant. Under this scenario manufacturing industry's energy consumption fell initially but eventually rose by 4% between 1995 and 2020 due to growth in output overwhelming gains in efficiency. In a third, technical potential scenario, all existing plant and equipment were assumed to be replaced immediately by state-of-the-art, high efficiency alternatives. Energy consumption then fell by 8% over the 25-year period.

6.18   Just over a quarter of manufacturing industry's energy requirement is for electricity.[16] Greater use of combined heat and power (CHP) stations (3.40), which supply both electricity and heat for industrial processes and space heating (usually in the form of steam or hot water), is assumed to play a leading role in reducing manufacturing's total demand for energy in all of these scenarios, including business as usual. In 1990 CHP supplied 11% of industry's own electricity demand.[17] Under ETSU's business as usual scenario, this is projected to grow to 18% in 2020. Under the economic potential scenario the contribution is put at 76%. The speed at which CHP spreads through industry will depend heavily on the terms on which surplus electricity can be marketed into the grid. It may also depend on expanding opportunities to export heat to nearby homes and businesses (8.8-8.9).

MEASURES FOR REDUCING ENERGY CONSUMPTION

Taxation-the climate change levy

6.19   The ETSU projections suggest that UK manufacturing industry could gradually reduce its total energy consumption while expanding the value of its output. The government's planned climate change levy, which will come into force in April 2001 and apply to almost all use of gas, coal and electricity outside the household sector, will encourage industry to move onto this path by raising energy prices and providing accompanying incentives for investments in energy efficiency. The bulk of the revenue will be allocated to reducing employers' National Insurance Contributions (NICs), but the government's intention is to devote some 15% (£150 million a year) to incentives for improvements in energy efficiency and for switching to non-fossil fuel alternatives; £100 million will be taken up in the form of 100% first year capital allowances for approved energy-saving investments. The £50 million balance will be used to fund energy efficiency advice, particularly to small and medium enterprises, to increase training in energy efficiency, and to increase research, development and deployment of energy saving technologies and renewable energy sources. The levy will impinge 'downstream', at the point of sale, and households will be exempted from it. Companies which find their overall costs increase as a result of the levy may pass some or all of these on to consumers but for many less energy-intensive companies overall costs will fall, because of the reduction in employers' NICs.[18,19]

6.20   Fears have been expressed that the international competitiveness of UK manufacturing industry will be damaged by the levy but this seems unlikely. According to DTI, there are only four sectors – water, iron and steel, cement, lime and plaster manufacture and brick making – in which energy expenditure exceeds 10% of total production costs. It exceeds 20% in none of them.[20] Furthermore, industrial gas prices in the UK are among the lowest for OECD countries, while UK industrial electricity prices are in the middle of the range.[21] The illustrative rates for the climate change levy set out in the Chancellor of the Exchequer's Pre-Budget Report of November 1999 would add 11% to the average industrial user's annual electricity bill and 27% to its annual gas bill but rebates of 80% of the tax have been offered to energy-intensive sectors that negotiate agreements with government to save energy or to reduce carbon dioxide emissions (6.22).[22] The reduction in employers' NICs will also tend to increase industrial competitiveness.

Negotiated agreements between the government and industry

6.21   In 1997 DETR and the Chemical Industries Association signed an agreement to improve the industry's specific energy use (energy consumption per tonne of product) by 20% between 1990 and 2005. This was the first agreement of its kind in the UK. The association estimated that its members had already achieved a 14% reduction from the 1990 baseline in the years before the agreement was signed; thus it was already well over half way to the target before half time.[23] Government undertook to provide verification of the improvements and some free guidance and advice, including up to five consultant days for each manufacturing site.

6.22   The government is now planning a major expansion of such agreements, with energy-intensive manufacturing sectors undertaking to make specified energy savings (or reductions in carbon dioxide emissions) per unit of output in return for an 80% rebate from the planned climate change levy. Such agreements will only be effective if the trade association includes all, or almost all, of the companies in a sector among its membership. They are unlikely to work if many small and medium enterprises are involved because of the problems in monitoring all of their performances.

6.23   The agreements will need to be underpinned by a credible threat to apply the full weight of the levy in the event of a company failing to achieve its agreed reduction. There may, however, be scope for firms achieving less than their commitment to purchase the balance from those exceeding their target figure through trading arrangements, which we discuss below. The energy consumption of firms in the sectors involved will need to be monitored closely to ensure compliance. **We recommend that a body with a degree of independence from government, such as the Environment Agency or the new Sustainable Energy Agency we recommend, undertake or audit the monitoring of negotiated agreements to reduce energy use and be given adequate funding to do so. We also endorse the House of Commons Environment, Transport and Regional Affairs Committee's recent recommendation that draft negotiated agreements be made publicly available.**[24]

6.24   Individual firms and entire sectors will differ in the ease with which they can make energy efficiency gains. In negotiating energy- and carbon-saving agreements, government will find it difficult to judge what target reduction in consumption it should bid for without reliable, detailed information on the economic potential for saving energy across each sector. Negotiated agreements with manufacturers will only prove a worthwhile alternative to taxation (6.19-6.20) or regulation (6.25-6.31) if they achieve substantial reductions in emissions with equal or greater cost-effectiveness.

Regulation – the IPPC Directive

6.25   Regulations implementing the European Union's new Integrated Pollution Prevention and Control Directive (the IPPC Directive) will soon cover the energy consumption of much of the UK's manufacturing industry. This builds on the concept of integrated pollution control advocated in the Commission's 5th Report in 1976 and introduced in the UK in 1990. The Directive seeks to minimise the overall environmental impacts of the most polluting installations by compelling their operators to demonstrate that they have adopted best available techniques (BAT) and that they are meeting plant and site-specific emission limits for significant pollutants. By 2007 it is expected to cover some 6,000 installations in the UK, which, between them, are responsible for some 60% of the manufacturing sector's total energy use.[25]

6.26   Under the IPPC Directive, EU Member States are charged with ensuring – through their pollution control agencies – that industrial sites and plants are operated in such a way that energy is used efficiently. They must also ensure that the determination of BAT for a particular process takes energy efficiency into account. The UK government's current thinking is that the Directive's requirements for energy efficiency should be met mainly through site-specific permit conditions based on lists of technologies and benchmarks of cost-effective energy efficiency measures developed by ETSU, DETR's energy efficiency consultants.

6.27   However, the government intends to treat industrial sites which have undertaken to cut their energy consumption as having demonstrated compliance with the energy efficiency aspects of the IPPC Directive. They will be exempted from site-specific conditions. These undertakings would be made as part of agreements negotiated between energy-intensive industrial sectors and the government under which the former avoided most of the climate change levy (6.22).

6.28   What impact the Directive will have on manufacturing industry's energy demand remains to be seen. Many small and medium enterprises do not come within the IPPC Directive's remit. Furthermore, major advances in the energy efficiency of industry have arisen – and will continue to arise – from redesigning products to reduce their embodied energy content as well as from changing manufacturing processes. The IPPC Directive is restricted to regulating the latter and has little influence on this crucial area of product design. We note, however, that an integrated product policy is under discussion within the EU.

6.29   The UK's three main pollution control agencies (the Environment Agency, the Scottish Environment Protection Agency and the Northern Ireland Environment and Heritage Service) and local authorities, which have a role in applying IPPC to less polluting industries, are unlikely to go beyond insisting on energy efficiency measures whose cost-effectiveness is proven and which have relatively short payback periods. If the agencies went any further, they would risk accusations of driving industries out of business or overseas.

6.30   However, given the evidence that many companies fail to implement all cost-effective energy-saving measures, we believe that the UK's environmental regulators could, in implementing the IPPC Directive, play a new and important role in raising industry's baseline standards of energy efficiency. **Government must encourage and enable the Environment**

Agencies to raise industry's baseline standards of energy efficiency in implementing IPPC.
Energy efficiency achievements of more advanced operators should be used as benchmarks in
order to raise the standards for laggards.

**6.31 Emissions of carbon dioxide and other greenhouse gases from a site should be
considered as pollutants in authorising processes subject to IPPC. As soon as it can be
established that disposal of carbon dioxide into deep geological strata (3.10-3.11) is
environmentally and legally acceptable, consideration should be given to designating
technology for removing carbon dioxide from the emissions from large combustion plants
(3.6) as the best available technique for the purposes of IPPC.**

Carbon trading

6.32   The government and a business group led by the Confederation of British Industry and
the Advisory Committee on Business and the Environment have been discussing the
establishment of a trading scheme in carbon dioxide emission permits as a means of cost-
effectively reducing industrial emissions.[26] A firm would be able to enter such a scheme if it
accepted a quota of carbon dioxide emission rights for a given period; in effect a cap on its
emissions. Those firms which found it cheapest to save energy and reduce emissions would
have an incentive to emit below their quota and sell the balance to firms which found it more
expensive to do so and preferred to exceed their cap. The price of quota would be established in
an open market. Such a trading scheme ought to minimise the overall costs to manufacturing
industry of increasing energy efficiency and reducing emissions.

6.33   We would welcome a trading scheme if it achieved this purpose, and also because it could
help the UK to play a leading role in the international trade in emission permits which is
expected to ensue (box 4A and 4.53). It will require some form of incentive to encourage firms
to join. It will also require complex rules, close monitoring and sanctions against companies
which fail to comply with their obligations. It will also need to achieve substantial emission
reductions by 2012. We note that stringent application to participating firms of the IPPC
Directive's energy efficiency requirements would tend to reduce the scope for trading by
pushing all companies towards the same high standard.

Advice and information

6.34   Another influence on manufacturing industry's energy consumption – and on the service
sector's – is government advice and information campaigns. The Energy Efficiency Best
Practice Programme (EEBPP), launched in 1989 and overseen by DETR, promotes energy
efficiency in the manufacturing, services, household and transport sectors through good
practice guides and case studies, demonstration projects, support for research and development
and benchmarking. The latter involves recording the energy consumption of a sample of
operators in particular sectors and processes, then disseminating this information to highlight
the energy savings which the best performers are achieving.

6.35   Government spending on energy efficiency best practice activities is expected to rise,
using revenues from the climate change levy. The government has estimated that by 1998 the
programme was saving primary energy worth more than £650 million a year, equivalent to an
average rate of about 6 GW.[27] DTI, DETR and the devolved administrations also run a similar,
but smaller Environmental Technology Best Practice Programme which promotes the
adoption of clean technologies and waste minimisation.

COMMERCIAL AND PUBLIC SERVICES

6.36   The final energy consumed by public and commercial services in the UK rose by 24% between 1973 and 1998. The sector's share of total UK final energy use rose slightly, from 11 to 13% over those 25 years.[28] As with the manufacturing and domestic sectors, there have been large shifts between energy sources with gas and electricity growing at the expense of solid fuels. The services sector's dependence on electricity is higher than any other's with 37% of all the final energy it consumed in 1998 arriving in this form.

6.37   Almost all of the increase in energy use has been on the commercial side of the services sector, where there has been trend growth of almost 3% a year since the early 1970s. Total consumption by primarily state-funded services such as health and education barely rose over this period.[29] The commercial side now accounts for some 60% of the sector's total energy use with shops, offices and hotel and catering establishments together accounting for well over half of commerce's consumption.[30]

6.38   Both the commercial and the public, state-funded parts of the services sector have increased output faster than energy consumption over the past two decades. However, since 1990 the trend towards decreasing energy intensity has been stagnant and may even have gone into reverse.[31] Several explanations have been advanced for this. A period of relatively low fuel prices following a recession removed earlier incentives to cut energy consumption. A growing proportion of large and medium sized buildings are centrally cooled as well as heated; more than a quarter of the non-domestic floorspace constructed since 1991 has full or partial air conditioning.[32] The amount of electrically powered equipment used in offices, particularly computers, printers, photocopiers and vending machines, has also been growing very rapidly and is expected to continue to do so. All of this equipment sheds heat, which increases the demand for the air conditioning needed to maintain tolerable indoor temperatures on hot days.

6.39   The bulk of all energy demand from both public and commercial services is for space heating and hot water, just as it is in households. But in some sub-sectors a large proportion of the total energy consumption is attributable to other uses. In shops, a third (including more than half of electricity consumed) is used for lighting. In offices, 10% of final energy use is devoted to cooling and 10% to computers and other information technology equipment.[33]

THE POTENTIAL FOR REDUCING ENERGY CONSUMPTION

6.40   An analysis of the prospects for saving energy in the services sector was carried out for the Commission, using the Building Research Establishment's Non-Domestic Energy and Emissions Model.[34] This model provides estimates of total energy consumption in ten sub-sectors, based on surveys of the energy use in individual buildings and businesses. The Commission's consultants concluded that if the technical potential was fulfilled the service sector's annual final energy consumption would fall by 18% between 1996 and 2010. If the economic potential was fulfilled the fall over this 14 year period would be 3%, with the reductions brought about by improvements in energy efficiency only just outweighing the increases associated with rising output. In the absence of any improvements in the rate at which the sector implements energy efficiency measures, its annual energy consumption would continue to rise by 0.5 to 1% a year.

MEASURES FOR REDUCING ENERGY CONSUMPTION

6.41   As with manufacturing, ways of reducing demand in the services sector range from simple housekeeping measures to the replacement of major infrastructure – including entire buildings-with more energy efficient alternatives. Improvements in heating, cooling ventilating and lighting offer the largest scope for energy savings in existing buildings. Often, this is a matter of improving controls so that buildings, or parts of buildings, are not overlit, overheated or overcooled. Sensors which switch off lights if no one stands or sits nearby for some time have been on the market for several years. Raising the efficiency of electrical appliances can also make a substantial contribution to reducing energy consumption in existing buildings-we discuss this further below (6.80-6.87). Combined heat and power (CHP) plants (3.40), generally with a much lower output than those used in manufacturing facilities, also offer energy savings by providing both warmth and electricity for a building at high efficiencies. As with the manufacturing sector, the spread of CHP in the services sector will depend largely on the ease and profitability with which surplus heat and warmth can be distributed and sold to other users.

Improving the energy efficiency of public and commercial buildings

6.42   In the long term, the greatest scope for advances in saving energy comes in the construction of new services buildings designed to consume a small fraction of the energy per square metre or per occupant which their older equivalents require. Several such buildings now exist in the UK (see box 6A). Devices such as light wells, atria and reflective surfaces are used to bring daylight into the centre of large floorplans, reducing electricity requirements. Sunshine is also used to provide much of these buildings' warmth, heating interior air behind glass. Ventilation systems, passive or forced, distribute this warmth through the building and-in combination with equipment which prevents too much solar energy entering-keep the interior comfortably cool in summer without the need for air conditioning. Such buildings generally feature high levels of insulation on all their external surfaces and advanced glazing with special coatings.

6.43   The main influences on the service sector's future energy consumption will be its underlying growth, the price of energy and the Building Regulations which set standards for the energy efficiency of new public and commercial buildings and for housing. These regulations are currently being reviewed by government for England and Wales, and amended ones setting higher standards are expected to be introduced in 2001. The Scottish Executive plans to consult in the autumn of 2000 on its proposals for higher energy efficiency standards for buildings.[37] Most commercial buildings are either demolished or extensively refurbished within 20 years of construction, so the application of higher standards to new build and refurbishment could have a major impact on energy demand over the medium to longer term. **The regulations should be amended to set more demanding criteria for the energy efficiency of lighting and introduce rigorous standards for air conditioning systems as well as heating systems, thereby encouraging architects and engineers to find less polluting ways of keeping buildings adequately lit and at comfortable temperatures.** They should also include requirements that ensure these systems are properly commissioned. And they should have a standard for ventilation; the UK is the only member of the EU to have no guideline for ventilation in public buildings.[38] The government is considering whether there is scope, under existing legislative powers, to raise energy efficiency standards in buildings already in existence.

6.44   **We recommend that government join with the construction industry to find an effective way of increasing the awareness and understanding of energy-saving methods and technologies among architects, engineers, surveyors and the building trades.** UK buildings which have been designed to attain high levels of energy saving have sometimes failed

BOX 6A	LOW ENERGY BUILDINGS

A university[35]

The University of East Anglia's Elizabeth Fry Building near Norwich contains offices, seminar rooms and lecture theatres (photograph V). It consumes less than half the energy of an air-conditioned building of comparable size and function while maintaining comfortable internal temperatures throughout the years.

The four-storey, 3,250 square metre building uses night cooling to keep temperatures down to comfortable levels on hot summer days. During the night, external air is pumped into the offices, seminar rooms and lecture theatres through cavities within the concrete slabs which form the ceilings and floors. This fresh air cools these slabs and the remainder of the building fabric. The slabs then act as a heat sink or 'cool store' during the day, reducing the build up of heat from people, electrical equipment and the sunlight streaming in through the windows. Warm external air pumped into the building for ventilation during hot summer days is also cooled by the slabs. Occupants can also open office windows or use integral sun blinds (which are sandwiched between the panes of glass) to adjust the temperature in their immediate surroundings.

In winter, the building is sealed at night to retain the daytime heat gains from people, lights and other and electrical equipment. During the day, the external air which has to be pumped through the building for ventilation is first warmed by outgoing, stale air in a heat exchanger and then further heated, if necessary, using three gas-fired boilers. Most of the heat required to warm the building is generated by occupants and equipment; the boilers are ordinary household-sized, high efficiency condensing types and all three are rarely required to operate. The walls contain 200 mm of insulation and the building, completed in 1995, is well sealed. Electricity consumption is reduced by making maximum use of sunshine to light the rooms, stairs and an atrium.

As well as having a low overall average energy consumption (some 90 KWh per square metre per annum), the Elizabeth Fry building also cost significantly less to construct than an air-conditioned equivalent and is easier and cheaper to maintain. Surveys of staff have found high levels of satisfaction with the building.

A supermarket[36]

J Sainsbury's new supermarket on the Greenwich peninsula site, in south east London, has been designed with the aim of having half the energy consumption of a conventional new foodstore of equivalent size (photograph IV). Supermarkets are among the most energy-intensive of buildings because they are air-conditioned, brightly lit, poorly insulated and have a great deal of refrigeration. The industry average is 1,087 kWh per square metre per annum from electricity and 152 kWh per square metre per annum from gas.

The store, which opened in September 1999, has its own 500 kW gas-fired combined heat and power plant which provides its base electricity requirement; any extra demand is met by importing power from the grid. Hot water from this CHP plant is used to pre-warm incoming air for ventilation and is also circulated in a network of pipes in the building's floor, providing space heating. In hot weather, cooling is provided by cold water pumped up from two boreholes; this cold water pre-cools the air used for ventilation and circulates through pipes in the floor.

Most of the time there is no need to force ventilation air through the building with fans. Instead, the air is drawn in from a void beneath the floor then, as it warms, it rises upwards to the roof. Winds flowing above the building create a suction effect, drawing the stale air out through vents whose aperture is varied by a control system. Conventional practice in supermarkets is to force cooled or warmed air down into the building from large ducts in the roof void. The Greenwich store also breaks with convention (and pleases both staff and customers) by having large skylights throughout the roof instead of relying entirely on artificial lighting.

For visitors and passers by, the most obvious sign that this £13 million building uses less fossil fuel is two wind turbines flanking the entrance which also carry photovoltaic panels. Their presence is largely symbolic, however, because they only supply enough electricity to power the store's external illuminated signs.

The energy saving elements are estimated to have added about £2 million to the construction costs. Even if energy consumption is halved, as is hoped, these improvements cannot be justified in conventional accounting terms. The supermarket chain broke with convention in order to develop energy efficiency technologies for use in future stores.

to realise them because of poor workmanship, lack of attention to detail and failure to understand specifications.[39] **We mean this recommendation to apply as much to the housebuilding sector, which we discuss below, as to larger commercial, industrial and public buildings.**

6.45   Tenure arrangements can also be inimical to energy efficiency improvements in buildings. The landlord may be responsible for the maintenance of boilers, air conditioning, insulation and other energy-related aspects of the building but has only a weak incentive to invest in improvements if she or he does not pay the fuel bills for a tenant's use of energy. If, however, the landlord does pay these bills and then passes them on to the tenants in fixed rental or services charges which do not reflect their precise, individual levels of energy consumption then the tenants have no incentive to reduce waste and use energy carefully. This suggests that tenants should pay individual, metered bills. Technical advances in metering (such as remote reading) and the liberalisation of meter reading services (box 5A) open up new opportunities for this.

6.46   But even if tenants did pay individual, metered bills they might face restrictions on the energy saving alterations landlords allowed them to make to buildings. Furthermore, they would have little incentive to make such improvements unless they were certain of remaining in occupancy for long enough to cover the investment through reduced fuel bills, or were awarded some offset to any dilapidations charge at the end of their lease.

6.47   In principle the energy efficiency of a building and its heating system and the landlord's energy billing arrangements might be reflected in the rent obtainable on the property, thus providing an incentive for mutually beneficial improvements. In practice, this rarely seems to happen.

6.48   **We recommend that government join with major property owners to develop means of tackling the 'landlord-tenant' problem which plagues attempts to raise energy efficiency in the services sector.** The starting point is to give tenants of offices, shopping centres and other multi-tenanted buildings information about how much energy they are consuming; only then will they have an incentive to reduce their own consumption and put pressure on their landlords to invest in measures which conserve energy. **We propose that government work with the property and energy industries to devise an incentive scheme which would encourage both landlords and tenants to move to individual meters for each tenant.**

6.49   **Where tenants cannot be individually metered, the landlord should be required to inform them of their building's overall annual energy consumption and fuel bill. At the same time, the landlord should be required to inform existing tenants and prospective tenants of the energy consumption and fuel bill for the average building with the same function and floor area as the one in which they rent, or propose to rent, space, as well as the equivalent figures for a high efficiency 'good practice' building of similar function and floor area.** The benchmark energy consumption figures required to make these comparisons have already been collected by the Building Research Establishment, which should be tasked and funded by the government to supply them free of charge to all landlords. The comparisons would motivate both landlords and tenants of low and average energy efficiency buildings to seek savings and could influence rent levels.

The climate change levy

6.50   DTI has estimated that average expenditure on energy in the services sector is only 0.9% of gross output and 0.6% of total production costs.[40] Therefore energy bills are not generally a major concern for management while most small enterprises give energy efficiency scant consideration. Given the fairly low price elasticities for energy in this and other sectors, which we discuss further below, the price increases resulting from the government's climate change levy are – on their own – likely to cause only small reductions in consumption. Advice, information and incentives will have an important role to play if demand is to be reduced.

6.51   We welcome the government's intention to use part of the £50 million fund from the climate change levy to improve energy efficiency advice and give more help to small and medium sized enterprises; these have proved to be the most difficult to influence. **The government should consider introducing to the rest of the UK the energy saving loan schemes which the Energy Saving Trust runs in Northern Ireland and Scotland.** These lend money to small firms at low rates of interest, enabling them to carry out energy efficiency investments with payback periods of up to five years.

HOUSEHOLDS

6.52   Households' share of UK final energy consumption stands at 29%, higher than the shares of the industrial and service sectors and second only to transport's.[41] Final energy consumption in this sector rose by just under a quarter between 1973 and 1998.[42]

6.53   Over the same period, however, the final energy consumed within the home by the average UK household fell by about a tenth.[43] This fall is mostly attributable to a decline in the average number of people per household, to an increase in insulation and draught proofing as new homes are built and existing dwellings are improved, and to the introduction of more energy efficient heating systems (gas central heating is much more efficient than open coal fires). But this gradual reduction in final energy consumption per household has not been sufficient to outweigh the rapid increase in the number of households. That growth is projected to continue, with an increase of nearly a fifth over the next quarter century.[44]

6.54   Four fifths of this final energy is used to heat rooms and water. The reduction in energy consumption per household brought about by improved insulation and heating systems has been offset by rising electricity consumption as the number of lights and the number and variety of electrical appliances grows. Given the very large amounts of energy wasted in fossil-fuel based electricity generation, the rise in household power consumption adds significantly to UK carbon dioxide emissions. Increasing ownership of freezers and fridge freezers, washing machines, clothes dryers, dishwashers, televisions and computers has been mainly responsible. The quantity and the proportion of total household energy consumption devoted to lighting and running appliances have almost doubled during the past quarter century[45] and households now consume a quarter of all UK electricity.[46]

6.55   A household's total energy consumption depends heavily on levels of insulation and draught proofing and the heating system it uses. The government's Standard Assessment Procedure (SAP) for the energy costs rating of dwellings is now widely used to measure the basic energy efficiency of UK homes (see box 6B) for space heating and hot water.[47] Although the existing housing stock has steadily improved, most of it is still far from having cost-effective levels of insulation.

THE POTENTIAL FOR REDUCING ENERGY CONSUMPTION

6.56   The Commission's consultants considered three recent studies into the technical and economic potential for saving energy in the UK's existing housing stock.[48] These concluded that savings of between 25 and 34% would be made on total current household energy

---

BOX 6B   **SAP – ENERGY LABELS FOR HOUSING**

A flat or house's SAP rating is based on its estimated annual fuel costs for space and water heating, assuming standard heating patterns and a standard number of occupants. The rating is normalised for floor area so house size does not strongly affect the result (a large house might have higher energy bills than a small one, even though the former was more energy efficient). The rating runs from 1 (extremely poor) to 100 (highly efficient) and while a highly-efficient house would achieve a rating above 100 the practice is to round the score down when this happens. The formula used is:

$$SAP = 115 - 100 \times \log_{10} E$$

where E is the dwelling's estimated annual space and water heating bill divided by its floor area in square metres. This estimate is made by taking account of the insulation levels in a dwelling's windows, walls, roofs and floors, its ventilation rate, the type of heating system and the unit price of the fuel it uses, the amount of solar heating the house will obtain through south facing windows and sheltering by other buildings. A site visit by an energy surveyor lasting about half an hour is needed to gather the necessary data (although it can also be obtained by viewing a building's plans and specifications). This is then followed by a series of calculations – usually made using a computer programme – based on the Building Research Establishment's Domestic Energy Model. A house with a SAP rating of 20 would have heating bills about twice as high as a similar sized dwelling with a 50 rating (slightly over the UK average) and four times as high as one with a 77 rating.

Compliance with the 1995 Building Regulations requires the builder of a property to estimate its rating but not to pass the information to prospective purchasers, although the government intends to amend the regulations to require this. The government's House Condition Surveys in England, Scotland and Northern Ireland now include SAP surveys on a large sample of dwellings. Combining the findings from the three nations, a picture of the energy efficiency of the UK housing stock emerges.

SAP rating	number of homes (millions)	%
0-20	1.8	8
20-39	6.1	27
40-59	11.4	51
60-79	3.1	14
80 plus	0.1	0
	22.5	

Analysis of SAP ratings from these surveys demonstrates that lower income households – those who can least afford to waste energy – live in the most inefficient, hardest to heat property. In all three nations the privately rented sector has a lower rating than owner-occupied, council and housing association homes. There is also a strong correlation between age of housing and SAP ratings with pre-1919 housing (which generally lacks cavity walls) having an average rating of 37. A new gas-heated home conforming to current building regulations would achieve a SAP rating of about 75. This improvement over time reflects successive revisions to the Building Regulations, which have gradually set higher standards of energy efficiency.

consumption if every household employed a range of energy saving equipment and techniques which are already on the market. In these analyses of technical potentials, the bulk of savings would come from improved wall insulation (either fitted to solid masonry walls in older buildings, or within the wall cavities of more modern ones) and from a switch to high efficiency boilers for central heating systems. Smaller reductions would come from the use of more efficient electrical appliances, insulation of lofts and hot water cylinders (many homes have too little of this most basic type of insulation, while a minority still lack any), the replacement of low efficiency, incandescent lighting with the modern, compact fluorescent type, universal installation of a higher standard of double glazing (with low emissivity glass), improved heating controls and draught proofing. These estimates of technical potential are conservative. They omit the small but not negligible reductions in the sector's overall energy consumption which could be made by installing small CHP power plants in existing blocks of flats (the type of housing where CHP could be most easily and cost-effectively fitted).[49]

6.57   As for the economic potential for saving energy, this depends on the period under consideration. The most favourable time for investing in energy efficiency is when old, worn out equipment and material – such as boilers, appliances and windows – have to be replaced in any case. But the installation of loft, hot water cylinder and cavity wall insulation, compact fluorescent light bulbs and draught proofing of windows and doors is generally cost-effective at any time. The three studies produced estimates for the economic potential of household energy savings ranging from 17% of current consumption in the short term to 34% over 20 to 30 years.

MEASURES FOR REDUCING ENERGY CONSUMPTION

6.58   We now consider existing government policies, regulation and economic instruments which influence household energy use and levels of investment in domestic energy efficiency.

Household energy prices, taxes and levies

6.59   While energy taxes have been increased on road users and will be on industry and commerce – both justified on environmental grounds – the government has been anxious to exempt households, arguing that to tax them would lead to increases in fuel poverty (6.6). On these grounds it cut VAT on electricity and gas from 8 to 5% in 1997.

6.60   But even setting aside this VAT cut, household electricity, gas and heating oil bills have fallen sharply in the UK in recent years, due to privatisation and market liberalisation at home, reinforced by statutory regulation, and low prices globally (see figure 5-IV). The declared aim of the government and the regulator of the gas and electricity industries is to bring about further price reductions for electricity. Spending on non-transport fuel accounts for only 4% of average household expenditure (while spending on transport fuel amounts to about 5%).[50]

6.61   A growing number of domestic consumers make fixed monthly payments by direct bank debit. Combined with the relatively low cost of fuel, this weakens the price signal and keeps consumers' attention focussed on the price per unit of energy rather than the amount they consume and their options for reducing this total. Changing supplier rather than investing in energy conservation measures has become the obvious way to cut fuel bills. The House of Commons Environmental Audit Committee recently commented that 'falling energy prices appear to send stronger signals than awareness campaigns and seem likely to overwhelm current efforts to promote energy efficiency.'[51]

6.62   A small energy efficiency levy has, however, been imposed on all households. From 1994 they paid £1 extra a year on their electricity bills. The 14 major electricity supply companies (the public electricity suppliers, see box 5A) have been required to use the revenue raised by this levy to finance measures and equipment which increase the efficiency with which electricity is used by households.

6.63   This Energy Efficiency Standards of Performance Scheme (EESOP) has been run by the public electricity suppliers and overseen by the regulator, with support from the Energy Saving Trust. It was the regulator who approved the £1 per customer figure. EESOP was introduced when the UK gas and electricity industries were privatised in order to enhance incentives for energy efficiency improvements by users. After the UK signed the UN's Framework Convention on Climate Change in 1992 the then government wanted to give EESOP a leading role in reducing household sector carbon dioxide emissions. But given the absence of any legislative backing for this role both the electricity and gas regulators resisted; hence the small size of the electricity levy and the absence of one for gas.

6.64   The National Audit Office has shown that EESOP has succeeded in bringing about cost-effective reductions in electricity consumption.[52] The total savings through reduced bills for customers have been considerably higher than the total cost of making the savings. About half of the households that have benefited have been in the low income bracket. The EESOP scheme has been, in effect, a small, hypothecated and broadly redistributive energy tax which very few consumers are aware of; it is not mentioned in their bills.

6.65   The new joint regulator of the gas and electricity industries has now extended this scheme to cover the gas supply industry as well as electricity, and it embraces all but the very smallest suppliers. The new scheme is to run from April 2000 to March 2002 as an interim measure, before new legislation on the regulation of utilities comes into force. The regulator envisages the scheme costing about £75 million a year, financed mainly by an annual charge of £1.20 on all domestic gas and electricity bills. Help with energy efficiency measures will continue to be focussed mainly on disadvantaged consumers who have difficulty paying their fuel bills.[53]

6.66   The government is planning to take over the running of future EESOP schemes, using powers set out in its Utilities Bill. It intends to launch a new scheme to run from 2002 to 2005, achieving about three times the level of annual household energy savings under the regulator's 2000 to 2002 scheme (equivalent to a reduction in carbon dioxide emissions of 0.75 million tonnes of carbon (MtC) a year).[54] This 'EESOP 4' scheme will continue to prioritise low income households. Because most of the savings will be taken up in increased warmth it is likely to achieve only a modest reduction of some 2% in total household energy use.[55] The government acknowledges that much larger annual savings in household energy consumption and carbon dioxide emissions – of the order of 10% – could be made by 2010 'with a substantial net saving for consumers and major financial and health benefits for low income householders in particular.'[56] In its draft Climate Change Programme, it says it intends to work towards these savings, taking into account the experience of the EESOP 4 scheme.

6.67   Electricity and gas suppliers will have an obligation to deliver specified energy savings under EESOP. Each will have to devise and then implement an energy efficiency programme, with the quantity to be saved determined by the regulator (from 2000 to 2002) and then the government (2002 to 2005) based on how many customers each has. If, under such a programme, all energy suppliers are required to deliver energy savings they will almost certainly pass some or all of the costs of achieving these onto their domestic customers. But their customers will have no way of knowing how much of their bills these costs represent. And, unless the programme reaches every household, some customers will pay towards an EESOP but derive no benefit from it.

6.68   We have concerns about the government relying mainly on EESOP-type schemes to deliver the bulk of reductions in energy consumption and carbon dioxide emissions in the household sector. On the plus side, energy suppliers would seek to improve the cost effectiveness of the energy saving investments they are obliged to carry out. They would want each pound they spend to produce the largest possible savings in kilowatt hours. The scheme might also prompt some of them to begin to position themselves as energy services companies, selling warmth and light, rather than as enterprises selling gas and electricity (5.23).

6.69   On the minus side, some of their customers might miss out on the benefits of energy savings even though all are likely to make a contribution to these through increased bills. Customers may, furthermore, be confused and wary when suppliers that had previously been offering them lower prices per unit, and incentives (including Air Miles) to consume more, begin to offer them the means of consuming less energy. A carefully monitored, well-publicised and broadly-based EESOP scheme which enables most gas and electricity customers to benefit can play an important part in reducing households' energy use. But further measures, which we discuss below, will also be necessary.

Improving the efficiency of the existing housing stock

6.70   The replacement rate of old homes by new, more energy-efficient ones in the UK is extremely slow; less than one tenth of 1% of the UK housing stock is demolished each year.[57] This means that there will have to be major improvements to the energy efficiency of the existing stock if household energy consumption is to be reduced. The EESOP schemes aim to deliver such improvements and various advice, promotion and incentive programmes run by the Energy Saving Trust and Environment Departments have also encouraged householders to undertake energy efficiency improvements. Successive government House Condition Surveys reveal a gradual improvement in the energy efficiency of the UK housing stock.[58]

6.71   The largest programme in this sphere is the Home Energy Efficiency Scheme (HEES) and its counterparts in other parts of the UK, which pay for the installation of energy-saving measures in households receiving state benefits because of low incomes or disabilities. Expenditure on HEES is increasing from £75 million in 1999/2000 to £175 million in 2001/02 and the maximum grant per dwelling is being raised from £700 to £1,800 in England for low income pensioner households; enough to cover the cost of installing a central heating system and some insulation. **We recommend that maximum grant levels in other parts of the UK should be raised to those applying under the new HEES in England.** The new HEES scheme will be concentrated on neglected and dilapidated homes in the owner-occupied and privately rented sectors, where most of the UK's fuel poverty is now to be found. The aim is to make 250,000 dwellings a year more warm and comfortable by cutting their energy wastage. We welcome the expansion of HEES and the reduction in fuel poverty it should bring. The scheme will not, however, have a large impact on energy consumption because most of the savings will be taken as extra warmth rather than reduced fuel consumption.

6.72   Improvements in the energy efficiency of low income households, particularly pensioner households, may bring important health benefits which could reduce demands on the National Health Service. There has already been some modest NHS expenditure on schemes which improve the heating and energy efficiency of housing.[59]

6.73   **We recommend that government set up a nationwide scheme which enables medical practitioners who believe their patients' health is being put at risk by fuel poverty to put their names forward for prompt attention under HEES.**

6.74   **We further recommend that government fund epidemiological research aimed at establishing how effective home energy efficiency measures are in terms of improving health and reducing overall health service expenditure.**

6.75   The Home Energy Conservation Act 1995, which originated as a Private Member's Bill but won government support, requires UK local housing authorities to draw up strategies for cost-effectively raising the energy efficiency of private and public sector homes in their area. Authorities have to submit their strategies to the Minister, as well as providing regular progress reports on implementation. The guidance they were given was to aim for a 30% reduction in household energy use by 2011 (34% in Northern Ireland). They were given no substantial new resources to achieve this; instead they were expected to act as facilitators and co-ordinators, encouraging householders and landlords to take advantage of cost-effective conservation measures.

6.76   A recent study indicates that the Act is unlikely to achieve such an improvement.[60] Most local authorities devote less than half of one officer's time to implementing the strategy. Many feel that 30% is an unrealistic target given the current resources available for improvements, and that central government lacks commitment to the Act and the target. The government, for its part, has complained that a quarter of the local authorities' strategies were inadequate and needed modification, that many had misunderstood or ignored their role as facilitators and that progress towards the 30% target was insufficient.

6.77   Local authorities can only have a strong influence on the energy efficiency of the dwellings they own; these constitute a dwindling minority of the total stock. They have little leverage on the privately owned majority. They also have problems in knowing how much energy is consumed by housing in their area – utilities do not provide that information – and therefore in knowing how much progress is being made towards the 30% target.

6.78   Domestic energy prices will need to rise and other incentives for domestic energy efficiency measures will have to be increased if household energy consumption is to be substantially reduced. We discuss the scope for price increases below (6.156-6.159). As for other incentives, we note that the government intends to legislate for 'sellers' packs' – a package of information which all house sellers in England and Wales will be required to make available to potential purchasers, giving them the information required before a final valuation can be established and a firm decision to purchase made.[61] A pilot scheme which has been run in Bristol aimed to include information on SAP ratings (box 6B) and energy efficiency in sellers' packs for 250 vendors. **We recommend that SAP survey findings should be part of information packs provided by sellers to house buyers, together with basic information explaining the SAP and general advice on making energy efficiency improvements.** This requirement would make SAP surveys mandatory at the point of sale. Within a decade of it being introduced a substantial proportion of the housing stock would have an energy label, given current rates of housing turnover. If this labelling began to influence the market value of homes it would lead to a higher take-up of energy efficiency equipment and measures. Home owners would know that an energy saving investment would not only cut their fuel bills immediately but give some lift to the sales price when they came to sell. The UK's high levels of home ownership would add to labelling's overall impact on energy consumption. The demand for new, more energy efficient housing would be stimulated which could, in turn, speed up the rate at which the most energy inefficient stock is upgraded and replaced. But energy labels for homes are unlikely to have much influence against a background of low and falling domestic energy prices.

6.79   **We recommend that purchasers who can demonstrate that they have raised the SAP rating of their property by 20 points should be entitled to a stamp duty rebate (up to a maximum of 1% of the purchase price).** A body such as the Energy Saving Trust could be tasked and resourced to administer this scheme. The purchasers would have to carry out the improvement works within a specified period of purchasing the dwelling, and submit energy surveyor's reports to the trust recording the SAP rating before the purchase and the new, higher rating. A system of audit and inspection run by the trust would prevent fraud.

Higher efficiency in household electricity use

6.80   A minority of homes are heated with electricity, which is expensive compared to gas and produces about two and a half times as much carbon dioxide per unit of heat.[62] So long as most UK electricity is generated by burning fossil fuels, gas is strongly preferable to electricity as a fuel for space and water heating on environmental grounds. (This would, however, change under the scenarios we consider in chapter 9 in which electricity generation is dominated by non-carbon sources.)

6.81   The quantity of electricity consumed by households is rising (6.54). This is mainly because the number of lights and electrical and electronic appliances has grown steadily. It has been estimated that universal use of the most efficient lights and appliances now available would cut domestic electricity consumption by a third.[63] The ordinary incandescent light bulb, little changed in almost a century, still consumes more than 80% of the energy used for lighting in UK homes, even though compact fluorescent lights which use a quarter of the electricity have been mass-marketed for a decade.[64] Although more expensive than incandescent bulbs they last much longer and achieve considerable savings over their lifetime.

6.82   Households should be inclined to buy the more energy efficient appliances and be prepared to pay a higher price for them. But when electricity bills are only a small proportion of most households' budgets and falling, other aspects such as appearance, price and performance assume greater importance. Governments have sought to raise efficiency levels for some products through mandating minimum energy efficiency standards, or negotiating voluntary agreements on standards with manufacturers. Prominent labels which give clear, simple information about a product's energy consumption and its rank order compared with its rivals also encourage consumers to buy more efficient appliances, provided these labels are on display in showrooms and sales staff have had the training required to discuss energy efficiency issues with prospective purchasers.

6.83   The UK's ability to act alone in this field is limited because of the legal requirements for a single European market within the EU. Progress on energy labelling, minimum standards and voluntary agreements with manufacturers has depended on the pace at which agreements can be reached between the EU Member States. So far, minimum standards have been set only for refrigerators and freezers and for oil and gas-fired boilers. Energy labelling has been introduced for refrigerators and freezers, washing machines, dryers and dishwashers; these labels rank each model on a scale from A (most efficient) to G (least). Energy labels for household lights will be introduced in 2001. Voluntary agreements have been reached with manufacturers covering the 'stand-by' power consumption of televisions and video cassette recorders and the removal of the most inefficient washing machines from the European market.

6.84   DETR runs a Market Transformation Programme with a budget of £500,000 a year. This aims to develop a consensus among manufacturers, consumers and government on achieving improvements in energy efficiency covering both domestic and office appliances and some electrical equipment used by industry, including motors. It has identified a large potential for improvement which could halt the overall rising trend in energy consumption by this spectrum of products.[65]

6.85   To enable this potential to be fulfilled, **we urge the government to take a lead within the EU in pressing for a broader range of household and office appliances to have mandatory energy labels and minimum energy efficiency standards.** Particular attention should be paid to those products which use the most electricity (such as refrigerators) and those with the fastest growing markets (such as computers and digital televisions with integrated decoder receivers). Standards should be set at the level achieved by the best performing appliances, then brought into force a specified number of years later; the process should then be repeated. This is the Japanese 'front runner' concept, which encourages manufacturers to innovate in improving energy efficiency.

6.86   At home, **we urge UK manufacturers and retailers to take a lead in marketing more energy efficient products, and government to encourage them to do so. Government Departments, local authorities, the NHS and government agencies should bulk purchase the more energy efficient products, expanding their market and helping to bring down costs.** The HEES (6.71) and EESOP (6.62-6.69) programmes have an important role to play in this.

6.87   **We recommend that the government consider subsidising some of the most energy efficient appliances;** the concept has already been applied to gas condensing boilers and cavity wall insulation. The subsidies could be funded from the revenues of the climate change levy or the carbon tax which we advocate below. Alternatively, VAT could be reduced to 5% for the highest performing appliances; this would, however, require a change in EU taxation law.

Higher efficiency standards for new housing

6.88   If new homes are constructed with high levels of energy efficiency they will tend to reduce energy consumption, to the extent that they gradually replace existing stock. But only some 10% of the new houses and flats completed in the UK each year replace existing homes; the remainder are additions to the stock. Nonetheless, given the projected increase in the number of UK homes between 1996 and 2021 of more than four million,[66] higher standards for new dwellings could make an important contribution to reducing energy consumption.

6.89   New houses can be designed with fuel saving as a leading objective, built in from the outset. The extra labour costs required to install energy saving equipment are lower than they would be for an existing dwelling because this can be combined with the rest of the construction work.

6.90   There are now ultra-energy efficient homes in the UK whose heating and lighting bills are negligible compared to their conventional counterparts; box 6C describes a current development. Internal spaces are heated by sunshine during the day (a domestic greenhouse effect) while the fabric of the building stores this heat and warms the interior through the night. Such homes have very high levels of insulation on all exterior surfaces. Instead of having radiators in every room, some use one or two small point sources of heat to keep the cold at bay in winter. The body warmth of the occupants and cooking heat also help to keep temperatures up. These houses tend to be well-sealed in winter, in order to retain warmed air. Some have mechanical ventilation systems with heat exchangers to recover warmth from the outgoing stale air.[67]

BOX 6C	NEW LOW ENERGY HOUSING

A pioneering development

The construction of the most ambitious low energy housing development in the UK to date began in Sutton, south London, in March 2000 (photograph VI). The 80 town houses, maisonettes, and apartments in the high density, mixed use Beddington Zero Energy Development will be heated mainly by sunlight streaming in through all-glass south facing walls. Additional warmth is provided by the body heat of the occupants and by cooking and electric lighting. Warmth gained during the days will be retained through the nights, due to the large thermal mass of the development (its fabric stores heat) and high levels of insulation. The buildings, which also include offices, are well sealed to prevent cold air leaking in. Ventilation is supplied through large wind cowls on the roofs, which draw in external air. As this cool air flows down ducts into the buildings it is warmed by stale internal air rising up through another duct enclosed within.

The heat for hot water supplies is generated by a small (110 kW) combined heat and power (CHP) station fuelled by wood chips derived from tree prunings from the streets and parks of the neighbouring borough of Croydon. Some of the heat is used to dry the wood chips. Each dwelling's hot water tank is uninsulated, but stowed in a well-insulated cupboard with louvres which can be opened to provide top-up space heating during particularly cold weather, or after the home has been left empty for some time. The electricity from the development's CHP station will be used for lighting and to power domestic and office appliances, all of which will meet high energy efficiency standards. Surplus electricity can be exported to the grid and power can also be imported when the CHP station is shut down or unable to meet peak loads.

The housing is being laid out on the site of an old sewage works, in seven parallel terraces running east west. The homes will be on the south facing, sunnier side with office accommodation on the north. The intention is to reduce the heating requirements to 10% of those of a conventional home; they would achieve a SAP rating (see box 6B) of well above 100. The office spaces, which also have high insulation and thermal mass and a passive ventilation system, will be kept at a comfortable temperature year round by exploiting the body warmth of the workers and the heat leakage from computers and other electrical equipment.

The transport-related carbon dioxide emissions associated with the BedZED should be considerably reduced compared to a conventional housing development of the same size. It is close to a station, a new tram line and four bus routes. It is hoped that some residents will work from home, or at the offices within the development. The developers plan to set up a car pool which will have several electrically powered vehicles, to be charged by photovoltaic panels on the roofs. Residents who keep a car on the site will pay a parking charge.

Despite this being a high density development, every dwelling will have its own garden (many of which will be roof gardens). The great majority of homes will be for sale on long leaseholds but at least 15% will be reserved for social housing. 300 potential purchasers had already expressed an interest before construction began. The BedZED is being developed by the Peabody Trust, one of Britain's oldest and largest housing associations, with architect Bill Dunster and a locally based environmental enterprise group, Bioregional.

A more conventional approach

Located two miles from the site of the BedZED, an ordinary looking home built by a volume housebuilder in Cheam, Sutton, uses about 40% less energy than the typical new dwelling built to the energy efficiency standards of the 1995 building regulations and of equivalent size. The former has a SAP rating of 100; the latter would achieve about 75. One of the three storey, 110 square metre town house's most important energy saving features is that it is part of a terrace; this substantially reduces heat losses through the walls. The 75 mm gap between the outer brick and inner masonry blocks is slightly wider than the industry norm and this cavity is filled with blown mineral fibre. There is also a layer of under-floor insulation. Space heating and hot water are provided by a high efficiency gas condensing boiler. The remainder of the three bedroom house's energy saving features, such as double glazing and loft insulation, are typical of all new homes. The company estimates that the extra energy saving features added £216 to the total construction costs.[68]

6.91   But levels of energy efficiency performance in the vast majority of new housing are determined chiefly by the Building Regulations. Revisions to these have gradually raised the standards of new housing over the past three decades. These regulations, which also affect commercial and public sector buildings and were being reviewed at the time of completing this report (6.43), have a central role to play in reducing UK carbon dioxide emissions.

6.92   The introduction of new regulations is preceded by lengthy discussions with the house building industry, landlords and others with an interest; this is a statutory requirement. House builders have, to date, resisted innovative energy conservation requirements that would achieve substantial gains in the energy efficiency in new housing. They have argued that these would push costs too high and that the introduction of any new technology in construction brings a risk of defects emerging a few years later on. The house building industry is reluctant to install insulation in the air gap within cavity walls, one of the most obvious and cost-effective energy conservation measures, in the more rainy and windswept areas of the UK because of problems with rain penetrating and being carried through to the inner wall. We believe that the house building industry should see this as a problem to be solved rather than an inescapable obstacle.

6.93   The latest, 1995 version of the regulations are meant to achieve a cost-effective level of energy conservation, with the extra expenditure on construction being covered by reduced fuel bills. Compared to the previous version, the 1995 regulations were estimated to reduce the energy consumption of a typical new house by 25% to 35%, worth £130 to £180 a year in savings to the householder, while imposing only an extra £675 to £1,350 (1.5% to 3%) on its construction costs.[69]

6.94   The government has estimated that a 26% reduction in the energy consumption of new detached and semi-detached homes could be achieved with further energy efficiency improvements beyond the 1995 Building Regulations level which added £1,200 to £1,300 to average construction costs per house.[70] This would imply a reduction in annual fuel bills of about £130; thus even with the current low level of domestic energy prices, major reductions in energy consumption are cost-effective, or close to being cost-effective. New regulations could deliver further, substantial gains in energy efficiency for new homes with only moderate increases in construction costs. Some of the modifications needed to conventional building practice have been discussed above (6.56-6.57). Others include more floor insulation and a wider cavity within the external walls allowing more insulation to be installed.

6.95   Building regulations in Scandinavian nations, the Netherlands and Canada have long set standards for energy conservation in new housing well in advance of those applying in the UK. We received evidence from the Royal Institute of British Architects indicating that a house built to the existing English and Welsh building regulations in 1993 would consume about four times as much energy for space heating as an identically sized house built to the then current Swedish regulations, and twice as much as one built to the Danish regulations.[71] These comparisons were made on the basis that the houses were exposed to the same climate. English and Welsh energy efficiency standards have been lifted since, but nowhere near enough to close the gaps.

6.96   The main objection raised by UK house builders to a substantial uprating of energy efficiency requirements is that it would require them to adopt alternative construction techniques. To achieve the necessary levels of insulation without resorting to extremely thick walls, they might have to abandon the traditional double masonry layer and move to timber or steel frame construction and single masonry layers instead. Some companies are wary about using timber frame construction after defects emerged in new homes built on this principle some years ago. However, almost half of new dwellings in Scotland are timber framed. The house building industry fears such major changes would prove unpopular with purchasers and might lead to problems emerging after the building has been completed and sold. The fact that it has to sell its products in competition with an enormous second hand market of conventional homes increases its resistance to innovation.

6.97   These arguments are tantamount to saying that UK households wish to be permanently disadvantaged in comparison to those of other north west European countries. **We recommend that government revise the Building Regulations to mandate much higher standards of energy efficiency in new homes and commercial and public sector buildings. For new housing Regulations that deliver a SAP 80 rating should be introduced forthwith. We further recommend that government announce its intention to move to a higher standard, based on achieving a SAP 100 rating, by 2005. We also recommend that the practice cease of rounding down very high SAP ratings to 100, in that a growing number of homes can exceed that level, or that the SAP formula be revised to take higher standards better into account.** A 100 rating would cut the energy consumption of new homes by a further third compared to a SAP 80 standard. The five year delay would allow the house building industry time to research and develop the most cost-effective and reliable ways for achieving the new standard.

6.98   The government intends to consult on a proposed new energy efficiency index for housing which would be used by builders as a basis for compliance with the regulations. This would be based on the overall carbon dioxide emissions associated with a building's energy consumption rather than its space and water heating costs. It would be similar to SAP and, in the great majority of cases, it would make only a small difference to a house's rating relative to other dwellings. **We support the introduction of a new energy efficiency index for housing based on carbon dioxide emissions and urge government to make this change as quickly as possible. But there is a strong case for retaining a rating based on energy costs when homes are sold because prospective purchasers wish to know about likely energy bills.** Government intends to retain the requirement for builders to calculate SAP for new homes, for the purposes of informing prospective purchasers.

6.99   The drive for much higher energy efficiency standards in housing will depend largely on improvements in insulation, draughtproofing and ventilation systems. But housebuilders should also be encouraged to install equipment for reducing fossil fuel use which, although fairly novel in the UK, is widely used elsewhere and could be as cost-effective as insulation improvements once a market was established. Subsidies, financed by the taxation measures we discuss below, could play a part in this. Sales of high efficiency gas condensing boilers have been boosted by Energy Saving Trust grants to individual owner occupiers.

6.100   Looking further ahead, **the UK government and devolved administrations should launch a long-term programme to bring about major reductions in the energy requirements of buildings. As well as reducing wastage, this will embrace wide use of technologies that enable occupiers of buildings, including householders, to obtain their own heat and electricity from renewable or energy-efficient sources such as solar heating, solar electricity, heat pumps and small-scale combined heat and power plants.**[72] **An integrated approach to heat management should become a central feature of the design of all new houses and other buildings, and should be applied to existing buildings wherever**

practicable, and building control legislation and the Building Regulations should be amended to bring that about. Also of great importance will be heat distribution networks, which we discuss further in chapter 8.

6.101   **We recommend that government investigate the carbon-saving potential and cost-effectiveness of heat pumps and solar water heating at the level of individual homes and larger buildings, with a view to devising subsidy arrangements, both for existing and new buildings, should the findings prove favourable. We further recommend that government provide greater incentives for the installation of small-scale CHP plants in existing and new blocks of flats.**

6.102   **The UK government and devolved administrations should examine the institutional, economic and social barriers to the large-scale growth of heat networks; consider, in conjunction with plant manufacturers, heat consumers and potential investors, what incentives could overcome such barriers; and support demonstration schemes.**

6.103   Intense debate surrounds the questions of how many new dwellings are required in the UK to provide for the underlying increase in the number of households, what form the new housing should take and what proportion should be accommodated within existing urban areas. A shift towards higher densities in new housing areas, with workplaces, shops, schools and other facilities provided as close to people's homes as possible, has been widely advocated and the government now wishes to see compact, mixed use development along these lines.[73] Whether this takes the form of new urban quarters built on brownfield sites within towns and cities, or urban extensions on their edge, this type of development offers scope for reducing households' energy use.

6.104   This comes partly from reducing the demand to travel, especially by car. Compact urban forms offer more facilities within walking and cycling range of homes and public transport services (which are, overall, considerably more energy efficient per person kilometre than cars) are likely to be more frequent and comprehensive in densely populated areas. But there is no certainty that simply raising density reduces travel demand, as was pointed out in the 18th Report.[74] Other factors, including the quality of public transport, the degree of restraint on car use and previous trends in land use, come into play.

6.105   There are other reasons why new, more compact neighbourhoods could consume considerably less energy than conventional post-war development. Homes which share walls share warmth. The building form can be used to create wind shields and microclimates which reduce the space heating requirement. Heat distribution networks become more economically viable as density rises; shorter lengths of pipe are needed, which reduces initial capital costs and heat losses. The priority should be to install heat networks in urban extensions and major brownfield sites which are being redeveloped.

6.106   **We endorse the impetus to higher densities and greater use of urban brownfield sites given in England by the revised Planning Policy Guidance on housing, and urge the devolved administrations to adopt similar policies.** A reduction in carbon dioxide emissions is one of the benefits that could flow from this change in direction.

TRANSPORT

6.107   The transport sector's final energy consumption rose by two-thirds between 1973 and 1998.[75] Its share of total UK final energy consumption grew from 21% to 34% over that period. These increases were largely due to rising volumes of road traffic which now accounts for 77% of the transport sector's energy use.[76]

6.108   During the recession of the early 1990s the growth in traffic volumes and in the sector's energy consumption halted briefly. Between 1992 and 1998, however, road traffic (in vehicle kilometres) increased by 11% while transport's annual energy consumption rose by 9%.[77, 78] Its share of UK carbon dioxide emissions rose from 22% to 24% between 1992 and 1998.[79]

6.109   These are worrying trends. In its 18th Report in 1994 the Commission argued that a change of direction and a new strategy were needed in order to avert the rising economic, social and environmental damage arising from the rapid growth in road traffic and to achieve sustainable development of the transport system. The Commission was particularly concerned with transport's fast growing contribution to UK carbon dioxide emissions. There are now a few hopeful signs. The growth in road traffic is slower than during previous periods of strong economic growth, and the number of railway passengers has grown rapidly since 1995, indicating that some drivers are switching from road to rail.[80] The government has published an important White Paper on transport policy[81] and, at the end of 1999, introduced a Bill in Parliament. However, the change in direction which the Commission believed was imperative has not yet taken place.

THE POTENTIAL FOR REDUCING ENERGY CONSUMPTION

6.110   Making estimates of the technical and economic potential for reducing this sector's energy use is particularly difficult because of the very broad scope for improvements in efficiency. Potentially cost-effective measures include raising the fuel efficiency of vehicles, reducing road congestion and motorway speed limits, sharing cars (car pooling) for the journey to work and reducing car use by making more use of alternative modes including public transport. Further contributions can come from telecommuting and tele-conferencing, reorganising distribution systems to reduce the empty running of freight vehicles and changing planning rules and guidelines to encourage more mixed-use, compact developments which reduce the need for travel (6.103-6.106).

6.111   The Commission's consultants estimated that, if the technical potential for reducing transport's energy consumption was fulfilled, the sector's demand in 2010 would be 28% lower than it was in 1996.[82] If the economic potential was fulfilled, energy demand in 2010 would be between 22% lower and 14% *higher* than the 1996 level. These estimates assumed that, under a business as usual scenario, transport's energy consumption would rise by 35% between 1996 and 2010. DTI's latest projection is that transport's energy consumption will rise by 28% over this period under a business as usual scenario, while carbon dioxide emissions from road transport would rise by 18%.[83]

6.112   DETR has recently published projections for road traffic volumes, congestion and carbon dioxide emissions in England in 2010[84] which are in contrast to DTI's. They are based on implementing, with varying degrees of intensity, measures set out in the 1998 Transport White Paper.[85] These illustrative scenarios range from modest and partial implementation of the policy options to widespread implementation, strong disincentives to private car use and much higher investment in public transport and other alternatives to the car. The scenarios project that overall road traffic volumes will increase by 16-29% between 1996 and 2010; none of them projects a decrease. All of them, however, project a decrease in annual carbon dioxide emissions from road vehicles, ranging from 1-10%. This divergence between the forecast growth in road traffic and the reduction in overall emissions is largely due to the expected major reduction in the fuel consumption of new cars which the European Commission has negotiated with manufacturers (6.123-6.124).

MEASURES FOR REDUCING ENERGY CONSUMPTION

6.113   In addition to the measures mentioned above, the transport sector's energy consumption can be influenced by the price of road fuels and the price of travel by public transport. The latter has been rising more rapidly than private motoring costs.[86] Improvements in the reliability, frequency and quality of public transport (cleanliness, better information systems, higher comfort and speed) can be important in persuading people to prefer it to their own cars. But relative cost is also a factor.

Taxation on vehicles, fuel, road use and workplace car parking

6.114   Successive governments have used annual, pre-announced increases in motor fuel duty – the fuel duty escalator – in order to encourage the development, marketing and purchasing of more fuel-efficient vehicles. This policy, introduced by the previous administration in 1993, was intended to let motorists and vehicle manufacturers know that the pump price of road fuel (the final price on petrol station forecourts) would continue to rise by well above the rate of inflation until at least the year 2000. The escalator started at 3% a year, rose after just one year to 5% and, after the change of administration in 1997, was steepened to 6% a year. Surveys of recent estimates of price elasticity suggest that in the long run (5 to 10 years), each 10% increase in fuel price causes a reduction in overall vehicle fuel consumption of about 6%.[87]

6.115   But the increases in duty have been offset, to some extent, by falls in the underlying price of crude oil and refinery products. After adjusting for general inflation, the pump price of diesel and petrol rose by some 20% between 1994 and 1999 while duty rose by more than 30%.[88] For most of this period there has been no detectable reduction in the overall fuel consumption of cars sold in Britain[89] and sales of high fuel consumption vehicles, especially 'all-terrain' four wheel drive cars, have been rising. Improvements in the energy efficiency of car engines and drive trains have been offset by increases in vehicle weights (as manufacturers install more safety and accessory equipment, such as air conditioning) and consumers' preference for larger models.

6.116   The Society of Motor Manufacturers and Traders has reported that the carbon dioxide emissions of the average new car sold in the UK in 1999 were 2.2% lower than in 1998 (following a 0.9% reduction over the previous year). It has said that the new car market is shifting towards smaller, more fuel-efficient vehicles. This trend is welcome, but the rate is not sufficient to achieve the very large reductions in new car emissions which manufacturers have agreed with the European Commission.

6.117   Recent increases in underlying fuel prices, combined with the steepened escalator, have led to a particularly sharp increase in pump prices and much criticism of the policy, particularly from the road freight industry which feared it would lose business to continental competitors. In November 1999 the Chancellor of the Exchequer announced that the escalator would end with immediate effect, and that future increases in fuel duty would be determined on a Budget by Budget basis. These will be less than 6% (after inflation adjusted duty increases are taken into account) and the revenue raised will go into a dedicated fund for improving public transport and modernising the road network.[90] The Budget in March 2000 increased fuel duty only in line with inflation. Before this change of policy, DETR had been projecting that continuing the fuel duty escalator up to 2002 would have reduced transport's annual energy consumption by some 5 to 12% by 2010, compared to what it would have been in the absence of these price increases.[91]

6.118   Government has introduced legislation which would enable local authorities to set up local road pricing schemes and workplace parking charges. Such schemes would be part of the new local transport plans (local transport strategies in Scotland). Under these, local authorities introduce packages of measures to improve transport and reduce congestion, including improvements to bus services, traffic management and walking and cycling facilities. The new charges are intended to reduce local road traffic (by raising the price of car travel) and to raise revenues which would fund local transport improvements, including alternatives to car use.

6.119   The government's draft Climate Change Programme includes a reduction in carbon dioxide emissions of up to 3.3 MtC a year below 'business as usual' levels in 2010, based on implementing integrated transport policies set out in the Transport White Paper. This reduction would be achieved by the most intensive application of policies envisaged in DETR's scenarios. Every urban local authority would have to introduce road pricing (cordon toll systems) and/or workplace car parking charges at the top end of the price range envisaged in these scenarios. There would also be tolls on the most congested 4% (by length) of inter-urban motorways and A roads accompanied by the construction of extra lanes on these roads. The real cost of fuel duty would rise by 19% between 1999 and 2010. There would also be a large increase in rail freight, a significant transfer of road freight to coastal shipping and a large transfer of drivers and passengers from cars to rail.[92]

6.120   If, however, only the lowest intensity implementation of policies envisaged in DETR's scenarios was applied, in which only 11 large urban areas introduced congestion charging, the reduction in annual carbon dioxide emissions would be 0.6 MtC.[93] Given the slow pace of implementation to date, this latter scenario seems by far the more likely of the two.

6.121   **If these new charging schemes are to be introduced on a scale that can make a significant national contribution to reducing transport's rising carbon dioxide emissions, local authorities which are considering implementing them will need sustained political and financial support from the UK government and devolved administrations. Progress will also depend on adequate government support for other aspects of local transport plans.**

6.122   The government has reduced vehicle excise duty (VED) for cars with smaller engines which generally produce less carbon dioxide per kilometre in the hope that some purchasers will switch from larger vehicles. It intends to introduce a graduated VED system for new cars, in which vehicles will be placed in one of four VED rate bands according to their carbon dioxide emissions per kilometre; owners of the highest emission vehicles will pay the highest rate. We welcome this decision, but **we urge a wide differential in VED between the highest and lowest bands and an increase in the number of bands or a sliding scale. We endorse the House of Commons Environment, Transport and Regional Affairs Committee's proposal for a revenue-neutral graduated purchase tax on new cars, with subsidy for low emission vehicles financed by tax on high emission vehicles.**[94]

Negotiated agreements with manufacturers

6.123   In 1998 the European Commission reached agreement with ACEA, the European Automobile Manufacturers Association, to reduce the average fuel consumption of new cars sold in the European Union by 25% between 1995 and 2008. This is expected to be achieved by selling a greater proportion of smaller cars and by improvements in technology, with an emphasis on diesel engines and direct injection petrol engines. The European Commission has now concluded similar agreements with Japanese and Korean car manufacturers. The UK government maintains that these agreements, together with the graduated VED (6.122) and proposed reforms to company car taxation, will make one of the largest contributions to the UK's programme for reducing carbon dioxide emissions. It estimates they will achieve a 4MtC reduction in annual emissions by 2010 (2.6% of total UK emissions in 1997).[95] **It is crucial that manufacturers comply with the agreements negotiated with the European Commission on reducing carbon dioxide emissions from new cars; and that, if they do not, mandatory standards are introduced rapidly.**

6.124   The European Union has a further target for a 35% reduction in the average fuel consumption of new cars by 2005, and by 2010 at the latest, compared to a 1995 baseline. This would be achieved not only through the agreements with manufacturers referred to above, but through giving car purchasers more information about the relative fuel economy of cars and by fiscal incentives.

THE 18TH REPORT AND ITS AFTERMATH

6.125   The Commission's 18th Report recommended a comprehensive package of measures which addressed the profound social, economic and environmental problems posed by current transport trends. The 20th Report considered progress since 1994 and made further proposals. The key objectives and recommendations are summarised in box 6D.

6.126   **We welcome the Transport White Paper, which adopted policies in line with much of the Commission's thinking.[96] But we continue to be disappointed at the slow progress in implementing the measures required and the delay in introducing the necessary legislation.**

6.127   The 18th Report recommended that the real price of road transport fuels should be doubled by 2005 through increases in duty. The Commission believed that the then current levels of taxation on motor fuels were below the level warranted by the external effects of noise, accidents, air pollution, congestion and global warming. Increases in fuel duty are especially important as an incentive to reducing fuel use; the Commission regarded it as essential that the intention to raise the price of fuel substantially over a period should be signalled in advance to give manufacturers and consumers an incentive to manufacture, market and purchase more fuel efficient vehicles. The Commission further suggested that much of the revenue raised by the increases should be spent on a package of measures which gave people improved alternatives to car use, especially public transport. We regret that the operation of the fuel duty escalator to date appears to have had little success in raising fuel efficiencies; with large increases in duty being partially offset by falls in the pre-tax price of oil. **We particularly regret that successive governments have not devoted more of the revenues from the fuel duty escalator to improving alternatives to car use. We welcome the recent increases in investment in public transport and hope these will be further enhanced.**

6.128   Now that the fuel duty escalator has been abandoned, or greatly scaled down, **we urge the government to do all it can through the EU to ensure further substantial reductions in carbon dioxide emissions from vehicles for the period beyond 2008.**

BOX 6D REDUCING CARBON DIOXIDE EMISSIONS FROM TRANSPORT

The Commission's 18th report, published in 1994, called for a fundamentally different approach to transport policy based on eight objectives, four of which had a direct bearing on reducing the quantities of energy used in transport. These were:

1) To ensure that an effective transport policy at all levels of government is integrated with land use policy and gives priority to minimising the need for transport and increasing the proportion of trips made by environmentally less damaging modes.

2) To increase the proportion of personal travel and freight transport by environmentally less damaging modes and to make the best use of existing infrastructure.

3) To reduce carbon dioxide emissions from transport.

4) To reduce substantially the demands which transport infrastructure and the vehicle industry place on non-renewable materials.

The report set out targets for moving towards these objectives, and recommendations for the measures required. Together these amounted to a programme which could slow the increase in passenger and freight travel by all modes to 10% a decade while stabilising road traffic at current levels. Targets for reducing annual carbon dioxide emissions from surface transport by 20% from their 1990 level by 2020 and for increasing the average fuel efficiency of new cars sold by 40% between 1990 and 2005 were proposed. A doubling of the real price of road fuel by 2005 through fuel duty increases and a steeply graduated annual excise duty on cars, based on their fuel efficiency, were also proposed to stimulate the development, marketing and purchase of more fuel-efficient vehicles.

The Commission called for major improvements in the quality, reliability and frequency of public transport services between and within towns and cities in order to give car users an alternative to private vehicles. To achieve this large increases in investment in public transport and in revenue expenditure would be necessary; up to £1 billion a year more on investment at 1994/95 prices and up to £2 billion a year on revenue. The Commission believed much of these increases would need to be financed by public expenditure and noted that by 2000 the additional revenue raised by the fuel duty increases it advocated 'would comfortably exceed the additional requirements for public expenditure identified in this report'. It also recommended that if road-pricing schemes were introduced for motorways and urban areas then the surplus revenue once the installation and running costs had been covered should be spent on increasing the attractiveness of alternatives to the car.

The Commission proposed a target for raising the proportion of personal travel which used public transport from 12% of total person kilometres in 1993 to 30% by 2020 while the proportion of urban journeys made by bicycle should increase from 2.5% to 10% by 2005. The 18th report also proposed targets for shifting substantial proportions of freight from road to rail and water. For air travel, the Commission recognised that the UK had little scope for unilateral action. It urged the government to negotiate within the European Union, and more widely, for an aviation fuel levy that would reflect the environmental damage caused by air transport.

Three years later the Commission returned to the subject, devoting its 20th report to developments since 1994. This found that, although there were signs of hope, the fundamental change in policies advocated in the 18th report had not occurred. Nor were there any signs of large changes in previous trends that had been pointing towards an unsustainable transport system – rapidly rising road traffic levels, declining patronage of public transport and freight shifting from rail and water onto roads. The 20th report stressed the need for an integrated transport system covering all modes and for transport policies to be closely linked to other relevant policy areas, especially land use planning.

AVIATION AND SHIPPING

6.129   Ships and aircraft make a large contribution to rising greenhouse gas emissions. Aircraft manufacturers have steadily improved the fuel efficiency of their products over the years, and the newest large passenger aircraft consume only one third as much kerosene per passenger kilometre as those built 40 years earlier. But the rapid growth in global passenger air travel – currently some 5% a year – has outweighed this technological improvement.[97] Aircraft greenhouse gas emissions are projected to increase by some 3% a year between 1990 and 2015. Aviation's share of total anthropogenic carbon dioxide emissions is about 2%, and rising. IPCC has projected that, in the absence of policy interventions designed to limit this growth, the total radiative forcing (or warming effect) due to aircraft will increase about fivefold between 1992 and 2050.

6.130   Because aviation and shipping movements are predominantly international it is extremely difficult for the UK or the European Union to act unilaterally in restraining the growth in the emissions. There is a case for internationally harmonised climate change taxes on aviation and shipping fuel, but to date there has been no serious attempt to negotiate one. Air passenger duty has been introduced in the UK in recent years, justified largely on environmental grounds. At the March 2000 Budget the Chancellor announced a halving of this tax for economy flights from the UK within Europe. This will substantially reduce the UK's overall tax take from air passenger duty, and we regard it as a retrograde step which sends entirely the wrong price signal.

6.131   **The government should press for an international tax on aircraft fuel while maintaining or increasing its own taxes on aviation. If, as seems likely, global agreement proves impossible in the current decade, then the government should use its best efforts to secure an OECD aviation fuel tax or, if that also proves impossible, a harmonised climate change levy on landing fees. Either of these could be applied solely within the European Union if a wider agreement cannot be negotiated.** The revenues raised by such taxes would be distributed among national governments for them to spend as they saw fit, but a proportion of these might go into a collaborative fund which supported international projects addressing the threat of climate change.

COMBINING THE POTENTIAL FOR REDUCING ENERGY USE FROM ALL FOUR SECTORS

6.132   Combining the economic potentials for saving energy in the four sectors discussed above provides an estimate of the UK's overall potential for cost-effective savings in final energy consumption in the short to medium term. The projections are set out in table 6.1 below. This suggests that by 2010 the UK's final energy consumption could be 2-15% lower than the 1998 figure if households, manufacturing industry, the transport sector and public and commercial services undertook those energy conservation measures that would save them money. In contrast, the government's most recently published 'business as usual' forecast projected growth in final energy consumption of 8-23% over this period.[98]

6.133   We conclude that UK final energy consumption could be reduced over the coming decade without any impact on competitiveness and with a strong benefit to the economy and living standards. Many other 'bottom up' analyses of the potential for energy conservation, carried out in the UK and other nations, have reached the same conclusion.[103]

6.134   These broad findings have changed little with the passing of time. After 10 or 20 years, a fresh analysis of a sector will generally find that there remains ample scope for cost-effective

Table 6.1

The scope for reducing UK final energy consumption

Sector	Final energy consumption rate in 1998 (actual), GW	Projected energy consumption rate in 2010 (business as usual), GW	Projected energy consumption rate in 2010 if economic potential for efficiency gains fulfilled, GW	% change, 1998 to 2010 – business as usual	% change, 1998 to 2010 – economic potential fulfilled
Domestic[99]	61.1	61	52	0	-15
Manufacturing[100]	46.4	51	44	+10	-6
Transport[101]	71.1	86	54-80	+21	-23 to +12
Services[102]	28.8	32	27	+11	-5
Total	207.4	230	177-203	+11	-15 to -2

energy saving measures – even though many such measures have already been undertaken during the intervening years. It has been commented that: 'It seems a curious feature of energy efficiency studies that they seem regularly to identify cost-effective potentials of around 20-30% of current demand, almost irrespective of the potential already exploited.'[104]

6.135   There is little mystery about this. As existing energy saving technologies are adopted, new ones are continuously being developed. In absolute terms the scope for savings will decline; a vehicle must consume some energy in order to move and a house will consume some energy in winter in order to maintain comfortable warmth. But the large, current potential for savings, and the fact that the most energy-efficient products are so far ahead of the rest of the field, suggests that demand reductions could continue for many decades to come.

6.136   Some analysts believe that a range of emerging or vigorously developing technologies, notably microelectronics, biotechnology and nanotechnology, could allow much more rapid gains in the efficiencies with which we exploit natural resources and energy in the 21st century than have occurred in the 20th. They envisage these advances leading to enormous reductions in the flows of materials and energy required to provide goods and services. They argue that companies will need to take advantage of these improvements in resource efficiency in order to remain competitive. Reductions in wastage will come about through changing the products and services on offer and through changing the ways they are made or delivered. Services, especially those related to information, will take an ever growing share of the global economy relative to manufacturing.

6.137   Proponents of these 'Factor Four' and 'Factor Ten' reductions in the natural resources required to produce each unit of output emphasise that a single efficiency improvement in a process or machine can permit further improvements, which can in turn allow yet more.[105] The example often cited is the car. Only one-fifth of the energy content of the fuel burnt in a conventional car's cylinders is actually used to propel the vehicle – the remainder is wasted. The engine's maximum power output is also much higher than the vehicle requires for most of the time it is running, in order for it to be able to accelerate and climb hills; the engine is heavier as a result. Once ways are found of making the car much lighter and of reducing its aerodynamic drag, the engine's power capacity and weight can be reduced which, in turn, allows further reductions in power capacity and weight.[106]

6.138   The demand for travel – one of the main drivers of rising energy consumption – may itself be reduced by technological progress. Major advances in the quality of private, real-time transmission of images and sound, and large cost reductions, can be expected in the next decade. These improvements may give much greater scope for conducting virtual meetings between two or more people without them having to travel to a meeting place. But while the need to travel for work purposes may be reduced, there is no reason to believe that the trend for people to travel more for pleasure as economies grow will be reversed.

6.139   There will continue to be very large gains in energy and resource efficiency but *on current trends* we find no reason to believe that these improvements can counteract the tendency for energy consumption to grow. Even if energy consumed per unit of output were reduced by three-quarters or 'Factor Four', half a century of economic growth at 3% a year (slightly less than the global trend for the past quarter century) would more than quadruple output, leaving overall energy consumption unchanged.

6.140   There are significant barriers to progress in improving energy efficiency. Individuals, businesses and public services routinely fail to use available equipment and known procedures which are blatantly cost-effective – they would pay back the initial investment through energy savings in five years or less. People leave lights burning in empty rooms and overfill electric kettles. Companies struggling to make profits in highly competitive market places miss obvious opportunities to make savings.

6.141   There is no reason to believe that people are more wasteful of energy than they are of any other abundant, relatively cheap commodity. But, for many, economising is a boring, even a depressing subject with penny-pinching and miserly associations. Our culture encourages consumption and expenditure, not thrift. Those who would promote the conservation cause need to be aware of these negative associations.

6.142   Among the barriers to energy efficiency improvements is a lack of information. Individuals and businesses are often unaware of how much energy they are wasting and the extent to which they could cost-effectively reduce this. Gathering and processing information takes time and effort; individuals and firms lack the motivation to do this. They may not know whom to turn to for trustworthy, independent advice.

6.143   Many business decision-makers and households demand much higher rates of return for investments made to cut costs than they do for investments which increase income. Energy conservation investments generally have to pay back their costs through savings within three to five years if they are to be justified. It is difficult to explain this preference, but it acts as a high barrier to energy efficiency improvements.

6.144   Capital may be lacking. In theory, low income households ought to be strongly motivated to conserve energy, for they spend a large proportion of their incomes on fuel. And they often end up paying more per unit of energy than better off consumers because they are unable to pay bills by bank direct debit (and thereby obtain a discount) or are compelled to use prepayment meters. As we have seen, they also tend to live in more dilapidated and less energy efficient housing (box 6B). Thus energy saving would be highly cost-effective for poor households, but they lack the savings and the ability to borrow which are required to make worthwhile energy conserving investments.

6.145   They also face a further hurdle if they rent from private sector landlords with little interest in making investments on their tenants' behalf. The tenure with the highest proportion of households suffering from fuel poverty is private renting.[107] We noted above (6.45-6.47) that the 'landlord tenant' problem is also an important factor in the services sector.

6.146   In the 20th century, the outcome of the interaction between these various barriers to, and drivers of, energy efficiency improvements, set against a background of growth in output, population, and household numbers, was a long-run growth in energy consumption. The UK's population is expected to stabilise in the next few decades; this will improve the prospects for halting the rise in energy consumption. Latest government projections suggest some slowing down in the rapid growth in the number of households.[108]

6.147   The question is whether shifts in public attitudes and government policy could accelerate the rate of improvement in energy efficiency so that energy consumption will stabilise and then begin to fall. The current trends (6.139) would have to change, the barriers to energy efficiency improvements be lowered. The scenarios for energy supply and demand for 2050 which we discuss in chapter 9 demonstrate that a gradual reduction in UK final energy consumption could make a crucial contribution to major, long-term reductions in UK carbon dioxide emissions over the next half century. Indeed, it is very difficult to see how the UK could make the emission cuts necessitated by a contraction and convergence approach and a 550 ppmv upper limit for atmospheric carbon dioxide concentration (see table 4.1) without reducing its overall energy use.

6.148   We now consider policies which could help to overcome some of the barriers discussed above and deliver such a reduction in energy use.

GENERAL MEASURES FOR REDUCING ENERGY USE
ECONOMIC INSTRUMENTS

6.149   Economic analysis suggests that one way of dealing with the situation in which the use of any fuel causes pollution or other environmental degradation is to levy a corrective tax on it. Its users would thus be charged an amount that reflects the costs they impose on others, as externalities.

6.150   Several problems arise with this approach to 'making the polluter pay'. First, credible estimates of the damage caused by fuel cycles are extremely difficult to make because of the wide range of impacts on buildings, ecosystems, landscapes, human health and longevity, and problems in measuring the size of these impacts. Assessments of the damage caused by the climate change resulting from human activities are more problematic still (4.22-4.27). Deciding the level of an appropriate corrective tax is thus not an easy matter, just as deciding appropriate targets for emission reductions is difficult.

6.151   Second, such a tax could also cause energy-intensive UK-based industries to lose markets to rivals based in environmentally less friendly nations where the fuel tax is lower or non-existent. Such industries might contract as a result, or investment in these industries might be diverted to other nations; in the latter case there would be no overall reduction in carbon dioxide emissions, and possibly even an increase.

6.152   Third, such a tax is likely to impinge differentially on people of different means. Some of the things people use fuel for, such as heating the home, are necessities on which they spend relatively little more as they become wealthier and many poorer households occupy poorly insulated, inefficiently heated property which is relatively expensive to keep warm (box 6B). Thus some form of compensation, whether by raising their net incomes or, preferably, improving the relevant features of their homes, has to be a first charge on the revenues generated by the tax.

6.153   A similar argument can be applied to industries whose competitiveness in international markets would come under threat as a result of a fuel tax. It may be possible to use the tax revenue to limit the effect on competitiveness, for instance by cutting employers' National Insurance Contributions (NICs), as the government proposes with the climate change levy. Whether such compensation should apply to a relatively narrow group of industries, for instance by cutting NICs more for industries which are more intensive users of the fuel in question, or more widely, possibly at the level of the whole economy, involves difficult judgements.

6.154   In its 21st Report the Commission concluded (paragraphs 6.56-6.59) that economic instruments such as corrective taxes on particular fuels should be used in conjunction with other instruments. In the present context other instruments deployed would include, as a means towards democratically determined ends, regulation, the training of house builders, advice to fuel users, incentives for raising energy efficiency, the setting of targets, monitoring of performance and research and development of energy-saving technologies.

A CARBON TAX AS PART OF A PACKAGE OF MEASURES

6.155   We believe such a combination of policies and instruments, including taxation, could reduce the UK's primary and final energy consumption in the medium to long term without damaging competitiveness or inflicting hardship.

6.156   We have noted that no energy source is entirely benign and that a wide range of policies have been used to counter the harmful effects associated with various fuel cycles (5.29-5.37). Controls on emissions of carbon dioxide, which is emerging as among the most significant of the threats to the environment associated with energy use, are still at an early stage. We strongly favour a carbon tax placed on fossil fuels, based on the carbon dioxide produced, because it would encourage a shift to low-carbon and non-carbon energy sources. But it would also bring about an increase in the average cost of energy which would bring about some reduction in consumers' energy use, partly by increasing the attractiveness of energy saving measures and equipment.

6.157   The climate change levy, as currently planned, will be based on the energy content, rather than the carbon content, of fuels. This is mistaken. We welcome, however, the decision to exempt electricity generated by some renewable sources and some CHP installations from the levy. If the climate change levy is to be introduced, it should be seen as an intermediate stage in the introduction of a carbon tax.

6.158   A carbon tax would be applied upstream, and should cover all fuels including transport fuels and all sectors. Applied upstream, when the fuel is initially purchased, it would give all companies converting and distributing energy an incentive to do so more efficiently, as well as giving energy consumers an efficiency incentive, because some of the costs of the tax would be passed on. The operator of a fossil fuel power station would, for instance, have an additional incentive to raise its efficiency if the fuel it burnt was taxed.

6.159   The government is mistaken in keeping domestic fuel cheap for all households in order to help a minority of households who suffer from fuel poverty, when there are growing concerns about the environmental damage caused by indiscriminate, inefficient consumption of fossil fuels. Climate change may make its most devastating impacts on the poorest and most vulnerable of the world's peoples. The effectiveness of other measures to raise energy efficiency in the household sector is reduced when they take place against a background of cheap and falling fuel prices.

6.160   There should not, therefore, be a blanket exemption for households from taxation measures aimed at limiting climate change. But if they were to be included, the tax would fall hardest on low income households. We would expect the government to give careful consideration to this matter. At the very least, the numbers of people suffering fuel poverty should not be allowed to increase when a carbon tax is introduced. We urge the government to adopt a programme with the aim of eliminating fuel poverty over a specified time period.[109] It will need a better indicator of fuel poverty than the one it currently employs, and more information about the extent of the problem.

6.161   Cold weather payments are currently available for pensioners and households reliant on state benefits when average temperatures fall below freezing for a week and all pensioner households are now entitled to a £150 fuel payment each winter. These payments would have to be increased when a carbon tax was introduced, as would mainstream state benefits, and there would need to be outreach systems in place which ensured all eligible claimants were aware of their entitlement to these benefits and could take them up promptly. It might prove necessary to widen the eligibility for some of this help to low income households which, while not qualifying for state benefits nor depending on the state old age pension, would be at risk of being moved into fuel poverty by a carbon tax.

6.162   It would be preferable for households to be lifted out of fuel poverty through energy efficiency improvements which enable them to waste less heat rather than through recurring benefits which enable them to consume more energy. Given the dilapidated state of the UK housing stock (and particularly the private sector stock), using either of these routes to eliminate fuel poverty would be costly – although the revenues from a carbon tax could finance such a programme over the medium to long term. We appreciate that it will be difficult for government to achieve the right balance between the two strategies. With both, it will be necessary for government to work closely with a range of bodies, including local authorities and charities, to ensure that households entitled to help are reached.

6.163   However, there is a pressing need for further expansion of government programmes for raising energy efficiency and increasing warmth in low income homes, going beyond the existing EESOP and enhanced HEES schemes. This expansion would increase the rate at which homes are improved as well as aiming for a higher standard of energy efficiency. It would take several years for any programme of energy efficiency improvements to reach all eligible dwellings. It should be integrated with programmes for urban regeneration and for more general renovations or replacement of run-down housing.

6.164   Until fuel poverty is eliminated, a substantial proportion of the revenues from a carbon tax would need to be ring-fenced for low income households, funding benefit increases and a programme of domestic energy efficiency improvements. Some of the revenue should also be used to promote energy efficiency improvements among households in general, in industry, public and commercial services and the transport sector, and to promote the deployment of low-carbon and non-carbon energy resources.

6.165   This range of energy-related programmes could absorb most of the revenue from a carbon tax. Remaining revenues should be used to reduce taxes on employment and investment, limiting any decline in the international competitiveness of UK commerce and industry caused by the tax.

6.166   The price elasticities of demand for energy appear to be generally fairly low in both the long and short term.[110] This would imply that a carbon tax would have to be very large if it was to bring about appreciable reductions in final energy consumption (although much of the reduction in carbon dioxide emissions which it brought about would come through a switch to no-carbon and low-carbon fuels). Using DTI's estimates of price elasticities and its energy model, DTI's Energy Advisory Panel estimated what levels of carbon tax would be required to achieve various reductions in annual carbon dioxide emissions. According to this analysis, the carbon tax required to bring about a 20% reduction in emissions (compared to a 1990 base year) by 2010 would cause a 72% increase in domestic gas prices, a 23% increase in domestic electricity prices, a 125% increase in industrial gas prices and a 41% increase in industrial electricity prices.[111]

6.167   But, as the panel pointed out, this analysis relied simply on the price mechanism to achieve demand reduction and fuel switching. We believe price rises of this magnitude would not be politically acceptable and would be economically and socially damaging. As we argued above, a range of incentives, advice and publicity is required, to evoke a much larger response than could be obtained by the price mechanism alone and, in effect, alter the price elasticities. Businesses and households should be given more help than is currently available in reducing their energy consumption. This help should take the form of credible, easily understood advice on equipment and measures which increase energy efficiency, and subsidies for the most cost-effective, practicable and reliable of these. If these measures were combined with a carbon tax, announced in advance of its introduction, sales of existing energy-saving equipment would increase. The development of new technologies would be stimulated. Consumers would pay more attention to the energy consumption of new appliances, cars and homes when making purchases.

6.168   Recent experience with taxation of road fuels gives some useful guidance. As we noted above, the fuel duty escalator appears to have had a very limited effect in reducing road fuel consumption. From the consumers' perspective, governments failed to use the large extra revenues to make an appreciable improvement to alternatives to the car or lorry. Indeed, public transport fares rose more rapidly than private motoring costs.[112] Yet, in what is probably the most effective use of an economic instrument in UK environmental policy to date, the introduction of lower fuel duty for unleaded fuel *did* evoke a strong response from consumers and manufacturers. A small incentive for people to switch to a less environmentally harmful alternative and a clear message about the need for change were successfully used by government to phase out leaded petrol.

6.169   **A carbon tax should be announced at least a year in advance of its introduction, be set at a modest level initially, and be preceded by or launched alongside the other measures we recommend for raising energy efficiency, reducing energy consumption and reducing fuel poverty.** It would also have to be integrated with the existing taxes on road fuels; either

XI A large inland water power scheme in Scotland (Sloy) with a capacity of 0.13 GW

XII Wind farm at Blyth Harbour, Northumberland, with a capacity of 2.7 MW from nine 300 kW turbines, commissioned in 1993

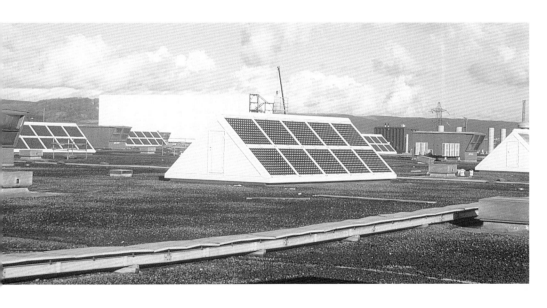

XIII Part of the UK's largest installation of photovoltaic technology, on the roof of the Ford Motor Company's engine plant at Bridgend, South Wales. The installation, completed in 1998, has a peak electrical capacity of 97 kW

XIV Short rotation willow coppice grown for project ARBRE near York (box 7B): visit by Commission June 1999

XV Tank testing of a 35th scale model of a Pelamis (sea-snake) wave power machine at Edinburgh University. It is envisaged that a full-sized, commercial machine would be 130 metres long with a peak electrical output of 750 kW

XVI The upper reservoir of the Dinorwig pumped storage scheme commissioned in 1983 with a capacity of 1.7 GW

7.92   The UK has a number of excellent tidal stream sites around its coastline, notably the Pentland Firth, Mull of Galloway, Barry Island and Portland Bill where tidal stream velocities range from 2.5 to 6 m/s. The factors which determine the size of the tidal stream resource are the tidal velocity and the volume through which the current flows. Tidal stream data is provided in Admiralty Tidal Stream Atlases. Taking into account factors such as normal shipping routes, the rating and the efficiency of the turbines (which result in a density of 37 turbines per square kilometre of sea-bed) and availability, the accessible tidal stream resource is estimated by ETSU to be about 4 GW. The true resource may be somewhat higher because there are numerous small sites with high tidal current velocities with insufficient information available to assess them.[101]

7.93   The environmental impact of tidal stream turbines would be broadly similar to that of offshore wave power devices (7.89). The rotors of the turbines might represent rather more of a hazard for fish and marine mammals, but it may be possible to erect protective screens.

FUTURE POTENTIAL

7.94   The sources these newer technologies seek to exploit resemble the second group of non-carbon sources discussed above in being widely dispersed. At the same time the amounts of energy present vary considerably from place to place; for shoreline and near shore wave energy, and still more so for tidal streams, the highest concentrations are in quite small areas. The studies so far carried out have focused on assessing the resources in such areas, and the costs and outputs of devices located there; the energy present elsewhere is likely to be too diffuse to be worthwhile exploiting. Some favourable areas, notably the Bristol Channel, are close to major demand centres; others (the Outer Hebrides, Orkneys and Shetlands for wave energy, and Alderney in the Channel Islands for tidal stream) are very remote.

7.95   The energy in tidal streams is available at predictable times, and for a much higher proportion of the time than would be the case for a tidal barrage, as the turbines can be reversible. Load factors for tidal stream turbines are very consistent, but site-specific, with typical values of between 0.28 and 0.4. Electricity generation from wave energy is likely to be possible at favourable locations, although output will be intermittent with a typical load factor of 0.25,[102] hence the amounts of energy available will vary considerably.

7.96   The amounts of energy it is practicable to obtain from tidal streams and shoreline wave energy seems likely to be quite modest. On present assessments that is also true for near shore wave energy. Larger resources are available offshore, but much less progress has been made in developing suitable technology for that zone.

7.97   Because of its long and exposed coastline the UK is one of the best endowed countries in terms of the energy available in waves. A study of the four most exposed lengths of the west and north coasts of Britain and of the Orkneys and Shetlands concluded that there is an accessible resource of about 0.22 GW of electrical output in the most favourable shoreline sites, 11.4-15.9 GW near the shore (in water depths of 10-25m) and 68.2-79.5 GW offshore (in water depths typically exceeding 40m). After eliminating areas that are likely to be uneconomic because of low energy levels, and taking into account environmental and other constraints on use of sites, the UK's practicable resource of wave energy was estimated to be 6 GW of electrical output, of which 5.7 GW is offshore, 0.24 GW near shore and 0.05 GW shoreline.[103] DTI's 1994 review of renewable sources nevertheless listed wave power as having no accessible resource, on the basis that the technology was too expensive to be competitive;[104] but it is now included among longer-term technologies expected to have potential after 2010 (see box 7E). ETSU's assessment for 2025 now points to an annual average output of 3.75 GW from wave power and 0.25 GW from tidal stream. The ultimate contribution from wave power could be much greater than that.

7.98   In many cases it may be desirable to deploy more than one technology on a single site. As well as minimising, for any given power output, both visual intrusion and disruption to other maritime activities, this approach should also produce significant reductions in the cost of support structures and electrical connections. Against that would have to be set any loss in potential yield if the same sites are not optimal for both sources. The OSPREY device for near shore wave power has been designed to incorporate a wind turbine. If wave power devices for deeper waters are designed to float, incorporation of a wind turbine may not be practicable. **We recommend that DTI commission studies of the feasibility of combining different offshore power generation technologies in a single structure so that, if the findings are promising, further development of the technologies can take place on that basis.**

7.99   Wave power appears to be a field in which the UK has a world lead. Estimated generating costs of electricity from both shoreline and offshore wave power are now much more competitive having fallen over recent years from around 15 p/kWh in 1980 to 5 p/kWh in 1999[105] (assuming an 8% discount rate and that research and development is completed successfully and that current designs will function as predicted without incurring additional costs). There has also been a significant amount of research elsewhere over the last 20 years, mainly in Scandinavia and Japan. Current interest is more widespread, and includes a 1 MW scheme planned in India[106] and a 1 MW pilot plant sponsored by the European Commission in the Azores.[107] If the technology is developed successfully, there could be a large export market.[108] The pace of development is now rapid, and concern has been expressed that the advantage the UK has at the moment could quickly be eroded.[109] Given its natural advantages, and the inventiveness its engineers have shown, it would be regrettable if the UK became dependent on imported technology, as has happened in the case of wind power.

7.100   The global market for tidal stream technology is assessed to be far smaller because of the high initial costs of devices.[110] Nevertheless this is also a field in which the UK has a world lead. The government has not provided any support for tidal stream technology; a grant towards the cost of the prototype device being constructed has been provided by the European Commission.[112] **We recommend that stronger support be given to wave power and tidal stream technology, which have considerable promise. Support can take the form either of funding research and development or of awarding contracts for electricity generated by these methods.**

CURRENT PROSPECTS FOR ALTERNATIVE ENERGY SOURCES

7.101   In the previous sections of this chapter we have reviewed the use made in the UK at present of the energy sources which provide alternatives to fossil fuels and their long-term potential. We now discuss their current prospects over the next two decades in the light of present government policies, including the proposals recently put forward for future support to renewable energy sources. We then consider public perceptions of alternative energy sources and the relevance these have for any strategy for their future development. In the next chapter we go on to consider the roles alternative sources could play in the longer term within the overall energy system for the UK.

7.102   Nuclear power is used on a substantial scale at present, but the capacity of nuclear power stations is starting to decline as the first generation stations are closed. A further large reduction is scheduled over the next two decades as the second generation stations are progressively closed. Figure 7-I shows the projection submitted to us in evidence by the company which owns and operates the newer stations.[113] In the absence of new construction, the third generation station, Sizewell B, is likely to be the only one still operating in 2025. The government's draft Climate Change Programme gives a broadly similar picture.[114]

Figure 7-I

Nuclear power: retirement pattern of existing power stations*

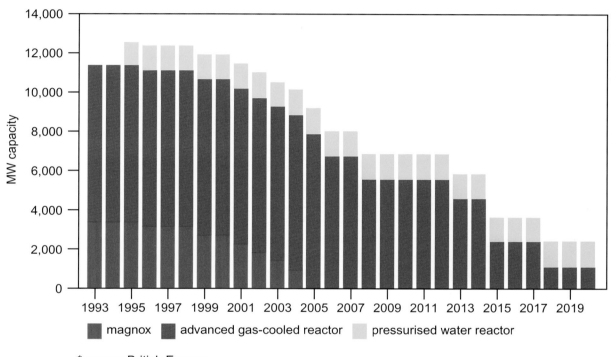

*source: British Energy

7.103   The prospects for nuclear power in the UK were reviewed by the previous government in 1995.[115] A second pressurised water reactor (Sizewell C) was identified as the best option for a new nuclear station in the short term. Estimated to produce electricity at a price of 2.9 p/kWh (with an 8% discount rate), it was not regarded as competitive with gas-fired stations. This cost is however below those of many of the other alternatives to fossil fuels.

7.104   In 1998 the House of Commons Trade and Industry Committee recommended that: 'A formal presumption be made now, for purposes of long-term planning, that new nuclear plant may be required in the course of the next two decades.'[116] This recommendation has been supported by a joint working group of the Royal Society and the Royal Academy of Engineering, which has further urged that:

> The timetable for such consideration should allow a decision to be taken early enough to enable nuclear to play a full, long-term role in national energy policy. This is likely to mean early in the next administration if a damaging decline in the role of nuclear is to be avoided.[117]

7.105   The government has recently said that: 'Questions of cost, waste disposal and public acceptability would need to be resolved before industry put forward any proposals for approval.'[118] We concur in that view. We emphasise however that, unless closure of nuclear power stations is offset by construction of new generating plants which do not emit carbon dioxide, there will be a direct conflict with any strategy to counter climate change, in that electricity generation will become more carbon-intensive.

7.106   In principle renewable energy sources could be developed on a scale that would compensate for the reduced contribution from nuclear power. But government policy does not provide for that. Its proposed target, still subject to consultation, is that the proportion of UK electricity requirements met from renewables should be increased from 2.5% now to 5% by the end of 2003 and 10% by 2010.[119] Nothing has so far been said about any further increase beyond 2010.[120,121] **We recommend that longer-term targets be set for expanding the contribution from renewable sources well beyond 10% of electricity supplies to cover a much larger share of primary energy demand.**

7.107   Whether the target for 2003 is achieved will largely depend on the successful implementation of renewable energy schemes which have been accepted by the government under the non-fossil fuel obligation (NFFO) (5.38), the system of support which has operated up to now. In principle this is a subsidy to renewable energy sources at the expense of consumers (albeit a much smaller one than the subsidy originally provided by consumers to nuclear power under the same procedures, but now removed). The size of this subsidy has been reduced because the system of competitive bidding under NFFO has halved the average declared price, so that in the fifth and final round it had fallen to 2.71 p/kWh, only marginally above the average pool selling price of 2.60 p/kWh in 1998.[122] As can be seen, this is below the most recently quoted cost for electricity from a new nuclear power station (7.103). There would nevertheless be a continuing subsidy under NFFO contracts already entered into: but in practice that may be overtaken by transitional arrangements being devised to ensure that contracts continue to be viable under the new system of support described below.[123]

7.108   In the liberalised electricity market consumers can now make a personal choice to support renewable energy sources by opting for a *green tariff*, either from a major supplier or from an independent supplier using only renewable sources. Some green tariffs involve payment of a premium which will be invested in a fund to support development of renewable sources. The Energy Saving Trust has established an accreditation scheme to ensure that green claims by suppliers are supported by independent auditing and that customers know the mix of generation used to fulfil the tariffs they are choosing.[124]

7.109   Support for projects which obtained contracts in the first two rounds of NFFO terminated at the end of 1998. They will be eligible for the new system of support described below, but for the moment are largely dependent on contracts negotiated with companies offering green tariffs. Such tariffs have not in most cases been marketed intensively, and they have not apparently met with an enthusiastic response from consumers. We regard support and incentives provided by government as a more appropriate and effective way of stimulating development of renewable energy sources. It is not clear how green tariffs will be affected by the new system of government support described below.

7.110   The government will provide a fiscal incentive for firms and public bodies to use electricity from renewable sources (other than large-scale hydro) by exempting such supplies from the climate change levy which will apply from April 2001. The expected rate for the levy in

7.125   A similar approach can be adopted at a more local level. In some other European countries there is a long tradition of ownership of energy utilities by local communities, which can benefit either through lower energy prices or through use of the profits for other local purposes. This gives them a direct interest in developing new energy sources. In contrast, the UK has liberalised markets for electricity and gas, with tariffs that apply nationally. Tangible advantages to the local community from construction of an energy installation are therefore confined to any employment provided and any incidental benefit by way of planning gain.

7.126   The principle that the price paid by customers for energy should not reflect their distance from the source of supply may be questioned now that clear distinctions have been drawn between responsibility for supply, transmission and (in the case of electricity) distribution, and these activities are being separately costed. If local communities found they could avoid increased prices for electricity by choosing suppliers which do not have to incur large charges for transmission and distribution, they would have a direct incentive to achieve greater self-sufficiency in energy.

7.127   The situation has changed in one respect since we took evidence. Whereas under NFFO the contract to purchase electricity from a specified renewable energy scheme preceded the grant of planning permission, electricity suppliers will now have to seek out generators who will enable them to comply with their obligation to obtain a given proportion of electricity from renewable sources. It will be prudent for companies wishing to undertake renewable energy schemes to open discussions at an early stage with the local planning authority and local people and develop proposals in consultation with them.

7.128   There is one type of renewable energy scheme in which the full involvement of the local community will be crucial, and which will also bring them direct advantage. That is the development of combined heat and power schemes using renewable energy sources and supplying residential neighbourhoods both with electricity and with heat through district heating networks.

7.129   Achieving very large reductions in carbon dioxide emissions is likely to involve the development of new energy sources on a scale that will raise issues of public acceptance at national level, as well as local level. For such policies to be acceptable to the public, they must have clearly understood objectives, be based on a full examination of the options, and represent an integrated approach which seeks to reconcile conflicting considerations. In the next chapter we discuss how an integrated approach can be based on an understanding of the dynamics of the UK energy system. Then in chapter 9 we consider some possible options for supplying given levels of energy demand while at the same time making deep cuts in carbon dioxide emissions, and what impacts those options would have on the environment in other respects.

There is great potential for the UK to obtain energy from renewable energy sources. Realising that potential will be dependent on adequate government support, careful attention to their particular characteristics and public acceptance for the necessary installations. Before new nuclear power stations are built, the waste management problem would have to be solved, not only to the satisfaction of the scientific community, but as a necessary part of gaining public acceptance

Chapter 8

PATTERNS OF ENERGY SUPPLY AND USE

What are the present patterns of supply and demand for energy? Can the requirements for different forms of energy be met in more efficient ways or by using alternative energy sources? If such sources are to be used on a large scale, what problems have to be overcome?

8.1 Having examined energy use sector by sector in chapter 6 and energy sources that might provide alternatives to fossil fuels in chapter 7, we now take a broader look at the energy system. In this chapter we discuss the present patterns of demand and supply for the three main forms in which energy is required, and possible alternative patterns. Those forms of energy are heat (8.4-8.16), propulsion for transport (8.17-8.25) and electricity (8.26-8.54). In the final section of the chapter we consider some cross-cutting and fundamental issues about storing energy and using energy carriers (8.55-8.65). This analysis provides the basis for the following chapter, in which we present illustrative scenarios for the UK energy system in 2050. It is also informed, in turn, by some of the results from that exercise.

8.2 The aspect of energy policy that has received most attention, both from governments and in public debate, is alternative ways of generating electricity. What may be more difficult to replace is the use of fossil fuels to provide heat and propulsion for transport.

8.3 Demand for primary energy is affected not only by demand from final users, but also by the overall efficiency of the energy system in matching the forms, times and locations in which energy is required with the forms, times and locations in which it is available. Energy losses within the system accounted for 30% of the UK's demand for primary energy in 1998, even without taking complete supply chains into account (see figure 5-I).[1] In particular, electricity generation usually involves the loss of large amounts of energy in the form of waste heat, as explained previously (3.39 and box 3A), and further losses occur in the course of transmission and distribution. The combined effect is that, whereas about one-sixth of the energy supplied to final users in the UK is in the form of electricity,[2] providing that electricity requires almost one third of the primary energy used in the UK.[3] In looking at requirements for particular forms of energy, we also consider whether there are ways in which the overall efficiency of the energy system could be improved. This might have major implications for the UK's ability to achieve very large reductions in carbon dioxide emissions over the next half century.

HEAT

8.4 In 1994, the most recent year for which figures are available, energy used for heating was, at 36%, the largest component of UK energy consumption by end use.[4] About 80% of energy used in the household sector, 75% in industry, and 65% in other non-transport uses is devoted to the provision of heat.[5] At present the greater part of that energy is provided by fossil fuels, the remainder by electricity.

8.5 Part of the demand from industry, at an average rate of 16 GW at present, is for heat at high temperatures for use in particular processes *(high-grade heat)*. This will continue to be provided by fossil fuels for the foreseeable future. It would be technically feasible to provide some of it by using energy crops or agricultural and forestry wastes as fuel, but that is unlikely to happen so long as other sources are available. Landfill gas is technically suitable for the purpose, but cannot be regarded as a source of energy in the longer term (7.80).

8.6   The greater part of the demand is for *low-grade heat* for industrial processes such as drying, and to maintain the temperature in buildings and heat water for domestic and other purposes. At the same time very large quantities of energy are being wasted because the greater part of the energy content of fuels used to generate electricity emerges as low-grade heat and is not at present put to use. In view of the importance of heat as a component of energy demand, and the scale on which it is being wasted at present, **the UK must develop a comprehensive strategy for the supply and use of heat.**

8.7   A more efficient way of using the energy in fuels is to burn them in combined heat and power plants (3.40) to provide both heat and electricity. Such plants have been used much more extensively in some other countries, notably in Scandinavia. In the UK they have hitherto predominantly served industrial sites with a large demand for low-grade heat. They declined in importance during the 1970s and 1980s,[6] but are now being promoted by entrepreneurial companies which have emerged following liberalisation of the electricity and gas markets, in some cases as subsidiaries of large energy companies (5.20). The commercial attractions of investing in a combined heat and power (CHP) plant have depended on the relative prices of gas and electricity and the terms on which top-up electricity can be bought from the grid and (not permitted until 1989) surplus electricity sold to the grid. It is only recently that the government has recognised the desirability from a national viewpoint of increasing the overall efficiency of energy conversion, and has adopted policies to encourage the wider use of CHP plants and set a target (5.45). There is a strong case for a much wider development of combined heat and power schemes for both the industrial and the domestic market. There are many opportunities in both the industrial (6.18) and services (6.41) sectors.

8.8   Using CHP plants to supply the needs of households entails either installing a separate plant in each dwelling or constructing networks to distribute the heat. Designs to serve individual dwellings have been developed, roughly the size of a domestic boiler, though much more complex, and fuelled by gas. There has been little progress as yet towards marketing such devices in the UK, despite much research and development by British Gas covering both fuel cells and microturbines.[7] A design using a fuel cell has been installed on a pilot scale in Germany.[8] There is a widespread expectation that within 20 years many households will have equipment of this kind.[9] With very large reductions in carbon dioxide emissions there might be sufficient fossil fuels available in 2050 to enable some households to have such plants, but certainly not all households. In the very long term such devices might be fuelled by hydrogen, produced using energy from sources other than fossil fuels (8.60-8.61).

8.9   Local distribution networks for heat are a more firmly established technology. Almost unknown in the UK, they are a familiar feature in Scandinavia, where networks can now convey heat economically over tens of kilometres. Box 8A describes systems which serve Stockholm and the surrounding area. Normal domestic central heating systems are supplied from the high-pressure system through heat exchangers, and individual households charged according to the metered amount of heat used.[10] There is likely to be major growth in small heat and power schemes serving blocks of flats (6.56), but it is unlikely that extensive schemes will be undertaken in the UK unless there is much stronger support from government. **We recommend that the UK government and devolved administrations carry out detailed studies to identify the most effective ways of promoting and facilitating the large-scale growth of heat networks.**

8.10   Heat networks become even more attractive as a method for reducing carbon dioxide emissions if heat can be obtained from sources other than fossil fuels. Most of the energy sources which are alternatives to fossil fuels cannot supply heat except indirectly, by first generating electricity. Nuclear power stations produce very large quantities of waste heat but it is likely to be impracticable to make any use of it, unless new stations were to be constructed under different siting criteria, and probably also on a much smaller scale than existing stations. Geothermal energy can supply heat, but the amount exploitable in the UK with presently foreseeable technology is very limited.

BOX 8A	MORE INTELLIGENT USE OF HEAT[11]

Large-scale heat distribution networks are found in many Scandinavian towns and cities. They are generally supplied by combined heat and power (CHP) plants, and frequently these burn wastes from the region's large forestry industry.

Stockholm has three large networks operated by Birka Energi, a company owned by the municipality and a Finnish group. These serve most of the blocks of flats in the city as well as many commercial and public buildings. These networks extend to communities outside the capital, as useful heat can be delivered 40 kilometres from the source.

One of these three networks, serving the centre of the city, is supplied partly by a large, coal-burning CHP plant and partly by heat pumps. The second, serving the south of the city, is supplied by the world's largest heat pump system at Hammarby and by a nearby CHP plant burning municipal waste. The electrically powered heat pumps supply on average some 70% of the heat. The third system, in the western districts of Stockholm, burns biofuels.

The main source of heat harnessed by the heat pumps is municipal wastewater. The temperature of this ranges from $5°C$ in winter to $22°C$ in summer. The heat pumps extract heat from the wastewater arriving at a large sewage works and use this to raise the temperature of the pressurised water in the heating network to $60-90°C$. After delivering heat to hundreds of buildings, this water returns to the heat pump at a temperature some $30°C$ lower. Another source of heat is seawater from the Baltic. The system supplies about 3.5 times as much energy as it consumes in electricity. During periods of extreme cold, when the heat pumps cannot supply sufficient heat, the network is topped up by burning oil and by using electricity for direct heating of the water.

The use of heat pumps on this large scale in Stockholm and some other Swedish cities stems in part from the oil crisis of the 1970s, which pushed up the cost of oil as a fuel for heating, and in part from an abundant supply of relatively cheap electricity generated by nuclear and hydroelectric plants.

Replacing fossil fuel-fired heating systems with systems based on electrically-powered heat pumps will reduce total carbon dioxide emissions if a substantial proportion of the electricity used is generated by non-fossil fuel sources. In Sweden that is the case. In the UK, most electricity is generated by burning fossil fuels; at present heat pumps would reduce carbon dioxide emissions only by comparison with oil- or coal-fired boilers. However, as the proportion of electricity generated by non-fossil fuel sources rises, there will be a growing potential for reducing carbon dioxide emissions by replacing fossil fuel-fired heating plants with heat pump systems.

8.11   The most readily available alternative sources for heat are carbon-based: energy crops, agricultural and forestry wastes, and municipal wastes. Although their use gives rise to carbon dioxide emissions, these are largely balanced by the carbon dioxide removed from the atmosphere by growing vegetation within a managed rotation, or in the case of municipal waste by preventing more damaging emissions of methane.[12] Until the last decade these alternative carbon-based sources provided more energy in the UK in the form of heat than in the form of electricity. Subsequently the position has been distorted by the non fossil fuel obligation; government policy has treated them as primarily fuels to generate electricity. That distortion should be corrected for the future. **Energy crops and wastes should be regarded in the medium to long term as having a premium role in supplying heat. They should be used in plants providing both heat and electricity to an urban area, and located close to the sources of the fuel in order to minimise transport.** Although all forms of waste should be utilised as energy sources to the extent that they continue to be available, the major long-term potential is in energy crops.

8.12   CHP plants vary in their heat-to-power ratio. The ratio in older plants was typically about 4:1. More recent plants, designed to maximise the amount of electricity generated, may have ratios as low as 2:1, and less flexibility to vary the ratio. **CHP plants should be regarded primarily as a source of heat. It may be desirable to keep a large part of their capacity to generate electricity in reserve, so that it can be used at those times at which there is a shortfall in supply from other sources.** If combined heat and power plants are viewed in that light, it would be preferable to design them as steam-cycle plants, rather than as combined cycle plants employing pyrolysis (7.56). The latter have a higher efficiency in terms of generating electricity but may have a lower overall efficiency, and offer less flexibility to vary the heat-to-power ratio. They therefore represent a less effective way of limiting carbon dioxide emissions.

8.13   The concept of regarding CHP plants as providing primarily heat is already well established in Denmark, where there is widespread use of district heating plants, sometimes fuelled by straw or wood.[13] During the summer, when demand for heat is substantially reduced, some plants are closed and electricity provided from other sources, including wind turbines. In some cases the generating capacity of such plants is being used to cover shortfalls in the supply of electricity from wind turbines.[14]

8.14   If the aggregate amount of energy that can be obtained in future as low-grade heat from fossil fuels and alternative carbon-based fuels is not sufficient to meet demand, the gap would have to be filled by electricity. Moreover, even with very extensive development of district heat networks, a substantial proportion of buildings would not be within reach of a district heat network, and for many of them use of gas might not be practicable; electricity, in contrast, is universally available. Conventional methods of electric heating for buildings are both more expensive than gas and, with the present mix of energy sources for electricity generation in the UK, give rise to two and a half times as much carbon dioxide for each unit of heat supplied (6.80).[15] However, the amount of heat that can be obtained from a given quantity of electricity is tripled if it is used to drive heat pumps (see box 3A), rather than provide heat directly. **To improve energy efficiency, government should promote use of heat pumps wherever electricity has to be used to supply low-grade heat.** Heat pumps can be used as the source of supply for heat networks (box 8A provides an example). On the basis of the UK's current mix of fuels to generate electricity, there would not be any advantage in terms of reduced carbon dioxide emissions in using heat pumps in preference to high-efficiency gas boilers. If however electricity comes to be generated predominantly from sources that do not give rise to carbon dioxide emissions, its use to drive heat pumps becomes much more attractive.

8.15   The purpose of the strategy for heat we are advocating is not only to increase the efficiency of supply, but also to obtain radical reductions in the demand for energy for heating. **A central policy objective must be a very large reduction in demand for energy for heating and cooling, achieved through much more sophisticated management of heat and much wider use of combined heat and power schemes for both the industrial and the domestic market. The resulting heat networks, supplied initially by fossil fuels, could ultimately obtain heat from energy crops and electrically powered heat pumps.** The general warming of the climate may make some contribution to this objective; but, without an intelligent policy response, any advantage in that respect might be outweighed by the growing demand for energy for cooling.

8.16   Greatly improved management of heat will require modifications on a massive scale, both to individual buildings and to the infrastructure of neighbourhoods. There will have to be not only a much higher standard of insulation in buildings but also a much more sophisticated approach to heat management, taking full advantage of microelectronics. Buildings must be designed to make full use of solar energy, both through passive heat gain by the building structure and through use of solar panels to heat water. The requirement for cooling in all types of building should be an integral part of the strategy right from the beginning, and heat exchangers should become a standard design feature in buildings of all types.

PROPULSION FOR TRANSPORT

8.17   Energy demand for transport is not only very substantial, but has grown rapidly. Oil at present supplies 99% of the energy used for transport in the UK, with almost all the rest provided by electricity.

8.18   Achieving a reduction in energy demand for transport over the next half century will require both radical changes in technology and effective and thoroughgoing implementation of integrated transport policies that will reduce the overall energy intensity of the transport system. This will involve reducing the need for mobility and making increasing use of modes which use less energy than private road transport. The Commission has explored these issues in previous reports (6.125 and box 6D).

8.19   Whatever degree of success is achieved in that direction, there will remain a very large demand for a readily portable energy source with a high energy density and power density suitable for propelling personal vehicles. It will be technically difficult to replace fossil fuels in that role, and for the time being it is likely to remain necessary to treat transport as the premium use for oil. The main emphasis in policy over coming decades therefore must be on finding ways of using fossil fuels in transport that reduce the amounts of carbon dioxide emitted. There have been big improvements in the conversion efficiencies of internal combustion engines. In the case of personal vehicles however these have been offset hitherto by increases in the size and weight of vehicles and in their ancillary equipment (6.115). European car manufacturers have entered into an agreement with the European Commission to reduce average carbon dioxide emissions per kilometre for new cars by 2008 (6.123). One immediate option for doing so is to switch between different forms of fossil fuel. However the implications for health-related pollutants such as particulates also have to be taken into account.

8.20   The Commission's reports on transport drew attention to the advantage that could be obtained (at that time assessed as a reduction of 20-30% in carbon dioxide emissions) if petrol were to be replaced by diesel as the fuel for cars and the smallest goods vehicles. Because of concern about health effects however they did not favour a major shift to diesel until more stringent limits had been placed on emissions of particulates and nitrogen oxides. Progress towards more stringent standards for emissions from diesel engines and improved technology to meet them has been slower than the Commission hoped would be the case. As the problem of reducing carbon dioxide emissions from transport receives more and more attention, both governments and manufacturers may well show increasing interest in the potential of diesel engines to contribute. Although diesel engines remain significantly more efficient, some much more efficient petrol engines have been developed since 1994; but there is some concern that such engines emit more particulates than conventional petrol engines. **We recommend that increased efforts should be made to develop and bring into general use methods of reducing substantially emissions of particulates and nitrogen oxides from diesel engines. The European Commission should promote this by setting technology-forcing standards for these pollutants.**

8.21   Gas has a similar efficiency advantage to diesel, and the additional advantage of containing less carbon in proportion to its energy content. It also has the great advantage as a transport fuel that emissions of health-related pollutants are lower; and for that reason the Commission has recommended its use as the fuel for heavy vehicles in urban areas. The UK seems to have lagged behind in adopting it as the fuel either for heavy vehicles or for cars (where the size and weight of the tank required is a disadvantage), and in developing appropriate infrastructure.

8.22   Fuel cells using methanol offer another way of using fossil fuels in transport that both safeguards air quality and is more efficient, and is currently attracting great interest. The high power density and energy density of fuel cells make them suitable for use in transport, and a particular advantage over the internal combustion engine is that they achieve a high efficiency over a much wider range of power outputs. Thus, although a vehicle powered by a fuel cell using methanol emits carbon dioxide, the emissions should be less than from an internal combustion engine. Whether there is an overall reduction in carbon dioxide emissions depends on how much energy has been used in producing methanol from fossil fuels, and the source of that energy. Hybrid engines may facilitate the transition to use of fuel cells in vehicles. We describe below the principles on which a fuel cell operates, and discuss the long-term option of relying on hydrogen as the fuel (8.61-8.62).

8.23   Electric batteries eliminate all emissions from vehicles. Despite extensive programmes of research and development on the use of batteries to propel vehicles however, technological progress has so far been disappointing. They still have a relatively low energy density and power density, and take a long time to recharge. A major breakthrough will be needed before battery-powered vehicles can offer a performance and range comparable to those offered by oil-engined vehicles, at reasonable cost. For this reason there is now much more interest in fuel cells as a method of propulsion for vehicles. The overall energy requirement for battery-powered vehicles however might be less than for vehicles powered by fuel cells using hydrogen because of smaller energy losses within the supply chain.

8.24   Liquid fuels for vehicles can be produced from crops. However the production processes can be polluting, and in some cases have a high energy requirement (7.77). To produce biofuels on a large scale a large area of land is needed to grow the crops. It is unlikely that sufficient land could be found for this purpose in the UK, especially if (as seems a more promising approach) large areas of land are to be devoted to growing crops to provide energy in the form of heat. We do not therefore regard biologically produced fuels as a valid option for large-scale use in transport in the UK in the foreseeable future.

8.25   Energy use in international air transport and the resulting emissions of greenhouse gases are not included in national statistics or the limits set as a result of the Kyoto Protocol. Although they so far represent only a small proportion of the global total of carbon dioxide emissions, it should be emphasised that emissions from this source are growing rapidly, and measures to limit their growth are therefore a significant part of the task of countering climate change. All the energy for air transport is provided by oil, and the only theoretical alternative so far identified is hydrogen.

ELECTRICITY

8.26   Demand for electricity is the most rapidly growing component of energy demand.[16] To assess the possibility of alternative patterns of demand and supply for electricity we look at three aspects in turn: increasing the efficiency with which fossil fuels are used in generating plants (8.27-8.31); the options for the UK to obtain electricity from non-carbon sources (8.32-8.41); and the nature of electricity networks and how that is changing (8.42-8.54).

USING FOSSIL FUELS MORE EFFICIENTLY

8.27   There are several approaches to reducing the amounts of carbon dioxide emitted when fossil fuels are used. As we have emphasised, when fossil fuels are used to generate electricity, most of their energy content emerges in the form of low-grade heat. Historically this element was ignored in the UK. The former Central Electricity Generating Board, which had a monopoly in England and Wales, had no legal power to sell energy except in the form of electricity.

8.28   Instead, the objective of more efficient electricity generation was pursued through successive increases in the size of plant used. The very large power stations that resulted produce heat on too large a scale to be a useful resource, and most of those in the UK were constructed on sites remote from potential markets for it. An important criterion for selecting the site for a power station was whether there was sufficient water available to remove the waste heat rapidly. As the amount of water available was often insufficient for direct cooling, perhaps the most conspicuous feature of large power stations became a cluster of giant cooling towers (see photograph II). With an eye to public safety (in the case of nuclear power) or urban air quality (if fossil fuels were used) most large power stations in the UK were constructed on sites remote from other activities which might have a demand for heat. They now stand as monuments to inefficiency and waste.

8.29   If there is to be a very extensive development of CHP schemes, plants generating electricity must be much smaller than in the past. Combined cycle gas turbines (CCGT) (see photograph III) are not only a more efficient technology, but also their efficiency does not increase significantly with size, in contrast to steam-cycle plants. Moreover, generating plants of modest size are more attractive commercially in a liberalised market. There could also be a large-scale development of plants of modest size using alternative carbon-based fuels such as energy crops, as described above.

8.30   Use of gas for electricity generation, in preference to oil or coal, is in any event advantageous because of its lower carbon content. As has been shown already (5.49) the 'dash to gas' in electricity generation significantly reduced UK carbon dioxide emissions, although it had other motivations. Coal remains the most important single fuel used in electricity generation.[17] There will not be a large further erosion of its position over the next few years unless there is a change in the government's current presumption that new gas-fired generating stations should not be built unless there are special circumstances.[18] Government policy on fuel choice for electricity generation is therefore in conflict with the need to reduce carbon dioxide emissions.

8.31   Even with the need to make very large reductions in carbon dioxide emissions we foresee a significant continuing role for fossil fuel plants in providing back-up and flexibility within electricity networks; we enlarge on the reasons for that in the next chapter. The amount of fossil fuels used for that purpose, and hence the carbon dioxide emissions, would not be large. There would be a different position if recovery of carbon dioxide produced at fossil fuel generating plants, and its subsequent disposal in geological strata, becomes established (3.4-3.11). That might happen either because this approach proved to be competitive in cost with alternative energy sources or because the prospective supplies from such sources were not sufficient to meet the expected demand for electricity. In that event, it is likely that, to ensure efficient operation of the processes involved, the generating plants would be very large ones of the kind familiar today, and would operate continuously to supply baseload. It might not be practicable to put to use the very large amounts of low-grade heat that would be produced at a few locations.

ELECTRICITY FROM NON-CARBON SOURCES

8.32   In chapter 7 we considered in turn the potential of a number of energy sources that might provide alternatives to fossil fuels. If fossil fuels are not used for large-scale electricity generation in future, that will create a fundamentally different situation, and it is necessary to consider how various alternative energy sources might be brought together to form a workable system for supplying electricity.

8.33   In the UK, and other countries which do not have large resources of inland water power, nuclear power is the only non-carbon source of energy already in use on a very large scale. It provides energy continuously and operates reliably.

8.34   The present role of nuclear power stations in meeting baseload demand suits their technical characteristics, in that the time needed to start them is long by comparison with fluctuations in demand. There would be scope for a substantial expansion of their baseload role. New designs of reactor may be capable of more flexible operation, and might therefore be able to meet part of the daily variation in demand,[19] although the network would also have to include a substantial capacity of other types of plant with shorter response times.

8.35   The renewable sources that are not carbon-based and that could make a substantial contribution to the UK's future energy supplies are all intermittent rather than continuous. The alternative energy sources that could be continuously available are carbon-based; although they can generate a significant amount of electricity if used in CHP plants, we consider they should be regarded primarily as sources of heat, rather than electricity (8.12).

8.36   The amount of electricity that intermittent sources can be expected to generate on average may be quite a small proportion of their capacity. For present designs of photovoltaic cells the output that can be obtained in the UK is only 17% of capacity. For wave and tidal power it is 33%, and for wind turbines 43% on average.[20]

8.37   The periods when intermittent sources can generate electricity are predictable to a large extent. Photovoltaic cells can operate only during daylight. The timing and height of tides can be predicted accurately a few days ahead. The energy available from wind and waves can be predicted accurately a few hours ahead; and predictions up to three days ahead are probably as reliable as the weather forecasts on which grid controllers already rely to assess future demand for electricity. The periods when intermittent sources are generating electricity however will often not coincide with the periods when demand for electricity is highest.

8.38   The low availability of generating plants using wind, wave and tidal energy can be compensated for to some extent by building a larger number of plants; if these are dispersed over a wide area, local variations in wind speed and sea conditions, and the times of high tide at particular locations, will be much less important. Even if changes in wind speeds were unexpected and relatively sudden, they would not occur simultaneously across the whole country. From time to time however there would inevitably be an overall shortfall in supply in any electricity network which placed heavy reliance on such intermittent energy sources. The energy available from wind and waves is lowest in summer. The greatest problem however might well arise in winter, when demand for electricity is much higher and high pressure could cause cold, still, overcast conditions that can persist over the whole of the UK for several days.

8.39   We discuss below the prospects for developing novel technologies for storing electricity. Unless that can be done, the security of electricity supplies would depend on having other sources of energy available on a substantial scale, so that they could be used, as and when necessary, to meet overall shortfalls in the supply of electricity from intermittent renewable sources.

8.40   Part of this back-up capacity could be provided if the operators of the large numbers of CHP plants we envisage, using alternative fuels (8.11), had the possibility and the incentive to vary the heat-to-power ratio of their plants (8.12) at such times in order to produce more electricity and less thermal energy than would normally be the case. This would be only a partial solution however. A limitation in practice could be that shortfalls in winter in the supply of electricity from intermittent renewable sources might coincide with peak demand for heat.

8.41   A system heavily dependent on intermittent renewable sources would therefore have to contain a correspondingly large capacity of back-up plants using fossil fuels. Although the total capacity of those plants would be substantial, it would be used only infrequently, and the resulting addition to the annual total of UK carbon dioxide emissions would not therefore be large. For some decades, this back-up capacity might be provided by the operators of existing fossil fuel plants, including some of those (mainly coal-fired) already operating in a reserve role. In the longer term new plants would have to be constructed for this purpose. The best prospect for ensuring that, and the most energy-efficient outcome, might be if the operators of CHP plants using alternative fuels were given an incentive to construct supplementary plants burning fossil fuels, which could then be brought into use to generate additional electricity as and when required. They would then be in a position to make the most advantageous use of the low-grade heat resulting from the burning of both kinds of fuel.

FUTURE EVOLUTION OF ELECTRICITY NETWORKS

8.42   In industrialised countries large networks have been constructed to deliver electricity, in the form of synchronised alternating current, from generating stations to users. The existence and nature of these networks has been determined in part by the quest for economies of scale in generation and the locations chosen for the resulting large power stations, and in part by the lack of any efficient method for storing electricity on a large scale, so that it has to be generated at the moment when it is required. An electricity network of this kind is a single vast entity operating in real time.[21] In England and Wales the function of controlling the network is undertaken by the National Grid Co plc, which also owns the bulk transmission system; in Scotland by two vertically integrated companies (Scottish Power plc and Scottish and Southern plc); and in Northern Ireland by Northern Ireland Electricity plc (see box 5A).

8.43   Grid controllers have the task of matching the generation of electricity to demand, which varies considerably according to the time of day, week and year. In England and Wales the minimum demand (which determines the level of *baseload*) is about 20 GW, but demand rises to 50 GW or more at day-time peaks in winter. Within technical constraints, the selection of sources of supply is determined by the prices charged by major power producers (box 5A). Figures 8-I and 8-II show the pool purchase price for each half-hour period during the day, and the large difference between the price for baseload electricity and the prices paid at times of peak demand.

8.44   Figures 8-I and 8-II also show how different types of power station have been deployed to meet demand in England and Wales on a typical winter day and a typical summer day. Baseload is met mainly by nuclear power stations and CCGTs, though with some contribution from large coal-fired stations and electricity imported from France; when demand rises, more use is made of large coal-fired stations, and other coal-fired stations and other types of plant are brought into use. The total capacity of plant available to supply the grid needs to exceed the predicted maximum demand in order to cope with breakdowns and other unexpected eventualities; in the year 1998/99 the margin of surplus capacity was 23%.[22] To ensure reliability of supply, the practice has been to have a capacity of 1.2 GW instantly available.[23]

8.45   Grid controllers also have responsibility for maintaining the quality of supply by keeping variations in voltage and frequency within the increasingly narrow limits acceptable in an economy that depends so heavily on complex electronic equipment. The National Grid Co plc enters into agreements with the operators of suitable generating plants to boost voltage as and when required, to have plant on stand-by in case of breakdowns and other unexpected fluctuations, and to provide a 'black start' capability for initiating restoration of the network if there were to be a total failure.

8.46   One way of obtaining flexibility in the operation of networks is through links with adjacent networks. The grid in England and Wales is linked to Scotland and to France, and the two networks in Ireland are linked. However such links generally have a relatively small capacity; if they are used to import electricity in normal operation, as happens for example with the link to France, they are less useful in responding to unforeseen events.

8.47   The far-reaching changes that have taken place, and are still taking place, in the market for electricity (5.19-5.26) are likely to have profound effects on the nature of electricity networks. The grid in England and Wales was originally controlled by the organisation which generated electricity, but is now controlled by a separate company answerable to its own shareholders. Another consequence of liberalisation and privatisation is a trend towards smaller and more numerous generating plants. The grid controllers cannot have the same close liaison with a much larger number of plants. Moreover the new plants often have more complex relationships with the network, either because they are using intermittent sources of energy

Figure 8-I
Daily pattern of electricity demand, supply and pool purchase price in England and Wales: winter

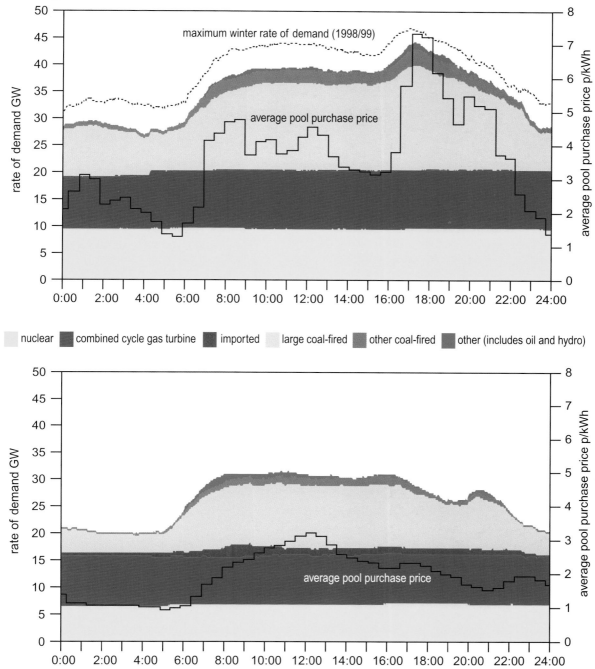

Figure 8-II
Daily pattern of electricity demand, supply and pool purchase price in England and Wales: summer

such as wind power, or because they are CHP plants which may only sometimes be in a position to supply electricity to the network and at other times may wish to take electricity from it.

8.48   The task of managing the national grid in England and Wales will be modified significantly when new electricity trading arrangements come into effect in October 2000. The effect will be to shift some of the burden of ensuring reliability of supply from the grid controllers to the major power producers by imposing heavy financial penalties if they feed into the grid either more or less than the amount of electricity to which they have previously committed themselves. Major power producers will now have an incentive, not only to increase the reliability of their plant, but also to maintain their own reserve plant. The situation in England and Wales will come closer to that in other networks, in which there are usually fewer significant producers.

8.49   The capacity of the bulk transmission system may impose constraints within a network, for example by limiting the transfer of electricity between the midlands and north of England (which have a disproportionate share of generating capacity) and the south. A recent proposal to build an overhead transmission line through Yorkshire, so that maximum use can be made of the link with Scotland, encountered strong opposition because of its effect on the landscape. Another difficulty about heavy reliance on intermittent renewable sources is that a large part of the resource is remote from centres of demand. Much of the wave energy available, for example, is off the west coast of Scotland. If it were necessary to use that to generate electricity to meet demand in England, it has been estimated that the cost of augmenting the high voltage link between the two countries for this purpose would be £400 million.[24] If advantage were also taken of the energy available in the same area from winds and tidal streams, the cost of augmenting the link would presumably be even higher. This does not seem an unacceptably large sum in relation to the total investments that will have to be made in new energy sources and systems, although the cost of strengthening the transmission system, and energy losses in the course of transmission, would affect the relative cost of electricity from the sources in question. A greater difficulty might be public opposition to the construction of new transmission lines through areas of high landscape quality. It remains to be seen whether the development of more efficient cables and less visually intrusive pylons can be successful in reducing such opposition, or whether it might be necessary to incur the considerable additional cost of laying cables underground.

8.50   There are also fundamental changes taking place at the level of distribution systems. Below a certain size, generating plants connect to the distribution system rather than the bulk transmission system. Major growth in *embedded generation* is a necessary concomitant of major growth in CHP plants and in relatively small generating plants using renewable sources of energy. It also has certain inherent advantages: generating electricity at or near the point of use reduces energy losses within the network; electricity is transmitted over shorter distances and undergoes fewer changes in voltage.[25] On the other hand embedded generation adds to the technical difficulties of ensuring security of supply and maintaining the stability of the network, including maintaining an appropriate element of reactive power among end users.

8.51   More radical developments are on the horizon. Small users, including individual households, may come to meet a greater or lesser proportion of their own requirements for electricity from sources of their own. As well as the micro-scale heat and power plants mentioned previously (8.8), another possibility is a significant growth in the use of arrays of photovoltaic cells to provide electricity for individual households. Manufacturers of equipment for these new markets will probably not find it profitable to size them to generate sufficient electricity to meet users' peak demands. To some extent, the gap can be bridged by incorporating storage in the system and/or by automatic disconnection of uses which are less time-sensitive, such as heating and refrigeration. It is probable nevertheless that users of small heat and power plants will want to retain a link to the public electricity network, if only as a precaution against plant failure. It is also possible that such plants will be designed to feed into the public network that part of the electricity generated that is in excess of the user's own requirements. The financial and contractual terms on which they are able to do either of those things will be an important consideration.

8.52   Embedded generation may require a structure for distribution networks which is more interconnected than is generally the case at present. While that is technically possible, it will be more expensive. The amount of electricity passing through the system may be reduced, without necessarily any reduction in peak flows.[26] It may well be necessary to construct more low-voltage transmission lines. Innovative techniques would have to be adopted for maintaining and improving the quality of supply. This might add to costs.

8.53   It has been argued that, because they are intermittent and dispersed, large-scale use of non-carbon renewable sources would complicate the task of controlling the grid to such an extent that, if the proportion of electricity being generated from such sources approaches 20-30%, it would be difficult to maintain frequency and voltage.[27]

8.54   There appears to have been no research as yet into these problems, either by the National Grid or by any other body. **We recommend that the government takes responsibility for promoting, and ensuring sufficient funding is available for, research into technologies that solve the problems of controlling electricity networks in which there is a high proportion of embedded and intermittent generation, and into the economic and institutional issues that will need to be resolved.** The technology for controlling such networks is a field in which the Engineering and Physical Sciences Research Council might well be able to play a key role in stimulating developments.

ENERGY STORAGE

8.55   The problems of incorporating intermittent sources into electricity networks would be considerably eased if some way could be found of storing the output of generating plants for later use. That would make management of the network much easier and avoid the need for extensive provision of back-up plant (8.40-8.41). What this requires is a technology that enables large amounts of energy to be stored in a form in which it can be rapidly and efficiently recovered in the form of electrical energy. We consider here mechanical storage, using pumped water systems, and chemical storage via hydrogen or electrolyte solutions.

8.56   In the national grid in England and Wales an element of storage is provided already. Pumped storage schemes use water power to generate electricity but, in contrast to direct flow inland water power schemes (7.20-7.21), they operate in a cycle. Low-cost electricity generated in the early hours of the morning is used to pump water up to a top reservoir (see photograph XVI), and electricity is generated at times of peak demand through releasing the water and letting it flow through turbines to a lower reservoir. The time needed to bring it into operation is very short: within 16 seconds it can produce electricity in large quantities (box 8B). The commercial attractiveness of operating pumped storage depends on the relative prices of the electricity used for pumping and the electricity sold from generation; at present the pumping is done with off-peak electricity, largely from nuclear stations, and the electricity generated is sold at peak times. Alternatively this capacity may be invoked to control the stability of the grid as part of the ancillary services for which the operator is paid a price different from the pool price.

8.57   Operation of a pumped storage reservoir involves significant energy losses: only three-quarters of the power needed for pumping is recovered at the Dinorwig and Ffestiniog power stations.[28] When considered as part of a system however, a pumped storage reservoir can be energy neutral because it becomes possible for other plants in the system to operate closer to their optimum efficiency.

8.58   Expanding this method of storing electricity, however, would require construction of large dams and reservoirs on elevated sites; because of the effects these would have on landscape and wildlife, it is unlikely acceptable sites could be found (7.21). Against that background there is considerable interest in developing alternative technologies for storing electricity, even though at the moment there is no experience anywhere in the world of large-scale use of any technique other than pumped storage.

BOX 8B   **DINORWIG PUMPED STORAGE SCHEME**[29]

The pumped storage plant at Dinorwig in north Wales, commissioned in 1983, has six 288 MW turbines with an installed capacity of 1.7 GW[30] and can operate for 5 hours at maximum output. The construction cost at today's prices would be £1 billion. There are no overhead transmission lines from the station, which is inside the Snowdonia National Park.

Dinorwig has three uses: peak lopping and trough filling; system reserve; and load following.

The first use is supply of electricity to the grid at times of peak demand (peak lopping) and use of cheap electricity from the grid between 2.30 am and 4.30 am (trough filling). System reserve capability is used for frequency control and Dinorwig may be asked by the National Grid Company to help keep frequency within 50 Hz +/- 1%. Its capability for load following is called upon when sudden surges in demand for electricity occur, as for example during half-time at major televised football matches. Dinorwig's large capacity and fast response time make it possible to save the large amounts of energy that would be used in keeping coal-fired plants on stand-by to generate for short periods. For example, the capacity of part-loaded steam plant that would have been required to supply demand at half-time during the World Cup game between England and Argentina in 1998 was 5GW.

Dinorwig helps in the more efficient overall use of primary fuel sources by:

> allowing other plants to operate closer to optimum efficiency
>
> reducing the amount of plant required to be on 'hot' stand-by

resulting in a net saving throughout 1998 at an average rate of 17 MW.

There are also savings in limiting nitrogen oxide and sulphur dioxide emissions. Dinorwig also has greater reliability (99.9%) than coal (80-90%) or CCGT (70-80%).

The availability of Dinorwig increases the efficiency with which other grid plant can be used. ETSU calculated in their 1999 Phase II study that Dinorwig would be energy neutral (electricity consumption at Dinorwig balancing savings from efficient use of other grid plant) if it generated 6.25 GWh/day in 1998/9. This situation will improve with the increased capacity of gas plant, giving a net saving by 2000. This also represents a net saving in sulphur dioxide and nitrogen oxide emissions equivalent to 0.4 and 0.02-0.25% of UK power station output respectively.

8.59   The second general approach is to store energy chemically. One way to achieve this is through use of a transportable *energy carrier;* the distinction between a primary fuel and an energy carrier is explained in box 8C. Hydrogen, the example taken there, is an attractive candidate. It would be used to power fuel cells (see box 8D) which provide an efficient way to convert chemical energy to electrical output, either for supply to the public network or to power vehicles.

8.60 Producing hydrogen in pure form from hydrocarbons (as in the reaction in box 8C) involves significant overall energy losses, although there is the possible advantage that the carbon in the fuel could then be recovered and disposed of in underground strata (3.4-3.11). Alternatively, hydrogen can be obtained from electrical energy by electrolysing water. In an electricity network with a large capacity of intermittent renewable sources, the hydrogen could be produced at times when supply exceeds demand. In the longer term, it is possible in principle that hydrogen could become an internationally traded energy carrier, produced in locations (such as Iceland or Quebec) where renewable energy sources greatly exceed local demand.

BOX 8C   **DISTINCTION BETWEEN PRIMARY FUELS AND ENERGY CARRIERS**

The principal constituent of natural gas – one of the main primary fuels – is the chemical compound methane (CH_4). The chemical energy stored is released by reacting the methane to form carbon dioxide (CO_2) and water (H_2O):

$$CH_4 + 2O_2 \rightarrow CO_2 + 2H_2O \qquad (1)$$

Alternatively, the energy might be released by some other route such as reforming:

$$CH_4 + 2H_2O \rightarrow CO_2 + 4H_2 \qquad (2)$$

The hydrogen produced from the primary fuel can then be used as an *energy carrier.*

Energy is released at the point of use by reaction with oxygen, either by direct combustion or by reaction in a fuel cell:

$$4H_2 + 2O_2 \rightarrow 4H_2O \qquad (3)$$

The sum of reactions (2) and (3) is identical to reaction (1), and the overall energy release from reactions (2) plus (3) is identical to that from reaction (1). Reaction (2) actually absorbs heat (usually provided by burning a fuel), so that hydrogen is a particularly intensive energy carrier. Given that there are thermal inefficiencies in the processes carrying out the reforming reaction however, the net energy released in practice by using the energy carrier through reaction (3) is less than the energy released by burning the primary fuel plus the theoretical energy absorption by reaction (2).

8.61   Hydrogen stored on a large scale under appropriate conditions represents one of the most efficient ways of storing energy. However, fuel cells are best suited to producing electricity on a relatively small scale (up to a few MW). Rather than using hydrogen for centralised storage to be recovered as electrical output to the grid therefore, a more plausible concept is that hydrogen would be distributed as an energy carrier into decentralised stores or as a transport fuel. Its advantage over electrical batteries, another form of decentralised storage or power for transport, is that it provides a much higher intensity of energy storage.

8.62   For the time being it is likely that extensive use of fuel cells will be based on producing hydrogen at the point of use from either a fossil fuel (gas) or a hydrogen-rich fuel manufactured from fossil fuel (methanol). The former route will be used for fuel cells providing heat and power for buildings (8.8), for which gas can be obtained from the existing distribution network); the latter route for vehicles, in that it requires only small modifications to the technology used to distribute petrol and diesel (8.22). Eventually however it will be necessary to obtain hydrogen by other means.

8.63   There is also a need, reflected in keen interest in the electricity industry, for other technologies for large-scale centralised chemical storage of energy in a form from which

---

BOX 8D	**FUEL CELLS**

A fuel cell utilises a chemical process to convert hydrogen or a hydrogen-rich fuel stream into electrical energy and heat. It can do so with high efficiency (i.e. high efficiency of conversion of fuel to useful energy), producing a stable (DC, non-fluctuating) power output. Most fuel cells operate with high power densities, that is, they produce a high power output per unit weight, volume or area. Different types of fuel cell are distinguished by their use of different electrolytes and the different temperatures reached during operation. Some of the range of fuels used in fuel cells could be supplied by renewable sources, which would promote diversity in energy supply and a transition to renewable energy sources.

There are limitations to fuel cell performance which mean that the *theoretical* cell voltage cannot be utilised entirely; these include the oxygen deactivation barrier at the cathode and mass transport problems caused by the diffusion of gaseous species and water through the cathodes, electrolyte and any catalyst layers in the fuel cell. Only about half of the energy of reaction (hydrogen + oxygen → water) can be converted into useful electrical energy. These limitations mean that a typical single fuel cell will have an area of about 50 cm^2 and a potential difference across it of about 0.7 volts. Generation of a usable voltage requires a fuel cell system to be built up of a stack, or several stacks, of cells, the anode of one cell being in contact with the cathode of another, and so on.

One of the principal advantages of fuel cells is that they display high efficiency across their output curve. The internal combustion engine (ICE) has a point of maximum operating efficiency, usually at high revolutions, either side of which it is less efficient. The fuel cell, in contrast, has a comparatively flat efficiency curve, and is generally more efficient operating at below 100% of its rated power. Although not a particularly important factor in stationary applications, in transport the engine of a vehicle is rarely at its ideal operating speed and the efficiency gain of a fuel cell vehicle over an ICE vehicle is much greater during a drive cycle than during continuous tests.

The main disadvantage of fuel cells is the large number of ancillary units which are required to deliver large scale power generation from fuel cells. The ancillary equipment includes fuel supply and water removal pipes, metering instruments, fuel reformers, pumps, compressors, and heat exchangers. Each of these ancillary systems will have a parasitic load which reduces the efficiency of the overall system. Fuel cells that are running are impressive in terms of reliability of performance but the *balance of plant* (BoP) that makes up the rest of the system means that, at present, a 200 kW phosphoric acid fuel cell generating unit is several times the size of a similar power diesel or natural gas CHP unit. The size of generating system is important in stationary applications but paramount in mobile systems where the power (or energy) density of the package rather than the fuel cell in isolation must be considered.

---

electrical energy can be recovered. Key factors in assessing such technologies are the cost, reliability and life of the installations; the risks they would pose to workers and the public; the capacity and efficiency of energy storage and recovery; and the rates at which electrical energy could be transformed to stored chemical energy and (more particularly) recovered again. One approach, based on regenerative fuel cell technology, is sufficiently promising that National Power has announced plans to build a 10 MW demonstration unit. It is described in box 8E.

8.64   Other means of storing energy have been proposed, but are at a much more speculative stage. Superconducting magnetic energy storage systems are devices based on the principle of storing energy by an electric current introduced into a resistance-free superconducting coil. The superconductor must be maintained at cryogenic temperatures, around $-269°C$ (liquid helium) or $-133°C$ (liquid air) depending on the type of superconductor. Devices using this principle however are extrapolations from laboratory observations, and are a long way from demonstration of technical or economic viability. It would be unsafe to assume that they can be developed and applied on a large scale by the middle of the century.

8.65   In our assessment, this leaves hydrogen and regenerative fuel cells as the technologies which could be in widespread use by the middle of the 21st century, but with rather different

---

BOX 8E   ENERGY STORAGE USING REGENERATIVE FUEL CELLS[31]

Innogy Limited, part of National Power's UK division npower, is planning to construct a 360 GJ installation using a technology called 'Regenesys'. This facility will be the largest energy storage plant of its type in the world. It will have a rated power output of 15 MW, which can be fed directly into the electrical distribution grid. Start-up time from complete shutdown is expected to be rapid. When running, the plant should be capable of switching from fully charging to fully discharging in about 20 milliseconds. Conversion of electrical to stored chemical energy can be repeated with high recovery efficiency.

Energy is stored chemically in two concentrated aqueous electrolyte solutions, of sodium bromide and of sodium polysulphide. The electrolytes are pumped through a regenerative fuel cell in which they are separated by an ion-selective membrane. The membrane is permeable to sodium ions but not to the anions present. A simplified overall chemical reaction for the cell is:

$$3\ Na\ Br + Na_2\ S_4 \quad \xrightarrow[\text{discharging}]{\text{charging}} \quad 2\ Na_2\ S_2 + Na\ Br_3$$

On charging, the bromide ions are oxidised to bromine which is complexed as tribromine ions, while sulphur in the polysulphide anion is converted to sulphide ions. On discharging, the sulphide ion acts as the reducing agent and the tribromide ion as the oxidising species. After charging, each cell gives a potential difference up to 1.5V. Cells are linked in series electrically, with electrodes shared between two cells, to generate the required total potential difference.

In addition to the 'Regenesys' fuel cells, the plant requires a power conversion system to act as the interface between the alternating 33 kV grid, and the DC fuel cells. However, the whole plant is compact, occupying less than half a hectare and housed in a low-rise building.

---

applications as explained above. In view of the uncertainty over their deployment however, we have taken a conservative approach in constructing scenarios for possible UK energy systems in 2050, by assuming that large-scale energy storage will not be available and that hydrogen will not be traded internationally as an energy carrier. We have taken the alternative approach of incorporating supplementary generating plant to the extent required to back-up supply from intermittent renewable sources. Availability or otherwise of energy storage primarily affects the back-up capacity needed, with much less effect on the overall energy balances which are the principal topic of chapter 9. Even though the scenarios have been constructed assuming no large-scale energy storage, we nevertheless regard it as very important that work to develop such technologies should be pressed forward and given a high priority. **We recommend that the government promote research and development into new technologies for large-scale energy storage, possibly on a collaborative basis in Europe.**

There is a vast, largely untapped opportunity for utilising the heat which is wasted when electricity is generated. Exploiting this heat will require the growth of heat networks and a shift from very large, all-electricity plant towards smaller and more numerous combined heat and power plants. The electricity distribution system will have to undergo major changes to cope with this development and with the expansion of smaller scale, intermittent renewable energy sources. The transition towards a low-emission energy system would be greatly helped by the development of new means of storing energy on a large scale

Chapter 9

POSSIBLE UK ENERGY BALANCES IN 2050

Can the UK make very large reductions in carbon dioxide emissions over the next 50 years without unacceptable effects on the quality of life of its population? What are the options for supplying given levels of demand for energy without adding to the greenhouse effect, and what are their implications?

9.1   We have recommended that the UK should promote the principle of contraction and convergence as the basis for a future global agreement to counter the threat of climate change (4.69). We have assumed that such agreements will have the objective of limiting the concentration of carbon dioxide in the global atmosphere to not more than twice the pre-industrial level, that is, to not more than 550 ppmv, and that they will be based on convergence by 2050 on a common figure for carbon dioxide emissions per head. If so, the requirement on the UK might be to reduce its present level of carbon dioxide emissions by almost 60% by 2050 and by almost 80% by 2100 (table 4.1). In this chapter we examine the practicability of a reduction of 60% in UK carbon dioxide emissions over the next 50 years, drawing on the analysis in previous chapters. We outline and discuss four illustrative scenarios that would reduce carbon dioxide emissions by about 60% (9.9-9.26), and consider what impacts they would have on the environment in other respects, certain common difficulties they present (9.27-9.29) and what can be said about their relative cost (9.30-9.34). We conclude this chapter by identifying the nature of the questions that consideration of such scenarios raises for UK policies (9.35-9.42). We go on to discuss those questions in the final chapter of our report.

9.2   If the UK's carbon dioxide emissions had to be reduced to the extent entailed by acceptance of the contraction and convergence principle, are scenarios possible in which the supply of energy will be sufficient to meet demand?

9.3   Four scenarios were constructed for meeting energy demand in 2050, while reducing carbon dioxide emissions by about 60% from their level in 1997 (the most recent year for which final estimates are available). They differ in three main respects: the assumed demands for energy, the use made of renewable energy sources, and whether there is a baseload capacity provided either by nuclear power or by fossil fuel stations at which the carbon dioxide is recovered and disposed of. Their key features are in box 9A and a fuller description in appendix E. We emphasise that these scenarios are illustrative, and designed to highlight the nature of the choices available for the UK.

9.4   For all combustion processes, whatever the fuel used, we envisage advanced techniques would be applied to protect air quality. We likewise envisage that installations of other kinds would be designed, built and operated to high standards so as to limit the damage they cause to the environment and the risks they present. Alongside benefits in reduced carbon dioxide emissions however, exploitation of any alternative energy source would have some impact on the environment and give rise to some direct or indirect risks, as chapter 7 showed.

9.5   One aim in examining possible energy balances was to assess the types, sizes and numbers of installations required to supply energy under different scenarios. The full results are in appendix E. If nuclear power is retained, as it might be in two scenarios, large numbers of nuclear power stations would have to be constructed on new sites. All four scenarios involve a very large expansion of renewable energy sources. The contributions that can be obtained from any energy source in practice, including fossil fuels, will depend on approval being obtained for each of the necessary installations.

9.6   The contributions the UK can obtain from particular renewable sources will also depend on the development of technology that can exploit the energy sources physically available without excessive cost. To quantify the energy that might be obtained cost-effectively in the middle of the 21st century, use was made in the case of most renewable sources of the Energy Technology Support Unit's recent estimates (table 7.1) of the amount of energy that could be available in 2025 at a cost of less than 7p/kWh (calculated using an 8% discount rate), after taking into account specified constraints on the siting of installations. The main exceptions are that some scenarios include a Severn Barrage and, for reasons explained in appendix E, some include much larger contributions from photovoltaic panels than would be indicated by ETSU's assessment. We return to the cost of the scenarios later in this chapter.

9.7   In all these scenarios fossil fuels still represent a major source of energy for the UK. To simplify, it was assumed oil would be the sole primary energy source for transport. A proportion of the fossil fuels available has to be reserved to meet periodic shortfalls in the supply of electricity (9.28). Beyond that, the preferred uses for fossil fuels are the provision of high-grade heat and micro-scale combined heat and power plants supplying low-grade heat and electricity. Even with use of fossil fuels for these purposes (to varying degrees in different scenarios) carbon dioxide emissions are reduced by 60% from their 1997 level, except in the first scenario where the reduction is only 57%. We also took into account the possibility that the recovery of carbon dioxide produced at power stations and its subsequent disposal in geological strata might allow continued use of fossil fuels on a much larger scale while still reducing carbon dioxide emissions to the atmosphere to the extent indicated. As indicated previously (8.31) we would see such stations as baseload stations supplying only electricity, and they therefore appear in the scenarios as a direct alternative to nuclear power stations.

FOUR ILLUSTRATIVE SCENARIOS

9.8   We now examine each of the four scenarios in turn. We emphasise that their contents do not represent a view on our part about what mix of alternative energy sources, including what combination of renewable sources, would be the most desirable in environmental or other terms in 2050, still less a prediction about which energy sources will in the event be in use by that date and on what scales. The intention is to throw light on the broad potential of different approaches and on how they relate to each other.

9.9   The distinctive feature of *scenario 1* is a higher demand for energy than in the other three scenarios: final demand in 2050 remains at the 1998 level in all four categories (low-grade and high-grade heat, transport, electricity). Stabilisation, however, represents a change from previous trends. For if final energy demand were to continue to rise by just over 0.5% a year – the mean rate over the last 40 and 10 years[1] – it would be 30% higher in 2050 than it is now. The DTI's latest energy projections show final energy demand rising by 0.9% a year between 1998 and 2010 (figure 6-I).[2]

BOX 9A   **FOUR SCENARIOS FOR 2050**

Four scenarios were constructed to illustrate the options available for balancing demand and supply for energy in the middle of the 21st century if the UK has to reduce carbon dioxide emissions from the burning of fossil fuels by 60%:

> *scenario 1:* no increase on 1998 demand, combination of renewables and *either* nuclear power stations *or* large fossil fuel power stations at which carbon dioxide is recovered and disposed of

> *scenario 2:* demand reductions, renewables (no nuclear power stations or routine use of large fossil fuel power stations)

> *scenario 3:* demand reductions, combination of renewables and *either* nuclear power stations *or* large fossil fuel power stations at which carbon dioxide is recovered and disposed of

> *scenario 4:* very large demand reductions. renewables (no nuclear power stations or routine use of large fossil fuel power stations).

The key parameters for these four scenarios are as follows:

	scenario 1	scenario 2	scenario 3	scenario 4
percentage reduction in 1997 carbon dioxide emissions	57	60	60	60
DEMAND (%)				
reduction from 1998 final consumption				
low-grade heat	0	50	50	66
high-grade heat	0	25	25	33
electricity	0	25	25	33
transport	0	25	25	33
total	**0**	**36**	**36**	**47**
SUPPLY (GW)				
annual average rate				
fossil fuels	106	106	106	106
intermittent renewables	34	26	16	16
other renewables	19	19	9	4
baseload stations (either nuclear or fossil				
fuel with carbon dioxide recovery)	52	0	19	0

A more detailed description of the scenarios is given in appendix F, which also describes the methodology used to construct them.

9.10   In chapter 6 we found that if the economic potential for energy saving was fulfilled – that is, if consumers took up cost-effective energy saving measures – demand would *fall* by between 2–15% below its 1998 level by 2010. We also noted the tendency for new opportunities for cost-effective energy saving measures to arise as existing ones were taken up (6.134-6.135). We conclude that a long-term stabilisation of demand, as envisaged in scenario 1, would require changes in energy policy but these need not be massive nor disruptive. We envisage that the real prices consumers had to pay for energy would have to rise gradually over this period. The replacement of the housing stock could continue at about its current low rate, although major energy efficiency improvements would have to be made to 19th and 20th century housing. The use of private cars and the quantity of air travel might conceivably be higher than today's levels in this scenario, with substantial improvements in the efficiency of vehicles and aircraft offsetting the growth in traffic. Most cars would run on fuel cells, with the hydrogen derived from oil or gas.

9.11   Meeting demand for energy on that scale, while also reducing carbon dioxide emissions by 60%, requires either a contribution from nuclear power that is more than four times as large as at present or an equivalent contribution from fossil fuel stations at which carbon dioxide is recovered. It also requires the largest contribution in any of the scenarios from renewable sources, a more than 20-fold increase from the present output of about 2.3 GW. Because the requirements for transport, high-grade heat and back-up plants pre-empt the fossil fuels available, most of the demand for low-grade heat in this scenario has to be met by electricity, half of that through use of heat pumps.

9.12   By 2050 all the present nuclear power stations will have long since closed. The required capacity of nuclear power in scenario 1 is equivalent to 46 of the UK's most recent nuclear power station (Sizewell B). That would involve developing a number of new sites, as well as constructing one or more new stations on the sites of previous stations. Some of the new stations might be based on groups of smaller reactors rather than a single large reactor. Alternatively, a similar number of fossil fuel power stations might be constructed with equipment for recovering carbon dioxide and transferring it to underground strata.

9.13   If energy supplied as heat is taken into account as well as energy supplied as electricity, the largest contribution from renewable sources comes from hundreds, or possibly thousands of small combined heat and power (CHP) plants located in or near urban areas and connected to district heating networks that have been constructed. These are fuelled by a combination of fast-growing crops cultivated for that purpose (probably short rotation coppice) and wastes from other agricultural and forestry operations. There is a significant increase in traffic in the areas around these plants, although building small plants supplied from their immediate vicinity would minimise the impact. On the basis of present productivity, cultivation of energy crops on the scale assumed would take up some 15% of the UK's present farmland area. Municipal solid waste is also burned in CHP plants (probably larger in size), and the environmental issues raised by that are broadly similar.

9.14   Almost as large a contribution comes from generating plants offshore. Almost 200 wind farms a kilometre or more out to sea, each with 100 turbines, exploit wind energy. There are some 7,500 small wave power devices in the stormiest seas where the depth of water exceeds 40m; and in the strongest tidal currents in shallower waters within a few kilometres of the coast a score of tidal stream farms, each with at least a dozen turbines. These latter installations have only a small visual impact; but offshore wind turbines are visible on the horizon from much of the UK coastline. It may be possible to combine at least two of these technologies in a single installation. As most of the offshore energy resource is remote from centres of demand, lengthy new high-voltage transmission lines are necessary. It is assumed that a barrage has also been built across the Severn Estuary.

9.15   Another large contribution comes from electricity generated by photovoltaic panels. These cover many large flat roofs, the south-facing side of most pitched roofs on houses and the upper parts of the south-facing walls of multi-storey office buildings.

9.16   The fourth largest renewable source is onshore wind, which provides 65 times as much electricity as it does today. Wind farms cover 2,000 km², slightly under 1% of the UK land area. On the assumption they would not have been permitted in areas designated for natural beauty or importance to wildlife, they occupy 10% of the remaining areas with the highest wind speeds, predominantly near coasts or on higher ground, and are visible from almost everywhere in those areas. A minor source, small water power schemes, has expanded 13-fold, through installation of several thousand turbines on rivers and streams throughout the UK.

9.17   *Scenarios 2 and 3* are based on an alternative assumption about energy demand: that there can be an overall reduction in final demand to 36% below the 1998 level over the next half century, with the largest reduction in demand for low-grade heat. Final energy demand, in these two scenarios, is 50% of what it would have been in 2050 had the trends of previous decades continued (9.9).

9.18   We envisage this degree of demand reduction being achieved by a sustained and vigorous implementation of the full range of policies discussed in chapter 6. The real price of energy would have been raised gradually but substantially through taxation, with much of the revenues spent on supporting energy efficiency improvements. Growth in road traffic and air travel would have stabilised in the early decades of the century and then fallen slightly. As in the first scenario, fuel cells have replaced the internal combustion engine in road vehicles. A much larger share of journeys is made by public transport than is the case today and the rapid growth in personal mobility which characterised the second half of the 20th century has ceased, partly as a result of the expansion in electronic communication. A large proportion of the population work from home, or in workplaces close to their homes.

9.19   There has been major restructuring of the UK's urban fabric. The rate at which the housing stock is replaced has accelerated and energy-efficient dwellings have taken the place of many of those built in the 19th and 20th centuries. As in our first scenario, heat distribution networks supplied by CHP stations and heat pumps are found in most towns and cities. Manufacturing industry has undergone radical improvements in resource as well as energy efficiency, with very low quantities of waste materials.

9.20   In *scenario 2* this lower level of demand is met by a combination of renewable sources and fossil fuels, without any use of either nuclear power or recovery and disposal of carbon dioxide. That entails large-scale development of renewable sources, but not quite on the extent of scenario 1 because demand is so much lower. In *scenario 3* the same demand is met by obtaining equal amounts of electricity from renewable sources and from either nuclear power or fossil fuel stations at which carbon dioxide is recovered and disposed of.

9.21   Scenario 2 would require a 20-fold increase, to 45 GW, in the energy obtained from renewable sources. The installations required and their environmental impacts are for most sources the same as in scenario 1, and the same area of land is required for growing energy crops. There are only half as many onshore wind turbines as in scenario 1 and only half as much electricity is obtained from photovoltaics.

9.22   In *scenario 3* a similar amount of energy in total is supplied by a smaller portfolio of renewable sources and the equivalent of 19 Sizewell B power stations (or alternatively a similar number of fossil fuel power stations of similar size with equipment for recovering carbon dioxide and transferring it to underground strata). There is no Severn Barrage, and sharply reduced contributions from the onshore renewable sources that would have the most obvious visual impact. Electricity and heat obtained from energy crops total less than 2 GW, and only about 2% of UK farmland would be required for growing short rotation coppice or other suitable crops. The average annual output from photovoltaic panels is only 0.5 GW, as against 5 GW in scenario 2, and output from onshore wind turbines is only slightly higher than at present, at 0.2 GW; onshore wind farms remain a fairly rare sight, confined to a few coastal and upland areas. Municipal waste is not used as an energy source, and alternative methods would have to be found for dealing with it without causing environmental damage. Offshore energy sources (wind, wave and tidal stream) are used on the same extensive scale as in scenarios 1 and 2, as are agricultural and forestry wastes.

9.23   Because of the much smaller use of energy crops in scenario 3, and the elimination of municipal waste as an energy source, the number of CHP plants is reduced very considerably. In both scenario 2 and scenario 3 a substantial proportion of the requirement for low-grade heat has to be met by electricity (half of that through use of heat pumps), but a higher proportion in scenario 3.

9.24   *Scenario 4* shows the implications for energy supply if an even larger reduction in final demand for energy could be achieved over the next half century. It is assumed that the requirement for low-grade heat has been reduced to one-third the present level by 2050 and the requirements for energy in other forms to two-thirds of the present level. That represents an overall reduction of 47% in final demand from the 1997 level, or a 59% reduction from what final energy demand would have been in 2050 if current trends had continued.

9.25   There is no nuclear power in this scenario, nor recovery and disposal of carbon dioxide. Nevertheless the very large reductions in demand mean that the total energy supplied by renewable sources (20 GW) is much less than in scenario 1 (or scenario 2) and somewhat less than in scenario 3. The outputs from energy crops and photovoltaic panels, and therefore the associated environmental impacts, are at the same modest levels as in scenario 3. For onshore and offshore wind the contributions are half those incorporated in scenario 1, with a corresponding reduction in the visual impact of wind turbines. No energy is supplied by municipal waste incineration and there is a lower output from agricultural and forestry wastes and from small-scale hydro. It is assumed that a Severn Barrage has been constructed; wave power and tidal streams contribute the same amounts of energy as in the other scenarios. The requirement for new high-voltage transmission lines still remains.

9.26   This fourth scenario provides a way of making deep cuts in carbon dioxide emissions while limiting the environmental impact of alternative energy sources. It is difficult to see how energy demand reductions on this scale could be achieved; they would involve even more far-reaching changes than in scenarios 2 and 3. There might have to be some reduction, or redefinition, of living standards. That has to be weighed against the substantially smaller capacity of energy installations that would be required.

COMMON FEATURES OF SCENARIOS

9.27   In all four scenarios difficulties are created by the assumed nature of the electricity networks. One difficulty, identified previously, arises from the intermittent nature of the renewable energy sources that would be used to generate electricity. The other difficulty is created by the large short-term variations in demand for electricity (see figures 8-I and 8-II). In none of the scenarios would the generating plants required to supply average demand over the year be capable of meeting the winter peak demand for electricity. Nor could they readily be expanded to do so.

9.28   The solution adopted in order to make the scenarios workable is to assume that very large capacities of fossil fuel generating plants would be available both to meet periodic shortfalls in the supply of electricity from renewable sources and to meet peak demands. Plant designated for one of those roles could not be assumed to be available for the other. Although the aggregate capacity of these plants would be very large indeed they would be used rather infrequently. The addition to carbon dioxide emissions from this cause would not therefore be large. The plant capacities in each scenario and the amounts of energy that would have to be obtained for this purpose from fossil fuels are shown in appendix E (table E.6). The reduction in carbon dioxide emissions shown for each scenario takes into account the use of gas to fuel these plants; that was treated as the first call on use of fossil fuels, after transport. If some of these plants were fuelled with coal rather than gas, carbon dioxide emissions would be higher (table E.7).

9.29   The need for these back-up and peak-lopping plants arises from the lack of a method for storing the output from generating plants. It is implausible that in practice there would be such an enormous capacity of infrequently used plant. The alternatives would be to devise ways of influencing demand, so that the peaks in winter demand for electricity could be smoothed out, or to develop new technologies that would allow electricity to be stored on a massive scale at an acceptable cost. In the latter case full advantage could be taken of renewable energy sources at times when they are able to deliver their full output but the demand for electricity is relatively low. Possible candidates for a new storage technology were discussed in chapter 8.

ELECTRICITY COSTS IN SCENARIOS

9.30   The plausibility of any scenario depends to some extent on the scale of the costs involved in implementing it. The present costs of generating electricity from a given source can be ascertained for those technologies that are already in use on a commercial scale. A combined cycle gas turbine supplies electricity at about 2 p/kWh.[3] The cost of electricity from a new nuclear power station was estimated in 1993 as 2.9 p/kWh.[4] The cost of electricity from onshore wind farms has fallen over successive NFFO rounds to 2.9 p/kWh. These figures represent direct costs (including, in the case of nuclear power an allowance for decommissioning and waste management), but do not include external costs.

9.31   Over a time-scale as long as half a century estimates of the costs of different ways of generating electricity can at best be made in terms of orders of magnitude. There are uncertainties about the long-term trend in the prices of fossil fuels on global markets. The most recent scenarios for global emissions discussed in part I of this report (2.22 and figure 2-VII) show fossil fuel use increasing globally for at least the next half century. While reserves would not have been exhausted, oil and gas production might increasingly be confined to a few regions of the world, with possible implications for price, availability and security. As the more easily exploited resources are exhausted, the cost of production is also likely to rise. On the other hand, if carbon-free technologies are taken up extensively, the demand for, and price of, fossil fuels will fall, thus lowering the cost of their use to generate electricity.

9.32   Progress in reducing the costs of carbon-free technologies for electricity generation will depend on the efforts devoted to developing them and the scale on which they are taken up. For most technologies it is likely to be the overall scale of their development globally that will the most important factor affecting their future cost. Within the UK however another important factor will be the characteristics of the locations in which they are deployed; the larger the contribution they are expected to provide, the greater the need to use less promising locations, thus raising the cost of the energy obtained.

9.33   For most renewable sources the maximum resource incorporated in the four scenarios is what ETSU has estimated could be available for electricity generation in 2025 at a cost of less than 7 p/kWh, without moving into those parts of the resource cost curves (7.6) in which costs would increase rapidly because less favourable sites would have to be used. In fact two-thirds of that resource is estimated to be available at less than 4 p/kWh. As these estimates are for 2025, it is reasonable to expect that further reductions in costs could be achieved over the following 25 years. The overall cost of supplying electricity in those scenarios in which heavy reliance is placed on intermittent and dispersed energy sources would however be raised by the substantial changes required to electricity networks and the provision of a very large capacity of back-up plants burning fossil fuels (or alternatively provision of a new form of large-scale storage for electrical energy). The output from the back-up plants would have high unit costs because they would be used relatively infrequently.

9.34   Taking all these factors into account, it might be unwise to count on electricity from renewable sources costing much less than 3-4 p/kWh in real terms in the middle of the 21st century. That can be compared with the estimate that recovering carbon dioxide from flue gases and disposing of it might increase the cost of generating electricity from fossil fuels by half or more (3.7). There are certainly grounds for assuming that renewable sources of energy could be utilised on a very large scale within the next half century at a cost that would not exceed double the present cost of generating electricity from fossil fuels.

THE WAY FORWARD

9.35   The four scenarios for 2050 outlined and discussed above are illustrative. Each of them would reduce UK carbon dioxide emissions by some 60%, the scale of reduction we concluded in chapter 4 is likely to be necessary by the middle of the 21st century. Their immediate purpose is to stimulate constructive debate about how reductions of that size can be achieved over that time-scale, and thus help the UK make a major contribution to the task of finding global solutions to the threat of climate change.

9.36   The main components of UK demand for primary energy are economic growth, the efficiency with which energy is utilised by end users and the extent of losses within the energy supply system. The energy intensity of the UK economy has fallen considerably (5.9 and figure 5-III), but economic growth still exerts a strong upward pressure on energy consumption. There would have to be substantial changes in the structure of the economy to neutralise that pressure, given that such a high proportion of demand is for transport and space and water heating. A necessary condition for achieving large reductions in carbon dioxide emissions is therefore likely to be more rapid improvements in the efficiency of end use than have been achieved in the past. If efficiency can be improved rapidly enough to reduce end use of energy in the UK by about 1% a year on average, this would reduce consumption by more than a third over the next 50 years, as envisaged in scenarios 2 and 3.

9.37   All four scenarios show consumption by final users diverging sharply from the previous trend. If that were not to happen, the only ways of meeting the resulting high level of demand, without consequences which we concluded in chapter 4 would be unacceptable on both moral and prudential grounds, would be a massive programme of nuclear power stations, or possibly a massive programme of separating carbon dioxide, liquefying it and injecting it beneath the sea bed. The programme of nuclear power stations indicated would have to be much larger even than in scenario 1, which itself involves obtaining four times as much energy from nuclear power as at present. It is certainly difficult to see the expansion of renewable energy sources over the next 50 years exceeding what is envisaged in scenario 1.

9.38   While all four scenarios assume the previous trend of growing energy use will not continue, they differ considerably in other respects, and highlight the key issues which have to be faced if carbon dioxide emissions are to be reduced to the extent likely to be required. None of them stands out as the obviously preferable option. Many people will recoil from the very extensive development of both nuclear power and renewable sources in scenario 1. Many will find scenario 4 attractive because it has no nuclear power and the smallest deployment of renewables in any of the scenarios. It will not be easy however for the UK to achieve the substantial reductions in its present use of energy which would be necessary to move beyond scenario 1, still less the deep cuts in energy use that are the most distinctive feature of scenario 4.

9.39   What these scenarios have in common is that they would all involve fundamental shifts over the next half century in the ways energy is obtained and used, and the associated infrastructures. In addition to development of renewable energy sources on a very large scale, they would all require extensive modifications to both the building stock and the transport system in order to reduce the need for energy. District heating systems, supplied by combined heat and power plants, would become commonplace in urban areas, as would use of heat pumps. Electricity networks would have to be restructured to accommodate the much larger numbers of smaller generating plants embedded within them, many supplying electricity only intermittently. The differences between the scenarios lie in the relative emphasis placed on each of these changes, the particular combinations of renewable sources assumed, and whether or not there are baseload stations using either nuclear power or recovery and disposal of carbon dioxide.

9.40   While these scenarios were constructed to achieve a 60% reduction in UK emissions, as a contribution to preventing the concentration of carbon dioxide in the atmosphere from rising above 550 ppmv, it should be emphasised that very large reductions would be required in UK emissions even if a different objective were selected for global action. For example, in order to prevent the concentration in the atmosphere rising above 1,000 ppmv (a level we concluded in chapter 4 was so high as to pose an unacceptable risk), the contraction and convergence principle, with convergence at 2050, would require UK emissions to be reduced by over 40% by 2050 (table 4.1). Even on that basis many of the same measures would be needed.

9.41   Accepting 550 ppmv as an upper limit on the concentration in the atmosphere would require UK carbon dioxide emissions to be reduced even further by 2100, to not much more than 20% of the 1998 level. When we invited evidence for this study however we took the view it was not sensible to try to look further ahead than the middle of the 21st century. Over a period as long as a hundred years energy technologies may change beyond recognition, and new technologies not at present contemplated may become available. It is certainly crucial that this should happen in the case of transport, which is the dominant use of fossil fuels in all four scenarios.

9.42   Even over half a century we have not attempted to map out specific pathways that will have to be followed if one or other of the four scenarios is to be realised. It would not be feasible or sensible to attempt to do so in detail at this stage. But the way in which successive governments handle the anticipated closure of all but one of the UK's nuclear power stations over the next quarter century will decide which, if any, of the four scenarios – or something like them – are attainable. If there are no measures to stabilise or reduce demand and the nuclear stations are replaced by fossil fuel plant, without any facilities for capture and then disposal of carbon dioxide, then it seems that no further substantial cuts in UK carbon dioxide emissions will be possible. There will also have to be a very substantial deployment of renewable energy resources by 2020 – far beyond the government's current target of 10% electricity generation by 2010 – if any of the scenarios are to be achievable. It is essential that the governments and citizens of today have a keen awareness of the issues, and begin to make radical changes in direction in the next few years. We discuss in the next chapter what changes in direction are needed, and how they can be brought about.

Curbing the UK's dependence on fossil fuels is technically feasible, but far from easy. Reductions in energy use, large-scale development of non-carbon energy sources and fundamental changes in electricity networks will all be necessary. If the demand for energy can be reduced, that makes it easier to avoid large programmes of new nuclear power stations or other technologies that might prove controversial

Chapter 10

ADOPTING A LONG-TERM STRATEGY

What policies should the government now adopt to begin the fundamental reshaping of the UK's energy system that is essential for the long term? How do present institutions and programmes need to evolve in order to create the impetus for radical change?

WHY A LONG-TERM STRATEGY IS NEEDED

10.1   When we announced our decision to study the interaction between energy and the environment (appendix A), the responses we received (see appendix B on the conduct of the study), and the seminar we held in July 1998 (appendix C), led us to the view that the most important issue to investigate was the prospects for energy use over the long term in the light of the threat posed by climate change. In September 1998 we invited evidence on what the implications would be of considerably reducing the use of fossil fuels as energy sources in the UK by 2050, or even phasing them out altogether. We posed a number of specific questions (listed in appendix A) covering not only the technological possibilities but the social implications of different energy policies and the environmental impacts that the alternatives to fossil fuels would themselves have.

10.2   We also invited evidence on the global context. In part I of this report we considered the causes and effects of climate change, the possibility of preventive measures, the actions so far taken by the world community to counter the threat and the prospects for a much more far-reaching international agreement in future. We concluded that it will probably be necessary for the UK to make very large reductions in the long run in emissions of greenhouse gases, and of carbon dioxide in particular.

10.3   Over the next decade the UK will not have difficulty in meeting its legal obligations to reduce emissions of six greenhouse gases in the years 2008-2012 to 12.5% below their 1990 level (5.52). Some of the favourable circumstances which have helped ensure that however will not persist into the following decade. This is strikingly true for carbon dioxide, the most important greenhouse gas. On the basis of present trends, and the policies that would be sufficient to meet the UK's legal obligations, carbon dioxide emissions will soon begin to rise again, and by 2020 are projected to be less than 2% below their 1990 level (5.51).

10.4   Compliance by developed nations with legal obligations stemming from the Kyoto Protocol (4.8) is important, not so much for the reductions in emissions that it will deliver, but as the first step towards more comprehensive and extensive global action to counter climate change. Even though it is not certain as yet that the protocol will be effectively implemented by all developed nations (4.55), it is right to proceed on the basis that this will indeed be the case, and observing the limit on emissions which the UK has accepted is an immediate priority.

10.5   In terms of energy policy, however, a decade is not a long time. Experience during the 1990s shows the dangers of regarding a specific international commitment covering a relatively short period as the main driver for government policies. Because the UK's carbon dioxide emissions were being reduced by favourable short-term trends, insufficient attention was paid to the fundamental changes that will be needed in the long run.

10.6   The present government's goal of reducing carbon dioxide emissions to 20% below the 1990 level by 2010 was an attempt to remedy that. It is much more demanding than the UK's share of the EU's obligation under the Kyoto Protocol, not only because of the larger percentage, but also because reductions will be more difficult to achieve for carbon dioxide than for the other five gases in the basket (box 2C). THE GOAL OF REDUCING ANNUAL CARBON DIOXIDE EMISSIONS BY 20% FROM THEIR 1990 LEVEL BY 2010 IS A MAJOR STEP IN THE RIGHT DIRECTION. IT SHOULD BECOME A FIRM TARGET AND GOVERNMENT SHOULD PRODUCE A CLIMATE CHANGE PROGRAMME THAT WILL ENSURE IT IS ACHIEVED (5.60). Even if the 20% goal for 2010 can be achieved, there will be strong upward pressures on UK carbon dioxide emissions after 2010, as we noted above.

10.7   Government policies must now begin to address the longer-term questions: what kind of international agreement might follow the Kyoto Protocol, what the implications will be for the UK, and how it can put itself in the position to respond. We have recommended (4.68) that THE UK SHOULD CONTINUE TO PLAY A FORCEFUL LEADING ROLE IN INTERNATIONAL NEGOTIATIONS TO COMBAT CLIMATE CHANGE, BOTH IN ITS OWN RIGHT AND THROUGH THE EUROPEAN UNION. THE GOVERNMENT SHOULD PRESS FOR FURTHER REDUCTIONS IN THE GREENHOUSE GAS EMISSIONS OF DEVELOPED NATIONS AFTER 2012, AND CONTROLS ON THE EMISSIONS OF DEVELOPING NATIONS.

10.8   The implication is that further large reductions will be required in the UK's own emissions of carbon dioxide and other greenhouse gases. The key issue is the basis on which the burden will be shared internationally. THE GOVERNMENT SHOULD PRESS FOR A FUTURE GLOBAL CLIMATE AGREEMENT BASED ON THE CONTRACTION AND CONVERGENCE APPROACH (4.47-4.50), COMBINED WITH INTERNATIONAL TRADING IN EMISSION PERMITS (4.53-4.54). TOGETHER, THESE OFFER THE BEST LONG-TERM PROSPECT OF SECURING EQUITY, ECONOMY AND INTERNATIONAL CONSENSUS (4.69).

10.9   The scale of the reductions required will also depend on the date by which national emission quotas converge and on the agreed objective for the carbon dioxide concentration in the atmosphere. We have proposed (4.32) that 550 ppmv, twice the pre-industrial level, should be regarded as the upper limit for the concentration of carbon dioxide in the atmosphere, and that convergence should take place in 2050. On that basis, the UK would be required to reduce carbon dioxide emissions by about 60% between 1997 and 2050, and by about 80% between 1997 and 2100 (table 4.1). Even if a much riskier objective were agreed for atmospheric concentration, the reduction required from the UK by 2050 would be very large: upper limits of 750 ppmv, or even 1,000 ppmv (more than three and a half times the pre-industrial level), would still require carbon dioxide emissions to be reduced by more than 40% from the 1997 level (table 4.1).

10.10   THE GOVERNMENT SHOULD NOW ADOPT A STRATEGY WHICH PUTS THE UK ON A PATH TO REDUCING CARBON DIOXIDE EMISSIONS BY SOME 60% FROM CURRENT LEVELS BY ABOUT 2050. THIS WOULD BE IN LINE WITH A GLOBAL AGREEMENT BASED ON CONTRACTION AND CONVERGENCE WHICH SET AN UPPER LIMIT FOR THE CARBON DIOXIDE CONCENTRATION IN THE ATMOSPHERE OF SOME 550 PPMV AND A CONVERGENCE DATE OF 2050. There will be some flexibility over how to comply with the eventual national limit because of mechanisms such as trading in emissions permits contained in the Kyoto Protocol. That does not alter the fundamental fact that far-reaching modifications to the UK's energy system will be essential.

The content of a long-term strategy

10.11   In chapter 9 we analysed some illustrative scenarios for the UK's energy system in the middle of the 21st century. That exercise showed why a long-term strategy is crucial if there is to be any prospect of cutting carbon dioxide emissions by 60% while continuing to meet requirements for energy in its various forms. It also indicated what areas the strategy needs to cover. Change of the kind envisaged in the scenarios will be far-reaching and take many years to bring about. That does not justify pessimism about its feasibility. The 20th century has seen several radical transformations in energy use: electrification, the internal combustion engine, gas central heating. They have typically taken place with a half life of 30 years. In view of the scale of the transformation now required, it is essential, not only that a long-term strategy is drawn up, but that implementation starts immediately and rapidly achieves considerable momentum.

10.12   Over the coming decades there will in any event be massive investments in the energy system in order to respond to changing demands and replace installations that reach the end of their lives. The decisions taken about these new assets will have big implications for future carbon dioxide emissions. For example, a major power station for which planning starts in the next few years may still be in operation in 2050. A looming issue is how the UK's present nuclear power stations will be replaced (7.102-7.105). WHILE UK CARBON DIOXIDE EMISSIONS ARE FALLING AT THE MOMENT, THEY ARE EXPECTED TO BEGIN RISING AGAIN. ALL BUT ONE OF THE NUCLEAR POWER STATIONS, THE MAIN SOURCE OF CARBON-FREE ENERGY AT PRESENT, ARE EXPECTED TO CLOSE BY 2025. THE GOVERNMENT SHOULD SET OUT, WITHIN THE NEXT FIVE YEARS, A PROGRAMME FOR ENERGY DEMAND REDUCTIONS AND DEVELOPMENT OF ALTERNATIVE ENERGY SOURCES THAT WILL PREVENT THIS FROM CAUSING AN INCREASE IN UK EMISSIONS.

10.13   There are even more daunting lead times for bringing about any significant changes in the present urban fabric and stock of buildings. The UK carries the massive historical burden of a housing stock that is very inefficient in energy terms by comparison with other north European countries. Part of the major improvement in energy efficiency that will be needed has to come through changes to existing buildings. For the small proportion of buildings that are of architectural or historic interest or located in conservation areas, that will require particular care and sensitivity. But the standards of energy efficiency that will have to apply generally in future cannot be achieved through modifications to existing buildings. There need to be substantial improvements in the standards set for new homes being built today, many of which are likely to be in use at the end of this century, with further improvements to follow in the coming decades. The need for radical improvements in energy efficiency may become a factor in determining the rate at which existing homes are demolished and replaced. It is not only design of individual buildings that is important, but the infrastructure of neighbourhoods. To make extensive use of combined heat and power plants possible, district networks for the supply of heat have to be established on a very wide scale. Neighbourhoods must also be planned in ways that reduce the distances people have to travel, and encourage them to reduce carbon dioxide emissions by walking or cycling or using public transport.

10.14   Decisions taken now about such long-lasting investments must have full regard to the long-term implications for the environment. Designing in energy efficiency is much less expensive than achieving the same level of efficiency through subsequent alterations, even where that is feasible. A high proportion of the relatively recent housing and other buildings now being demolished have been rejected because they were built to poor standards in one or other respect. If improvements in efficiency are to be obtained on the scale required, in a timely way and without excessive cost, a start needs to be made as soon as possible. **Both for the building stock and for other capital assets, maximum advantage must be taken of new construction and the replacement cycle in order to make major improvements in energy efficiency.**

10.15   To provide a consistent framework which will give companies confidence in making long-term plans and putting them into effect, it is essential that the long-term strategy adopted should reflect a broad national consensus, and should be pursued continuously, in its essentials, through a number of Parliaments. There must be the social and political will to face the radical challenge posed by climate change.

10.16   The long-term strategy will have at its core a set of long-term targets. These are essential to provide a clear framework for investment decisions. At the moment no such targets exist. Renewable energy is an example. The government has proposed as a target that 10% of electricity should come from renewable sources by 2010 (7.106), with corresponding obligations placed on electricity suppliers (7.111). But nothing has so far been said about any further increase beyond 2010. A 10% contribution would fall far short of the minimum contribution from renewable sources envisaged in the scenarios for 2050 discussed in the previous chapter (see box 9A). Nor are there long-term targets for improving energy efficiency or (reflecting the continuing failure to appreciate the importance of heat as a component of energy demand) for establishing combined heat and power schemes.

10.17   ABSOLUTE REDUCTIONS IN ENERGY DEMAND AND A LARGE DEPLOYMENT OF ALTERNATIVE ENERGY SOURCES WILL BE NEEDED IF THE UK IS TO MAKE DEEP AND SUSTAINED CUTS IN CARBON DIOXIDE EMISSIONS WHILE PROTECTING ITS ENVIRONMENT AND QUALITY OF LIFE. LONGER-TERM TARGETS SHOULD BE SET FOR EXPANDING THE CONTRIBUTION FROM RENEWABLE SOURCES WELL BEYOND 10% OF ELECTRICITY SUPPLIES TO COVER A MUCH LARGER SHARE OF PRIMARY ENERGY DEMAND (7.106). A RANGE OF TARGETS SHOULD BE DEVELOPED FOR RAISING ENERGY EFFICIENCY IN ALL SECTORS OF THE ECONOMY (6.172). A CENTRAL POLICY OBJECTIVE MUST BE A VERY LARGE REDUCTION IN DEMAND FOR ENERGY FOR HEATING AND COOLING, ACHIEVED THROUGH MUCH MORE SOPHISTICATED MANAGEMENT OF HEAT AND MUCH WIDER USE OF COMBINED HEAT AND POWER SCHEMES FOR BOTH THE INDUSTRIAL AND THE DOMESTIC MARKET (8.15).

10.18   The other essential ingredient of a long-term strategy is instruments that will make it possible to achieve the targets adopted. They will not come about through the unaided operation of the present liberalised markets for gas and electricity (5.27-5.28). Indeed, there are respects in which the operation of those markets has been inconsistent with environmental objectives (5.22). We discuss below what we see as the key instruments for implementing the long-term strategy: economic instruments, creation of a new agency, powerful research and development programmes, and new approaches in other key areas of policy such as building control.

10.19   One contribution to reducing emissions could be recovering the carbon dioxide produced at fossil fuel power stations and disposing of it in underground strata (3.4-3.11). Fossil fuel stations with such equipment could be considered as an alternative option to nuclear power stations for meeting baseload demand for electricity (8.31). But, before this approach is adopted, confirmation is needed that it will not itself give rise to environmental hazards.

10.20   Stimulating vegetation growth and increasing the organic content of soils help limit the concentration of carbon dioxide in the atmosphere (3.15-3.22). Because the UK has a relatively small land area however, these forms of action can have only a small effect on its net emissions of carbon dioxide. Nevertheless, tree-planting programmes bring some benefit in limiting emissions and other benefits as well, provided they are carefully planned with regard to all aspects of their impact on the environment. THE TARGETS IN THE UK'S LONG-TERM STRATEGY SHOULD COVER PROTECTION AND EXPANSION OF CARBON SINKS THROUGH TREE PLANTING AND APPROPRIATE LAND USE POLICIES.

10.21   Whatever the ultimate success of international agreements in limiting concentrations of greenhouse gases in the atmosphere, some change in climate and a rise in sea level now seem inevitable as a result of emissions that have already taken place or will take place before further preventive measures can have an effect (2.39). Although the exact consequences for the UK are difficult to predict, they are likely to be significant (box 2D). Another part of the long-term strategy therefore must be to avert or minimise the more damaging consequences of climate change. **We welcome the start the government has made in developing policies to minimise consequential damage in the UK as a result of climate change.** Comprehensive monitoring and further research will be needed to underpin those policies (10.54).

10.22   Adaptive measures will have to be taken in a wide variety of fields, including town and country planning, flood protection, coast protection, agriculture, forestry, nature conservation and countryside recreation. As part of the study of environmental planning we are now conducting, we intend to examine how legislation and administrative procedures should be modified and extended in recognition of this issue.

THE EUROPEAN DIMENSION

10.23   The European Union has an important role in international negotiations on countering climate change, and has moved further and faster than other parts of the developed world in setting targets for reducing greenhouse gas emissions (4.8). **The sharing out between Member States of the EU's limit under the Kyoto Protocol must now be given a firm legal basis, and effective mechanisms must be established for monitoring compliance with their respective limits, with sanctions for non-compliance.**

10.24   Some key measures needed to achieve deep cuts in carbon dioxide emissions require action by the EU rather than Member States. Reductions in the fuel consumption of personal vehicles, for example, are dependent on the European Commission's agreements with associations of manufacturers (6.123). In general the European Commission has not been proactive in putting forward proposals for reducing carbon dioxide emissions. There are important fields in which the EU could be making major contributions to countering the threat of climate change, but is not doing so at present. They include economic instruments; for example, proposals have been put forward for either an EU carbon tax or an EU energy tax, but so far without success. Another aspect is fundamental reform of the Common Agricultural Policy, which may be a necessary condition for realising the full potential of energy crops as an energy source. **The government should continue to press for thoroughgoing integration of environmental considerations into EU policies, both in the energy field and in other fields.**

ECONOMIC INSTRUMENTS

10.25   Incentives must be provided to encourage both firms and individuals to act in ways that will help reduce carbon dioxide emissions. Corrective taxes provide a way of ensuring that decisions by those using a resource take into account, not only its market price, but also the external costs being imposed through its use. The case for a corrective tax is especially strong in the case of energy because the effect of low, and falling, energy prices (5.28) may have been to encourage inefficiency in energy use. Any use of energy is likely to impose some external costs, if not at the point of use then through the chain of activities by which energy is supplied.

10.26   Emissions of carbon dioxide are expected to impose very high external costs on the world. Corrective taxes in the energy field therefore should be targeted directly towards fuels that give rise to carbon dioxide emissions. This will bring about some reduction in the amounts of energy used by firms and individuals, and it will provide a direct incentive for them to use those energy sources which do not contribute, or contribute less, to carbon dioxide emissions. We criticised the government's original proposals for a 'climate change levy' because they amount to an energy tax rather than a carbon tax, and because they do not cover domestic use of energy. Although energy from renewable sources and from the most efficient combined heat and power plants will now be exempt, this tax will still be a very imperfect instrument for bringing about the far-reaching changes needed in order to achieve deep cuts in carbon dioxide emissions (6.157). The number of energy sources and consumers covered by exemptions, reduced rates and negotiated agreements has been growing in the run-up to the levy's introduction. We agree with the description of it by House of Commons Environment, Transport and Regional Affairs Committee as 'an extremely complex and cumbersome market instrument which will result in a relatively modest emissions reduction.[1] THE UK SHOULD INTRODUCE A CARBON TAX, REPLACING THE CLIMATE CHANGE LEVY WHICH IS DUE TO BEGIN NEXT YEAR. IT SHOULD APPLY UPSTREAM AND COVER ALL SECTORS. It should be set at a modest level initially.

10.27   We appreciate the concern for vulnerable groups in society that has led many people to oppose any tax that would affect energy prices for ordinary customers. But keeping energy prices low for all domestic customers is not the right way to deal with the particular UK problem of 'fuel poverty'. The tax we are advocating can provide funding for measures that will be much more effective in improving quality of life for the vulnerable (6.159-6.160). THE FIRST CALL ON THE REVENUE FROM THIS CARBON TAX SHOULD BE TO FURTHER REDUCE FUEL POVERTY BY BENEFIT INCREASES AND MORE SPENDING ON HOUSEHOLD ENERGY EFFICIENCY MEASURES.

10.28   Even with the carbon tax in place, some measures that would be effective in reducing carbon dioxide emissions may not be sufficiently attractive to elicit an adequate response from firms or individuals, and additional incentives may be required. THE REMAINDER OF THE REVENUE SHOULD BE USED TO RAISE INVESTMENT IN ENERGY EFFICIENCY MEASURES IN ALL SECTORS, TO INCREASE THE VIABILITY OF ALTERNATIVE ENERGY SOURCES, AND TO REDUCE THE IMPACT OF THE NEW TAX ON UK INDUSTRIAL COMPETITIVENESS. This use of the revenue builds on what the government is already proposing; devoting the bulk of the revenue to reducing employers' National Insurance Contributions while retaining £150 million a year for improvements in energy efficiency and promotion of alternative sources.[2]

10.29   A carbon tax would improve the economic viability of nuclear power as well as renewable energy sources. But cost is not the only consideration. Before any new nuclear power plants are built in the UK, the problem of managing nuclear waste must be solved to the satisfaction of the scientific community and the general public (7.19). It seems unlikely that public opinion will permit the construction of new nuclear power stations unless they are part of a strategy which delivers improvements in energy efficiency and gives equal opportunity for the deployment of other alternatives to fossil fuels which can compete in terms of cost and reduced environmental impacts.

10.30   Several EU Member States now have energy taxes aimed at reducing carbon dioxide emissions. There would be less ground for concern about the impact of such a tax on the international competitiveness of UK firms if it were being levied on a consistent basis across the EU. If the UK acted unilaterally by introducing a domestic carbon tax, it would be imposed on fossil fuels sold in the UK, both imported and domestically produced. Any imports of electricity which had been generated using fossil fuels would then have a price advantage over electricity generated in the UK from fossil fuels. One solution to this anomaly would be to impose a 'shadow carbon tax' on imports of electricity, to reflect the quantity of carbon dioxide emitted during their generation. That could, however, fall foul of EU laws.[3] **If there is not to be an EU-wide carbon tax, EU law ought to be amended to enable Member States which wish to impose internal carbon taxes to levy reasonable shadow carbon taxes on imported electricity.**

10.31   At present the only substantial electricity imports into the UK are from France. If a carbon tax is introduced in the UK, those imports would gain a price advantage over UK electricity generated from fossil fuels. The great majority of French electricity however is generated at nuclear power stations, and would not therefore be subject to a carbon tax.

10.32   THE UK SHOULD PRESS FOR A CARBON TAX WITHIN THE EUROPEAN UNION, BUT PROCEED ON ITS OWN IF AGREEMENT CANNOT BE REACHED WITHIN THE NEXT FEW YEARS. Taking into account the other measures we are recommending, a package of policies that includes a carbon tax could reduce the UK's carbon dioxide emissions significantly in the medium to long term without damaging competitiveness, or increasing hardship.

EFFECTIVE INSTITUTIONS

WHITEHALL DEPARTMENTS

10.33   The long-term strategy for deep cuts in carbon dioxide emissions that we are advocating will be drawn up and successfully implemented only if there is a comprehensive and far-sighted vision at the heart of government about energy policy and its environmental dimension. The Department of Trade and Industry (DTI) is responsible for the energy industries (5.44) throughout Britain (but not in Northern Ireland). The Department of the Environment, Transport and the Regions (DETR) is responsible for negotiation of, and compliance with, international environmental agreements and EU environmental legislation, and for energy efficiency in England. The division of responsibilities between the two Departments could be regarded as cutting across both the essential nature of the challenge posed by climate change and the promotion of key concepts that span energy use and energy supply, such as energy service companies and making use of waste heat (through large-scale development of combined heat and power, including micro-scale plants).

10.34   The House of Commons Trade and Industry Committee has spoken of 'a crying need for the integration of environmental priorities with energy policy, rather than the one being a tardy intrusion into the latter'.[4] We have considered whether the situation would be improved by a transfer of responsibilities between Whitehall Departments. One option would be to recognise the critical importance of energy issues by creating once again a Department of Energy. The retention of a Department of Energy in the USA provides part of the explanation for the comprehensiveness of the research and development programmes the US government continues to carry out in this field. In responding to the threat of climate change, on the other hand, the USA has often shown signs of dragging its feet. We did not find the idea of a separate Department attractive in a UK context. With the completion of privatisation and liberalisation, and the extensive powers given to the energy regulator, a Department of Energy would now have, at most, far fewer functions than the former UK Department with that title. It is doubtful whether it would be large enough to be viable as a separate Department. It would certainly carry little influence in Whitehall or Westminster.

10.35   Another option would be to bring together in DTI all the surviving functions of the former Department of Energy. That would mean transferring responsibility for energy efficiency from DETR. This would have the disadvantage of weakening the crucial links between energy efficiency and DETR's responsibilities for building control, housing and transport. It would be interpreted as signifying a lack of political will to make fundamental changes in the way the UK obtains and uses energy.

10.36   Denmark provides the alternative model of a ministry (formed by merger in 1994) which combines responsibility for energy and the environment. The counterpart in UK terms would be to transfer from DTI to DETR sponsorship of the energy industries and responsibility for promoting new energy technologies, and probably also responsibility for the energy regulator. We would see serious objections however to combining in the same government Department sponsorship of industries which are potentially major sources of pollution and DETR's primary function of protecting the environment. Support for UK energy technology firms in world markets could also suffer from the change. In Denmark, policy-making and administration are largely located in subordinate agencies such as the Danish Energy Agency, leaving the combined ministry with an oversight role. While that extent of delegation would go beyond normal UK practice, the key to improvement may well lie in creating a more effective executive body in the energy field, rather than in reshuffling responsibilities within Whitehall. We propose such a body below.

10.37   There is one respect in which we have concluded that existing responsibilities should be changed. At present the Energy Minister gives consent for new generating plants with a capacity of 50 MW or more and separate approval for new overhead transmission lines (5.32). This seems undesirable for two reasons. First, it means proposals for generating plants can be examined and approved in advance of any consideration being given to the infrastructure needed to link them to the transmission system. Second, it represents an undesirable exemption from the normal land use planning system. **We recommend that all proposals for new generating plants and overhead transmission lines should in future be considered under land use planning legislation, and that planning applications for generating plants should be required to cover all the transmission lines and other infrastructure that will be needed for their operation.** In cases where transmission lines would cross the areas of several local planning authorities, it would be appropriate for the Environment Minister to call in the case and take the decision on it.

The Gas and Electricity Markets Authority

10.38   Because the distribution networks for gas and electricity give rise to residual natural monopolies, creating and maintaining competitive markets in those industries in itself requires a high degree of regulation. The issue is the terms on which economic regulation should be conducted. There has been much discussion about the extent to which economic regulation of the electricity and gas industries ought to concern itself with environmental objectives, in particular with energy efficiency.

10.39   Although there were originally separate regulators the Office of Gas and Electricity Markets has been established administratively, and the current Utilities Bill[5] will create the Gas and Electricity Markets Authority.[6] This will have the primary duty to exercise its functions in a manner best calculated to protect the consumer interest. The duty will relate to the interests of gas and electricity consumers taken together, and will extend to non-domestic consumers, potential consumers, and consumers who are not customers of licensed suppliers. It will 'subsume' the present duty to ensure that reasonable demands for gas and electricity are met. The regulatory authority will have to pay particular regard to the interests of groups of consumers who are most vulnerable to difficulties in obtaining satisfactory energy supplies: those on low incomes, the elderly, the chronically sick and disabled, and those living in rural areas. The secondary duties which the regulator has at present to promote efficiency and economy and to take environmental effects into account will be retained. The removal of the duty hitherto placed on the electricity regulator to exercise his functions so as to promote research and development in the fields of generation, transmission and supply[7] can be regarded as acceptance of inevitable changes in the role of the regulated companies in funding research and development (5.64).

10.40   The government nevertheless recognises 'the importance of the utility industries in helping to achieve social and environmental objectives, and the importance of securing the right engagement of the regulatory system in that process'. It therefore intends to follow the model already established in the water industry and issue guidance to the regulator on social and environmental matters, after full consultation and subject to parliamentary approval. Although there will be a statutory duty to have regard to this guidance, it will be for the regulatory authority to decide how these social and environmental objectives 'are to be reflected in the way they carry out their functions'.[8]

10.41   Experience with nationalised industries and the Environment Agencies shows it is difficult to frame ministerial guidance or directions in such a way as to be precise and effective. Where social or environmental measures will have significant financial implications, the government will not rely on guidance to the regulatory authority, but will introduce specific legal provisions. One measure already identified as requiring that approach is the energy efficiency standards of performance scheme for gas and electricity,[9] discussed earlier in this report (6.62-6.69).

10.42   We do not consider it part of the economic regulator's function to form an independent view about what is desirable or undesirable in environmental terms. Environmental objectives should be formulated explicitly and clearly by those responsible for environmental policy, after full consultation. The extent to which those objectives are taken into account in decisions affecting the energy industries should be deliberated openly and recorded publicly. With particular reference to environmental interests, the government has said it is taking measures to ensure that 'all parties with an interest in regulation . . . have a full opportunity to participate effectively in the decision-making process, and . . . understand the outcome'.

10.43   While the proposed structure for economic regulation of the electricity and gas industries is logical in principle, there are worrying signs that sufficient weight is not being given to environmental objectives and the achievement of long-term policy goals. In particular, the new electricity trading arrangements, which will provide the framework for the wholesale electricity market in England and Wales (8.48), have very unfavourable consequences for the competitive position both of renewable energy sources and of combined heat and power schemes. This experience highlights the need, not only for a comprehensive and far-sighted vision at the heart of government, but also for an effective executive body which can act as a powerful and well informed advocate for the creation of a more sustainable energy system.

A SUSTAINABLE ENERGY AGENCY

10.44   Improving energy efficiency is a crucial dimension of energy policy. There is widespread agreement that the present arrangements for achieving that aim are complex and fragmented (see figure 5-VI). The Environmental Audit Committee has concluded that: 'While Government believes its arrangements can be made to work, this view is not shared by significant partners outside Whitehall.'[10] The Committee's suggested solution was 'a new unit with a dedicated staff' reporting jointly to DETR and DTI Ministers which would be given responsibility for 'driving and co-ordinating policy on energy efficiency; its integration into other policy areas; and for identifying barriers to effective action'.[11] The government response to that recommendation said that the Energy, Environment and Waste Directorate of DETR already fulfils the role envisaged.[12] DTI and DETR officials assured us that they work well together, and that the division of responsibilities between the two Departments (10.33) does not have any adverse effect on the content or implementation of government policies.[13] We have reached the conclusion however that the achievements of present policies in this field have fallen well short of what will be required from now on (6.170).

10.45   Rather than some fine tuning of responsibilities in Whitehall, what is needed is an effective executive body charged with carrying forward sustainable energy policies. Much excellent work has been done by bodies such as the Energy Saving Trust (which is itself about to be reviewed), and DETR is justified in claiming that 'no single agency could cover all aspects of energy efficiency'.[14] There are nevertheless important functions related to energy efficiency which would benefit from a higher profile, sharper focus and better targeting.

10.46   A similar conclusion can be reached about the effectiveness of arrangements for promoting renewable sources of energy. Moreover, we share the view of the Environmental Audit Committee that there is 'the potential for synergy between efforts to promote energy efficiency and efforts to promote the development of renewables'.[15] WE RECOMMEND THAT A SUSTAINABLE ENERGY AGENCY SHOULD BE SET UP TO PROMOTE ENERGY EFFICIENCY MORE EFFECTIVELY IN ALL SECTORS AND CO-ORDINATE THAT WITH THE RAPID DEVELOPMENT OF NEW ENERGY SOURCES. This Agency would be in essence a money-moving and promotional body. Its principal statutory aim should be to promote the development and implementation of sustainable energy options. It should be required to take account of the economic and social consequences of its activities, and have among its specific aims reducing inequalities in access to warm homes.[16] For comparison, the Netherlands Agency for Energy and the Environment (Novem), with rather similar functions, has an annual budget of about £65 million and 400 employees.[17] We were also impressed with the effectiveness of the Energy Conservation Centre which promotes energy efficiency in Japan.

10.47   The Sustainable Energy Agency would take over from government Departments responsibility for funding research and development on efficient use of energy, renewable energy technologies, fuel cells and system integration issues. It would negotiate for inclusion of provision for renewable energy projects in regional and structure plans. It would take over staff from the Energy Saving Trust, and possibly from the Energy Technology Support Unit of AEA Technology plc (ETSU), DETR and DTI. It would provide funding to EAGA and related fuel poverty organisations.[18]

10.48   The initial annual budget of the Agency would be about £150 million. The largest element would be the funding provided to EAGA for the Home Energy Efficiency Scheme. Other elements would be DTI's research and development budget for new and renewable

10.66   There is a third, equally important aspect of the research required to underpin the long-term strategy we are advocating. Many of the key issues discussed in this report are not primarily scientific or technical. Economic and ethical considerations also inform policy choices, as chapter 4 showed. More generally, research in the social sciences has a crucial role in assessing the current situation and moving towards a more sustainable energy future. For example, we need to understand the extent to which the risks associated with obtaining and using energy are socially constructed, and why different groups respond to them in the ways they do. If we seek to modify patterns of production and consumption, an understanding of the social, cultural and political determinants of behaviour is vital. We have to develop a more sophisticated conception of how both natural and social scientific knowledge impinge on the policy process. In addressing these and many other issues, the need is to draw contributions from across the social sciences, and integrate them with scientific and technical perspectives. We welcome the interdisciplinary nature of the new jointly funded Climate Change Centre.

IMPLICATIONS FOR OTHER POLICY AREAS

10.67   Many of the measures that will have to be taken in order to bring about deep cuts in carbon dioxide emissions involve fields other than energy policy. THE NEED TO REDUCE EMISSIONS OF GREENHOUSE GASES, PARTICULARLY CARBON DIOXIDE, SHOULD BE TAKEN INTO ACCOUNT IN ALL GOVERNMENT POLICIES. THAT IS NOT THE CASE AT PRESENT. There are four fields—the built environment, transport, agriculture and offshore development—in which we see it as especially important that a long-term strategic view should be taken.

10.68   We have emphasised the importance of the built environment, and the long lead times involved in bringing about the major changes needed in energy performance. THE UK GOVERNMENT AND DEVOLVED ADMINISTRATIONS SHOULD LAUNCH A LONG-TERM PROGRAMME TO BRING ABOUT MAJOR REDUCTIONS IN THE ENERGY REQUIREMENTS OF BUILDINGS. THIS WILL EMBRACE WIDE USE OF TECHNOLOGIES THAT ENABLE OCCUPIERS OF BUILDINGS, INCLUDING HOUSEHOLDERS, TO OBTAIN THEIR OWN HEAT AND ELECTRICITY FROM RENEWABLE OR ENERGY-EFFICIENT SOURCES SUCH AS SOLAR HEATING, SOLAR ELECTRICITY, HEAT PUMPS, AND SMALL-SCALE COMBINED HEAT AND POWER SCHEMES (6.100). IT WILL ALSO REQUIRE THE LARGE-SCALE CONSTRUCTION OF DISTRICT HEATING NETWORKS, SO THAT ADVANTAGE CAN BE TAKEN OF LARGER-SCALE COMBINED HEAT AND POWER SCHEMES.

10.69   The Commission has previously produced two comprehensive reports on transport, covering all aspects of its effects on the environment. REDUCING CARBON DIOXIDE EMISSIONS SHOULD CONTINUE TO BE A CENTRAL OBJECTIVE OF TRANSPORT POLICY. Towards the end of this year we plan to review progress since the Commission's second report on transport in 1997.

10.70   The extent to which renewable energy sources can be developed successfully, both on land and offshore, will also depend on a strategic view being taken that goes well beyond conventional issues of energy policy.

10.71   GROWING CROPS FOR ENERGY PURPOSES SHOULD BE REGARDED AS A PRIMARY USE FOR AGRICULTURAL LAND, AND POLICIES AND SUPPORT MEASURES SHOULD REFLECT THAT.

10.72   A COMPREHENSIVE STRATEGY IS NEEDED FOR DEVELOPING RENEWABLE ENERGY SOURCES OFFSHORE. THIS SHOULD COVER ASSESSMENT OF ENVIRONMENTAL IMPACTS, DESIGNATION OF APPROPRIATE AREAS, AND THE POSSIBILITY OF COMBINING MORE THAN ONE TECHNOLOGY WITHIN A SINGLE INSTALLATION.

THE CHOICES BEFORE US

10.73   All energy policies have both some potential to damage the environment and wider social and economic implications. They must command public assent, be compatible with an improving quality of life, and where possible contribute to extending social inclusion.

10.74   In this report we have focused on an issue, trying to avert dangerous modifications to the world's climate, which we regard as critical, not only for environmental sustainability, but for all aspects of sustainable development. Some of the actions we have advocated will have favourable social or economic implications in the short term. Big improvements in the energy efficiency of housing, for example, will contribute both to limiting long-term energy demand and to eliminating fuel poverty. Both sets of criteria should be used in judging the effectiveness of the measures taken. Developing new energy technologies and new forms of delivery for energy services will not only benefit the environment but could also provide the basis for new industries, hopefully including some new UK industries supplying global markets.

10.75   There will be conflicts of objectives and conflicts of values as the debate over the UK's future energy system continues. In some cases the conflict will be between different concerns and values related to the environment, in other cases the conflict will be between environmental concerns and the interests of particular groups. The UK is a major producer of fossil fuels; numerous companies and employees will therefore have concerns about the substantial reductions in fossil use which we advocate for the coming decades.

10.76   Even if most people accept our argument that there must be very large reductions in UK carbon dioxide emissions, conflicts of values may well arise over the way in which that should be achieved. The analysis in chapter 9 of illustrative scenarios for 2050 showed that, while there are several possible approaches for achieving a 60% reduction in emissions, all have consequences that some people and interest groups might regard as strongly objectionable. It is difficult, for instance, to see how major reductions in transport-related emissions could be made over the next few decades without the growth in road traffic and in air travel being stabilised.

10.77   Proposals to construct new energy installations may also arouse intense opposition. Although the main focus for such opposition will be more local, some may come from people over a much wider area. The most fiercely contested cases have been proposals for nuclear power stations, which give rise to particular concerns over safety, the fuel cycle and waste management. But proposals for wind farms, plants to generate electricity from wastes and overhead transmissions lines have also met strong opposition.

10.78   Recovery of the carbon dioxide produced at power stations and its injection into underground strata could have a part to play in countering climate change. But that would also lead to significant increases in the price of electricity. There is likely to be debate about the safety and sustainability of disposing of carbon dioxide in this way, and there may be public opposition to the installations required for recovery, transport and injection.

10.79   Without a general acceptance of the need for major emission reductions there are likely to be continuing difficulties and delays in obtaining authorisation for any form of new energy project, while policies and financial instruments for reducing energy demand may also face strong opposition. There needs to be much greater awareness, and much more debate, about the challenge of climate change and the case for major reductions in emissions. We hope this report will contribute to a much wider understanding of the issues involved. The ways in which this debate is conducted must allow for deliberations of a high standard and be capable of articulating deeply held values. We have described in our report on environmental standards some approaches that might be deployed in order to achieve that.

10.80   The great majority of recommendations in this report are aimed at government. We accept, however, that government will not be able to introduce the policies needed to achieve sustained and deep cuts in emissions without increased public awareness about the dangers of climate change and the means of addressing the challenge.

10.81   There is an important role for government in increasing that awareness, but it cannot act alone. It falls also to politicians of all parties, to the press and broadcasters, to local authorities, educators, voluntary organisations, local government, industry and commerce to spread awareness and understanding of the threat and of the options for countering it.

10.82   People and organisations should be encouraged to take responsibility for making their own reductions in fossil fuel consumption. But the framework in which energy and environment policies are devised must ensure that sectors which are emitting large quantities of carbon dioxide are likewise committed to reductions. If this is not the case, many people will not feel inclined to 'do their bit.'

10.83   In the medium term the measures needed to achieve the very large emission reductions that are necessary may add appreciably to the price of energy services, whether they take the form of regulation or economic instruments such as a carbon tax or tradeable emission quotas. The increased price of using fossil fuels would both substantially reduce the demand for energy and encourage the development of alternative energy sources or techniques for recovery and disposal of carbon dioxide. The higher price that would be paid by energy users would impose three distinct types of cost. The first would be borne by those who reduced their demand for energy, making some sacrifice as a result. Most people and businesses would, however, decide not to cut their energy consumption by the full amount needed to maintain their bills at the previous level. The second type of costs would be the payments made in taxes, if the higher price was the result of a carbon tax. These would provide extra revenues for the Treasury, which would be available to replace other taxes or finance additional public expenditure; there is therefore unlikely to be a substantial net cost to society over the medium to long term. The third type of costs is the cost of the additional resources required to supply energy without emitting carbon dioxide to the atmosphere.

10.84   From the evidence we have received it seems likely that a carbon tax that doubled the price of energy from fossil fuels could, in the medium to long term, very substantially reduce carbon dioxide emissions by reducing energy demand or by eliciting substitution of carbon free sources of energy. We estimate that, at present prices, energy accounts for about 7% of global economic output. An extreme case would be that of a carbon tax which doubled the global price of energy from fossil fuels, had no effect on overall energy use while inducing complete displacement of fossil fuels or complete capture and disposal of all of their carbon dioxide emissions. If so, it might almost double the resource cost of energy supplies. Thus 7 % would be an upper limit to the additional proportion of world resources required to achieve emission reductions of the magnitude required to respond to the challenge of climate change. If real global output grew by anything over 2% a year, this programme would, at most, set back the net production of other goods and services cumulatively by some three years. It would, in other words, absorb some three years worth of global economic growth. This seems a reasonable price to pay to reduce the environmental dangers set out in Part I of this report. Given the scale of the risk humanity is running in altering climate, it would not be excessive as an insurance premium even if climate change turns out to have less impact than we currently envisage.

10.85   We are not arguing for a rapid doubling of fossil fuel prices; this would have unacceptable distributional effects and leave assets stranded. We are maintaining that a range of measures, including economic instruments, which substantially reduced the demand for energy and brought about the large-scale deployment of non-fossil fuel sources over the coming decades would be acceptable even if they did raise the price of energy services significantly, albeit gradually.

To knowingly cause large-scale disruptions to climate would be unjust and reckless. We stand on the threshold of doing just that. If the United Kingdom cannot demonstrate that it is serious about doing its part to address this threat, it cannot expect other nations – least of all those which are much less wealthy – to do theirs

RECOMMENDATIONS

We bring together here all the recommendations which appear (in bold type) elsewhere in this report: first 19 key recommendations, which are also included (in capitals) in the relevant contexts in chapter 10; and then a number of other recommendations on particular aspects

KEY RECOMMENDATIONS

1.   The goal of reducing the UK's annual carbon dioxide emissions by 20% from their 1990 level by 2010 is a major step in the right direction. It should become a firm target and the government should produce a climate change programme that will ensure it is achieved (5.60).

2.   The UK should continue to play a forceful leading role in international negotiations to combat climate change, both in its own right and through the European Union. The government should press for further reductions in the greenhouse gas emissions of developed nations after 2012, and controls on the emissions of developing nations (4.68).

3.   The government should press for a future global climate agreement based on the contraction and convergence approach, combined with international trading in emission permits. Together, these offer the best long-term prospect of securing equity, economy and international consensus (4.69).

4.   While UK carbon dioxide emissions are falling at the moment, they are expected to begin rising again. All but one of the nuclear power stations, the main source of carbon-free energy at present, are expected to close by 2025. The government should set out, within the next five years, a programme for energy demand reductions and development of alternative energy sources that will prevent this from causing an increase in UK emissions (10.12).

5.   The government should now adopt a strategy which puts the UK on a path to reducing carbon dioxide emissions by some 60% from current levels by about 2050. This would be in line with a global agreement based on contraction and convergence which set an upper limit for the carbon dioxide concentration in the atmosphere of some 550 ppmv and a convergence date of 2050 (10.10).

6.   Absolute reductions in energy demand and a large deployment of alternative energy sources will be needed if the UK is to make deep and sustained cuts in carbon dioxide emissions while protecting its environment and quality of life (10.17). Longer-term targets should be set for expanding the contribution from renewable sources well beyond 10% of electricity supplies to cover a much larger share of primary energy demand (7.106). A range of targets should be developed for raising energy efficiency in all sectors of the economy (6.172). A central policy objective must be a very large reduction in demand for energy for heating and cooling, achieved through much more sophisticated management of heat and much wider use of combined heat and power schemes for both the industrial and the commercial and domestic markets. The resulting heat networks, supplied initially by fossil fuels, could ultimately obtain heat from energy crops and electrically powered heat pumps (8.15).

199

7.   The targets in the UK's long-term strategy should cover protection and expansion of carbon sinks through tree planting and appropriate land use policies (10.20).

8.   The UK should introduce a carbon tax, replacing the climate change levy which is due to begin next year. It should apply upstream and cover all sectors (10.26).

9.   The first call on the revenue from this carbon tax should be to further reduce fuel poverty by benefit increases and more spending on household energy efficiency measures (10.27).

10.   The remainder of the revenue should be used to raise investment in energy efficiency measures in all sectors, to increase the viability of alternative energy sources, and to reduce the impact of the new tax on UK industrial competitiveness (10.28).

11.   The UK should press for a carbon tax within the European Union, but proceed on its own if agreement cannot be reached within the next few years (10.32).

12.   We recommend that a Sustainable Energy Agency should be set up to promote energy efficiency more effectively in all sectors and co-ordinate that with the rapid development of new energy sources (10.46).

13.   We recommend that the government should take the lead in a fundamental review of how electricity networks can best be financed, managed and regulated in order to stimulate and accommodate large contributions to energy supplies from combined heat and power plants and renewable sources, while maintaining reliability and quality of supplies (10.50).

14.   We recommend that the fall in government spending on energy research and development should be reversed, and annual expenditure as a proportion of gross domestic product quadrupled over the next decade to bring the UK up to the present EU average (10.59).

15.   The need to reduce emissions of greenhouse gases, particularly carbon dioxide, should be taken into account in all government policies. That is not the case at present (10.67).

16.   The UK government and devolved administrations should launch a long-term programme to bring about major reductions in the energy requirements of buildings. As well as reducing wastage, this will embrace wide use of technologies that enable occupiers of buildings, including householders, to obtain their own heat and electricity from renewable or energy-efficient sources such as solar heating, solar electricity, heat pumps, and small-scale combined heat and power plants (6.100). It will also require the large-scale construction of district heating networks, so that advantage can be taken of larger-scale combined heat and power schemes (10.68).

17.   Reducing carbon dioxide emissions should continue to be a central objective of transport policy (10.69).

18.   Growing crops for energy purposes should be regarded as a primary use for agricultural land, and policies and support measures should reflect that (10.71).

19.   A comprehensive strategy is needed for developing renewable energy sources offshore. This should cover assessment of environmental impacts, designation of appropriate areas, and the possibility of combining more than one technology within a single installation (10.72).

OTHER RECOMMENDATIONS

THE GLOBAL CONTEXT

20. On the basis of current scientific knowledge about human impact on climate, we support the proposal that an atmospheric concentration of 550 ppmv of carbon dioxide should be regarded as an upper limit that should not be exceeded (4.32).

21. Our view is that an effective, enduring and equitable climate protocol will eventually require emission quotas to be allocated to nations on a simple and equal *per capita* basis. There will have to be a comprehensive system of monitoring emissions to ensure the quotas are complied with (4.47).

22. We urge government to facilitate and encourage the creation of a national trading scheme, to help position the City of London - which has the necessary skills and capacity - as the world centre for international trading in emission permits when that emerges from the negotiations on implementing the Kyoto Protocol (4.64).

A CARBON TAX

23. A carbon tax should be announced at least a year in advance of its introduction, be set at a modest level initially, and be preceded by or launched alongside the other measures we recommend for raising energy efficiency, reducing energy consumption and reducing fuel poverty (6.169).

BETTER MANAGEMENT OF HEAT

24. The UK must develop a comprehensive strategy for the supply and use of heat (8.6)

25. We recommend that the UK government and devolved administrations carry out detailed studies to identify the most effective ways of promoting and facilitating the large-scale growth of heat networks (8.9). They should examine the institutional, economic and social barriers that might prevent that; consider, in conjunction with plant manufacturers, consumers and potential investors, what incentives could overcome such barriers; and support demonstration schemes (6.102).

26. Energy crops and wastes should be regarded in the medium to long term as having a premium role in supplying heat. They should be used in plants providing both heat and electricity to an urban area, and located close to the sources of the fuel in order to minimise transport (8.11).

27. Combined heat and power plants should be regarded primarily as a source of heat. It may be desirable to keep a large part of their capacity to generate electricity in reserve, so that it can be used at those times at which there is a shortfall in supply from other sources (8.12).

28. An integrated approach to heat management should become a central feature of the design of all new houses and other buildings, and should be applied to existing buildings wherever practicable, and building control legislation and the Building Regulations should be amended to bring that about (6.100).

29. To improve energy efficiency, government should promote use of heat pumps wherever electricity has to be used to supply low-grade heat (8.14). Government should investigate the carbon-saving potential and cost-effectiveness of heat pumps and solar water heating at the level of individual homes and larger buildings, with a view to devising subsidy arrangements, both for existing and new buildings, should the findings prove favourable (6.101).

Recommendations

ENERGY USE IN BUILDINGS

30. Both for the building stock and for other capital assets, maximum advantage must be taken of new construction and the replacement cycle in order to make major improvements in energy efficiency (10.14).

31. We recommend that government revise the Building Regulations to mandate much higher standards of energy efficiency in new homes and commercial and public sector buildings (6.97). That should include more demanding criteria for the energy efficiency of lighting and introduce rigorous standards for air conditioning systems as well as heating systems, thereby encouraging architects and engineers to find less polluting ways of keeping buildings adequately lit and at comfortable temperatures (6.43).

32. We recommend that government join with the construction industry to find an effective way of increasing the awareness and understanding of energy-saving methods and technologies among architects, engineers, surveyors and the building trades. We mean this recommendation to apply as much to the house building sector as to larger commercial, industrial and public buildings (6.44).

33. We recommend that government join with major property owners to develop means of tackling the 'landlord-tenant' problem which plagues attempts to raise energy efficiency in the services sector. We propose that government work with the property and energy industries to devise an incentive scheme which would encourage both landlords and tenants to move to individual meters for each tenant (6.48).

34. Where tenants cannot be individually metered, the landlord should be required to inform them of their building's overall annual energy consumption and fuel bill. At the same time, the landlord should be required to inform existing tenants and prospective tenants of the energy consumption and fuel bill for the average building with the same function and floor area as the one in which they rent, or propose to rent, space, as well as the equivalent figures for a high efficiency 'good practice' building of similar function and floor area (6.49).

DOMESTIC ENERGY USE

35. Major improvements in the energy efficiency of UK housing are required (6.6).

36. We recommend that SAP (Standard Assessment Procedure) survey findings should be part of the information packs provided by sellers to house buyers, together with basic information explaining the SAP and general advice on making energy efficiency improvements (6.78).

37. We recommend that purchasers who can demonstrate that they have raised the SAP rating of their property by 20 points should be entitled to a stamp duty rebate (up to a maximum of 1% of the purchase price) (6.79).

38. We urge UK manufacturers and retailers to take a lead in marketing more energy efficient products, and government to encourage them to do so. Government Departments, local authorities the NHS and government agencies should bulk purchase the more energy efficient products, expanding their market and helping to bring down costs (6.86).

39. For new housing Building Regulations that deliver a SAP 80 rating should be introduced forthwith. We further recommend that government announce its intention to move to a higher standard, based on achieving a SAP 100 rating, by 2005. We also recommend that the practice

REFERENCES

Energy: Definitions and Units

1.   The international system of units (6th edition). HMSO, 1993.

Chapter 1

1.   Annual rates of global energy use have been taken from Odell, P.R. (1999). *Fossil fuels in the 21st century.* Financial Times Energy. The Commission Secretariat has converted from tonnes coal equivalent to watts. To obtain estimates of global energy use in terms of tonnes coal equivalent, Odell expressed energy derived from hydro and nuclear power as the heat value of the electricity produced. Statistics of world population have been taken from Durand, J.D. (1974). *Historical estimates of world population: an evaluation.* University of Pennsylvania Population Studies Center, Philadelphia; United Nations (1966). *World population prospects as assessed in 1963.* United Nations, New York; United Nations (1998). *World population prospects: the 1998 revision.* ESA/P/WP.150. United Nations, New York.

2.   International Energy Agency (IEA) (1998). *World Energy Outlook 1998 Edition.* IEA/Organization for Economic Co-operation and Development, Paris. The most recent year for which global data are available is 1995.

3.   Tolba, M.K., El Kholy, O., El Hinnawi, E., Holdgate, M.W., McMichael, D.F. and Munn, R.E. (eds) (1992). *The world environment, 1972-1992: two decades of challenge.* Chapman and Hall.

4.   Tolba *et al.* (1992).

5.   IEA (1998). See page 413.

6.   Department of Health, Committee on the Medical Effects of Air Pollutants (1998). *Quantification of the effects of air pollution on health in the United Kingdom.* The Stationery Office.

7.   World Commission on Environment and Development (1987). *Our common future.* Oxford University Press, Oxford.

Chapter 2

1.   Intergovernmental Panel on Climate Change (IPCC) (1996a). *The Science of Climate Change 1995.* Cambridge University Press, Cambridge.

2.   Houghton, J.T. (1997). *Global Warming.* Cambridge University Press, Cambridge.

3.   IPCC (1996b). *The Science of Climate Change 1995. Summary for Policymakers.* Cambridge University Press, Cambridge. See page 31.

4.   Karl, T.R., Knight, R.W. and Baker, B. (2000). The record breaking global temperatures of 1997 and 1998: evidence for an increase in the rate of global warming? *Geophysical Research Letters,* **27**, 719-722.

5.   The disparity between the rapid increase observed in surface temperature and the relatively minimal temperature increase observed during the last 20 years in the lower to mid-troposphere does not invalidate the conclusion that surface temperature has been rising: National Research Council, Panel on Reconciling Temperature Observations (2000). *Reconciling observations of global temperature change.* National Academy Press, Washington DC.

6.   Barnola, J.M., Raynaus, D., Korotkevich, Y.S. and Lorius, C. (1987). Vostock ice core provides 160,000-year record of atmospheric CO_2. *Nature,* **329**, 408-414.

7.   The average concentration of carbon dioxide in the atmosphere in 1997 was around 363 ppmv: Keeling, C.D. and Whorf, T.P. (1998). *Atmospheric CO_2 concentrations – Mauna Loa Observatory, Hawaii, 1958-1997.* Carbon Dioxide Information Analysis Center, Oak Ridge National Laboratory, Tennessee;
The average concentration reported from observations at the Mauna Loa Observatory throughout 1998 was 367 ppmv: http://cdiac.esd.ornl.gov/ftp/maunaloa-co2/maunaloa.co2

8.   IPCC (1994). *Climate Change 1994: Radiative forcing of climate change and an evaluation of the IPCC IS92 emission scenarios.* Cambridge University Press, Cambridge. See page 34.

9.   Rotty, R.M. and Marland, G. (1986). *Production of CO_2 from fossil fuel burning by fuel type.* Report NDP-006. Carbon Dioxide Information Analysis Center, Oak Ridge National Laboratory, Tennessee.

10. Carbon dioxide is released into the atmosphere through the calcining of limestone during cement manufacture. For an assessment of the cement industry's contribution to carbon dioxide emissions, see *Greenhouse Issues* (newsletter of the IEA Greenhouse Gas R&D Programme), **46**, January 2000.

11. IPCC (1996b), page 8.

12. IPCC (1996a).

13. The flows shown in figure 2-III are averages of estimates for the years 1988-1997.

14. The figure of 260 GtC includes carbon dioxide emissions from cement manufacture.

15. Keshgi, H.S., Jain, A.K. and Wuebbles, D.J. (1996). Accounting for the missing carbon sink with the CO_2 fertilisation effect. *Climate Change,* **33**, 31-62.

16. Etheridge, D.M., Steele, L.P., Langenfields, R.L., Francey, R.J., Barnola, J.M. and Morgan, V.I. (1996). Natural and anthropogenic changes in CO_2 over the last 1,000 years from Antarctic ice and firn. *Journal of Geophysical Research,* **101**, 4115-4128.

17. Petit, J.R., Jouzel, J., Raynaud, D., Barkov, N.I., Barnola, J.M., Basile, I., Bender, M., Chapellaz, J., Davis, M., Delaygue, G., Delmotte, M., Kotlyakov, V.M., Legrand, M., Lipenkov, V.Y., Lorius, C., Pepin, L., Ritz, C., Saltzman, E. and Stienhard, M. (1999). Climate and atmospheric history of the past 420,000 years from the Vostok ice core, Antarctica. *Nature,* **399**, 429-436.

18. See endnote 7.

19. Berner, R. A. (1994). Geocarb II: a revised model of atmospheric CO_2 over Phanerozoic time. *American Journal of Science,* **294**, 56-91.

20. IPCC (1996b), table 1.

21   IPCC (1994), page 245.

22. Hoffert, M.I., Caldeira, K., Jain, A.K., Haites, E.F., Harvey, L.D.D., Potter S.D., Schlesinger, M.E., Schneider, S.H., Watts, R.G., Wigley, T.M.L. and Wuebbles, D.J. (1998). Energy implications of future stabilization of atmospheric CO_2 content. *Nature,* **395**, 881-884. The power produced by 'carbon-emission-free' sources in 2050 would be 10TW (figure 2), equivalent to the power provided by all today's energy sources combined, and global energy intensity would have to be reduced by 1% a year over the next 50 years (notes to figure 3).

23. Meteorological Office (1999). *Climate change and its impacts: stabilization of CO_2 in the atmosphere.* The Meteorological Office, Bracknell. This projection assumed there would be no net addition to the greenhouse effect from other substances, and may therefore be an under-estimate.

24. Information supplied by The Hadley Centre, February 2000. In 1990 global emissions from burning of fossil fuels were 6.1 GtC (IPCC (1996a), page 78). The calculation assumes that carbon dioxide emissions resulting from land use changes also continue at the 1990 level.

25. Meteorological Office (1999).

26. United Nations Framework Convention on Climate Change (UNFCCC) (1992). Adopted 9 May 1992, New York.

27. Brown, B.E., Dunne, R.P. and Chansang, H. (1997). Coral bleaching relative to elevated sea surface temperature in the Andaman Sea (Indian Ocean) over the last 50 years. *Coral Reefs,* **15**, 151-152.

28. Meteorological Office (1999).

29. Oppenheimer, M. (1998). Global warming and the stability of the West Antarctic Ice Sheet. *Nature,* **393**, 325-332.

30. Meteorological Office (1999).

31. Turner, R.K., Adger, N. and Doktor, P. (1999) Assessing the economic costs of sea level rise. *Environment and Planning A, 27*, 1777-1796.

32. The most comprehensive assessment is that by the UK Climate Change Impact Review Group (CCIRG): Department of the Environment (1996). *Review of the potential effects of climate change in the United Kingdom.* HMSO.

33. UK Climate Impacts Programme (1998). *Climate change scenarios for the United Kingdom. Technical Report No. 1: Summary Report.* Climate Research Unit, University of East Anglia, Norwich.

34. Centre for the Study of Environmental Change and Sustainability (1999). *Climate Change: Scottish Implications Scoping Study.*

35. Meteorological Office (1999).

36. Evidence from Julian Morris (Director, Institute of Economic Affairs), December 1998.

37. A text published on the web-site of the Oregon Institute of Science and Medicine reviewing the research literature concerning the environmental consequences of increased levels of atmospheric carbon dioxide during the 20th century concludes that this has had no deleterious effects on global weather, climate and temperature;
    Robinson, A.B., Baliunas, S.L., Soon, W. and Robinson, Z.W. (1998). Environmental effects of increased atmospheric carbon dioxide. http://www.oism.org/pproject/

38. Twenty-first Report, paragraph 2.66.

39. In the four new scenarios increases in temperature and rises in sea level are measured from 1750, whereas in IPCC's 1995 scenarios they were measured from the 1860s; the difference in sea level between the two dates is negligible and the difference in temperature about $0.2°C$.

40. Meteorological Office (1999).

Chapter 3

1. Twenty-first Report, paragraph 3.32.

2. In certain types of deep bituminous coal deposits it would be possible to combine injection of carbon dioxide with recovery of methane adsorbed in the coal seam, in an approach akin to enhanced recovery from oil fields (information supplied by Dr K. Thambimuthu, February 2000).

3. Croiset, E. and Thambimuthu, K.V. (1999). A novel strategy for greenhouse gas abatement in coal-fired power plants: enriched oxygen combustion. *Combustion Canada '99.* Calgary, Alberta, Canada, 26-28 May 1999.

4. Herzog, H., Golomb, D. and Zemba, S. (1991). Feasibility, modelling and economics of sequestering power plant CO_2 emissions in the deep ocean. *Environmental Progress, 10,* 64-74.

5. Thambimuthu, K. and Freund, P. (1998). CO_2 capture and sequestration from power generation: studies by the IEA Greenhouse Gas R&D Programme. *Proceedings of the 1998 Electric Power Research Institute and Gasification Technology Council Conference, San Francisco, California, October 1998.* For calculating the costs of avoiding carbon dioxide emissions the IEA Greenhouse Gas R&D Programme uses a discount rate of 10% and a standard set of assumptions and conditions: a power plant supplying 500 MW of electricity to a grid, at which 85% of carbon dioxide is removed, dried and pressurised to 90 bar, and kept in a temporary store. Costs have been converted from US $ at the rate of $1.6=£1.

6. Supercritical fluids are highly compressed gases which combine properties of gases and liquids. The definition of a supercritical fluid usually begins with a phase diagram, which defines the critical temperature and pressure of a substance. For example, carbon dioxide becomes supercritical above a temperature of $31.1°C$ and a pressure of 73.8 bar, known as the critical point.

7. International Energy Agency Greenhouse Gas R&D Programme (IEAGGP) (1994). *Carbon dioxide disposal from power stations.* Cheltenham.

8. Holloway, S. *et al.* (1996). The underground disposal of carbon dioxide. British Geological Survey, Keyworth, Nottingham.

211

References

9.   Workshop organized by IEAGGP and Statoil on the geological storage of carbon dioxide in saline aquifers, 4-5 April 2000, Noorwijkerhout, Netherlands.

10. Schmidt, K. (1998). Coming to grips with the world's greenhouse gases. *Science, 281*, 504-505.

11. Under existing circulation patterns the turnover of water between surface and deep layers of the ocean ranges from 250 years in the Atlantic to 550 years in the Pacific: Into the abyss, *New Scientist*, 15 May 1999, 14.

12. Greenpeace International (1999). *Ocean disposal/sequestration of carbon dioxide from fossil fuel production and use: an overview of rationale, techniques and implications.* Amsterdam, Netherlands.

13. Convention on the prevention of marine pollution by dumping of wastes and other matter (1972). A protocol updating and enhancing the environmental protection provided by the London Convention was agreed in 1996 but has yet to enter into force. A number of delegations at the twenty-first consultative meeting of the contracting parties supported the conclusion of the advisory scientific group that fossil fuel-derived carbon dioxide should be considered an industrial waste, the dumping of which is prohibited under the convention. Other delegations concluded that it was too early to reach a decision, that the convention should not be used to prevent research and that its terms could be changed if necessary. It was also pointed out that under article III(I)c of the convention (retained as article 1.4.3 of the 1996 protocol) the disposal or storage of wastes or other matter from offshore oil and gas activities is not currently covered by the provisions of the convention. The London Convention does not cover the disposal of carbon dioxide from land-based sources via pipelines. Delegations present at the twenty-first meeting agreed that the scientific group would maintain a watching brief on developments relating to carbon dioxide disposal.

14. UNEP (1999). *Global Environment Outlook 2000.* Earthscan.

15. Nilssen, A. (1992). *Greenhouse Earth.* John Wiley and Sons for Scientific Committee on Problems of the Environment.

16. Intergovernmental Panel on Climate Change (IPCC) (1996a). *Climate Change 1995: Impacts, adaptations and mitigation of climate change: scientific-technical analyses.* Cambridge University Press, Cambridge.

17. IPCC (1994). *Climate Change 1994: Radiative forcing of climate change and an evaluation of the IPCC IS92 emission scenarios.* Cambridge University Press, Cambridge.

18. IPCC (1996a).

19. Davison, J.E. and Freund, P. (1999). *A comparison of sequestration of CO_2 by forestry and capture from power stations.* IEAGGP, Cheltenham.

20. Dixon, R.K., Brown, S., Houghton, R.A., Solomon, A.M., Trexler, M.C. and Wisniewski, J. (1994). Carbon pools and flux of global forest ecosystems. *Science, 263*, 185-190;
     Schlesinger, W. H. (1997). *Biogeochemistry: An analysis of global change.* Academic Press.

21. Friend, A.D., Stevens, A.K., Knox, R.G. and Cannell, N.G.R. (1997). A process based terrestrial biosphere model of ecosystem dynamics (HYBRID v3.0). *Ecological Modelling, 95*, 249-287.

22. Meteorological Office (1999). *Climate change and its impacts: stabilization of CO_2 in the atmosphere.* The Meteorological Office, Bracknell.

23. Nilssen (1992).

24. Cooper, D.J., Watson, A.J. and Nightingale, P.D. (1996). Large decrease in ocean surface CO_2 fugacity in response to *in-situ* iron fertilization. *Nature, 383*, 511-513.

25. Denman, K., Hofmann, E. and Marchant, H. (1996). Marine biotic responses to environmental change and feedbacks to climate. Pages 487-516 in IPCC (1996b). *The Science of Climate Change 1995.* Cambridge University Press, Cambridge.

26. Ritschard, R.L. (1992). Marine algae as a CO_2 sink. *Water, Air and Soil Pollution.* **64**, 289-303;
     IEAGGP (1998). *Ocean fertilisation as a CO_2 sequestration option.* Cheltenham.

27. Convention on the Conservation of Antarctic Marine Living Resources (1982). Hobart, Tasmania, Australia. http://www.ccamlr.org/

28. Sarmiento, J.L. and Orr, J.C. (1991). Three-dimensional simulations of the impact of Southern Ocean nutrient depletion on atmospheric CO_2 and ocean chemistry. *Limnology Oceanography, 36*, 1928-1950.

29. IPCC (1996b).

30. International Energy Agency (IEA) (1999). *Energy balances of non-OECD countries 1996-1997*. Paris: IEA/Organization for Economic Co-operation and Development (OECD).

31. IEA (1998). *World Energy Outlook – 1998 Edition*. Paris: IEA/OECD.

32. Chadwick, M.J. (1997). Industrial ecocycles: rate adjustments and dematerialization. *Philosophical Transactions of the Royal Society of London A*, **355**, 1439-1447.

33. Energy intensity is the ratio between consumption of primary energy and output of goods and services. Between 1971 and 1997 global output of goods and services rose by 3.2% a year, whereas global energy use rose by 2.2% a year: IEA (1998).

34. Nakicenovic, N. (1996). Freeing energy from carbon. *Daedalus*, **125(3)**, 95-112.

35. Patterson, W. (1999). *Transforming electricity*. Royal Institute of International Affairs/Earthscan.

36. Twentieth Report, paragraph 2.35.

37. Evidence from Dr L. Brookes, April 1999;
     Herring, H. (1998). *Does energy efficiency save energy: the economists debate*. The Open University, Milton Keynes.

38. Watt Committee on Energy (1990). *Technological responses to the greenhouse effect*. G. Thurlow (Ed.). The Watt Committee on Energy, Rooster Books Limited.

39. Presentation by Professor Peter Odell, May 1999.

40. Reference efficiencies of power plant taken from IEAGGP (1994).

41. DTI (1998). *Conclusions of the review of energy sources for power generation and government response to fourth and fifth reports of the Trade and Industry Committee*. Cm 4071. See paragraph 9.57.

42. Carbon emissions from the ARBRE biomass plant are estimated as 44-109 g/kWh whilst the equivalent figures for coal and gas fired power plants are 410 and 1,050 gC/kWh, respectively. Bauen, A. (1999). *Gasification-based biomass fuel cycles: an economic and environmental analysis at the regional level*. Unpublished PhD thesis, King's College London, University of London. See page 146.

43. Energy Technology Support Unit (1995). *Full fuel cycle atmospheric emissions and global warming impacts from UK electricity generation*. ETSU Report No. R-88. HMSO.

44. IEA. Appendix B - Photovoltaics, in *Benign energy: the environmental implications of renewables*. http//:www.iea.org.tech/pubs

45. Michaelis, P. (1998). *Life cycle assessment of energy systems*. A report prepared for the Royal Commission on Environmental Pollution. Centre for Environmental Strategy, University of Surrey, Guildford.

46. European Wind Energy Association/Forum for Energy and Development/Greenpeace International (1999). *Wind Force 10: a blueprint to achieve 10% of the world's electricity from wind power by 2020*. Birger Madsen BTM Consult, Ringkøbing (Denmark).

47. Thambimuthu, K. and Freund, P. (1998);
     Davison, J.E. and Freund, P.(1999).

Chapter 4

1. Netherlands, Ministry of Housing, Spatial Planning and the Environment (1999). *Environmental News from the Netherlands*, **4**, 3. The Hague.

2. Wigley, T. (1998). The Kyoto Protocol: CO_2, CH_4 and climate implications. *Geophysical Research Letters* **25**(13), 2285-2288. The comparison was with IPCC's IS92a scenario (2.20).

3. United Nations (1998). *World Population Prospects: The 1998 Revision*. ESA/P/WP.150. United Nations, New York.

4. Nordhaus, W.D. (1999). *Roll the DICE again: the economics of global warming*. Yale University Press, New Haven. The quotation is from page 47.

5. Heal, G. (1997). Discounting and climate change, an editorial essay. *Climatic Change*, **37**(2), 335-343.

6. Dasgupta, P.S., Mäler, K. and Barrett, S. (1999). Intergenerational equity, social discount rates and global warming. In Portney, P.R. and Weyant, J.P. (Eds.). *Discounting and intergenerational equity*. Resources for the Future, Washington DC.

7. Nordhaus, W.D. and Boyer, J.G. (1999). Requiem for Kyoto: An economic analysis of the Kyoto Protocol. *Energy Journal*, May 1999, 93-130.

8. Global Commons Institute's website, http:/www.gci.org.uk. The institute regards 450 ppmv as an upper limit.

9. Nordhaus, W.D. and Boyer, J.G. (1999).

10. The Council of Ministers first reached this conclusion in March 1998, on the basis that a 550 ppmv limit might prevent global temperatures from rising by more than 2°C. Community Strategy on Climate Change: Council Conclusions.

11. Wigley, T.M.L., Richels, R. and Edmonds, J.A. (1996). Economic and environmental choices in the stabilization of atmospheric CO_2 concentrations. *Nature,* **379,** 240-243.

12. International Energy Agency (1998). *World Energy Outlook 1998 Edition.* IEA/Organization for Economic Co-operation and Development, Paris.

13. Galeotti, M. and Lanza, B. (1999). Richer and cleaner? A study on carbon dioxide emissions in developing countries. *Energy Policy,* **27,** 565-573.

14. Wigley, T.M.L. (1997). Implications of recent CO_2 emission-limitation proposals for stabilization of atmospheric concentrations. *Nature,* **390,** 267-270.

15. Baumert, K.A., Bhandari, R. and Kete, N. (1999). What might a developing country climate commitment look like? *World Resources Institute Climate Notes,* May 1999. Washington DC. See also Sagoff, M. (1999). Controlling global climate: The debate over pollution trading. *Report from the Institute for Philosophy and Public Policy,* **19,** 1-6.

16. Wigley, T.M.L. (1997). But see also Ramakrishna, K., The Great Debate on CO_2 emissions. *Nature,* **390,** 227-228.

17. Table 4.1 has been calculated by the Commission Secretariat. The figures used for total allowable global emissions under different stabilisation scenarios are based on estimates in Intergovernmental Panel on Climate Change (1996). *The Science of Climate Change 1995. Summary for Policymakers.* Cambridge University Press, Cambridge.

18. The UK population in 2050 is assumed to be 57 million and the global population 8.9 billion: United Nations (1998).

19. Meyer, A. (1997). The Kyoto Protocol and the emergence of contraction and convergence as a framework for an international political solution to greenhouse gas emissions abatement. In Hohmeyher, O. and Rennings, K. (Eds.). *Man made climate change – economic aspects and policy options.* Proceedings of a ZEW conference. Mannheim; web-site of the Global Commons Institute. http://www.gci.org.uk

20. Auken, S. *(Minister for Environment and Energy, Denmark) (1999).* Kyoto and beyond. In: *The Sustainable Development Agenda 1999.* Campden. See page 18.

21. Grubb, M., Vrolijk, C. and Brack, D. (1999). *The Kyoto Protocol; a guide and an assessment.* Royal Institute of International Affairs/Earthscan. See page 270.

22. Emissions Trading Group (1999). *Outline proposals for a UK emissions trading scheme.* December 1999. The Group was set up in June 1999 by the Confederation of British Industry and the government's Advisory Committee on Business and the Environment. In the November 1999 pre-Budget report the Chancellor supported the group's work.

Chapter 5

1. Department of Trade and Industry (DTI) (1999). *Digest of United Kingdom Energy Statistics (DUKES) 1999.* Cited as DUKES 1999.

2. DUKES 1999, table 1.13.

3. DUKES 1999, table 1.12.

4. DTI (2000a). *Energy projections for the UK – working paper.* DTI EPTAC Directorate. This document, the first set of official energy projections since 1995, emphasised that it represented work in progress and had yet to be approved by Ministers. It was issued in this preliminary form to accompany the Draft UK Climate Change Programme, which took the DTI energy projections into account in projecting UK 'business as usual' carbon dioxide emissions. The energy projections cover six scenarios, based on different assumptions about future economic growth and energy prices. The projections quoted in the text, and used in constructing figures 5-I, 5-II, 5-III and 5-V, are for the central economic growth case (GDP increases at 2.5-2.75% a year between 2001 and 2020) and higher energy prices (oil traded at an average of $20 a barrel, at 1995 prices, over the period 2000-2020).

5. DUKES 1999, table 1.9; 228.9 million tonnes of oil equivalent is equal to an average rate of 304 GW.

6. DUKES 1998, tables 1.1 and 1.9.

7. DUKES 1999, table 1.9, page 35.

8. DUKES 1999, table 1.9.

9   DUKES 1999, tables 6.1 and 1.1.

10. DUKES 1999, page 17, paragraph 1.40.

11. DUKES 1999, table 1.13; in total final users consumed 156.2 million tonnes of oil equivalent, equal to an average rate of 207 GW.

12. DUKES 1999, tables 1.9 and 1.13.

13. Calculated from DUKES 1999.

14. GDP at 1995 prices; watts represent the average rate of consumption of primary energy in the year in question.

15. Parliamentary Office of Science and Technology (POST). Appendix 1 in House of Commons, Environmental Audit Committee (1999). *Energy efficiency.* Minutes of Evidence, HC159-II 1998-99.

16. The policies set out in the 1969 Energy White Paper might have constituted an exception, had it not been followed quickly by a change of government.

17. DTI (1998). *Conclusions of the review of energy sources for power generation and government response to Fourth and Fifth Reports of the Trade and Industry Committee.* Cm 4071. October 1998. See paragraph 1.1. In paragraph 2 of the government's response to the House of Commons Environmental Audit Committee's report, *Energy efficiency* this is described as 'the Government's central policy objective'.

18. DTI (1998), paragraph 1.2.

19. Covered in chapter 9 of DTI (1998). See paragraph 3 of the government's response to the Environmental Audit Committee's report (end note 57).

20. The current Utilities Bill provides for the formal merger of the two offices, which have already been combined administratively. There is a separate regulator for the electricity industry in Northern Ireland; there is no public supply of gas in Northern Ireland.

21. DTI (1998).

22. Blair's energy cave-in to US. Revealed: how threats forced U-turn on mines. *The Guardian,* 13 August 1999.

23. A Directive on liberalisation of the electricity market was adopted in January 1997 and should make it easier for independent producers to sell electricity; by 2003 it will give anyone using electricity at an average rate of more than about 1 MW the right to choose a supplier. A programme for liberalisation of the gas market was agreed by Ministers in December 1997 and provides for 33% of the market to be opened to competition five years after a Directive comes into force. Owen, G. (1999). *Public purpose or private benefit? The policies of energy conservation.* Manchester University Press, Manchester. See page 54.

24. The source for the structure of the gas industry is DUKES 1999, chart 4.1 and paragraphs 4.8-4.10; figures for market share are for 1998 for the industrial and commercial market and end April 1999 for the domestic market, number of companies as at the end of 1998;

    sources for the structure of the electricity industry are DUKES 1999, chart 5.1, paragraphs 5.4 and 5.52-5.53, and table 5.4; Electricity Association (1999). *Electricity Industry Review 3*, pages 19-23 and table on page 39 (using data supplied by NGC Energy Settlements and Information Services Ltd). Figures for market share are for 1997/98; number of second tier suppliers as at 1 October 1998.

25. It has been suggested, on the basis of modelling studies, that the actual effect of moving from the Pool to bilateral agreements will be to increase the power of the large generators and raise prices: Cheap power plan to backfire. *The Observer,* 22 August 1999.

26. In March 1998 a government advisory committee recommended that the electricity and gas regulators should incentivise suppliers to develop in that direction in relation to housing: Advisory Committee on Business and the Environment. *Climate change: a strategic issue for business.* Report presented to the Prime Minister, 31 March 1998.

27. Department of the Environment Transport and the Regions (DETR) (2000a). *Energy Efficiency Standard of Performance – 2003-2005. Consultation Proposals.*

28. The Environment Agency in England and Wales and the Scottish Environment Protection Agency in Scotland; integrated pollution control does not yet operate in Northern Ireland.

29. Council Directive 96/61/EC concerning integrated pollution prevention and control. *Official Journal of the European Communities*, **L257**, 10.10.96.

30. Information supplied by DTI, February 2000.

31. In Northern Ireland appeals are made to the Planning Appeals Commission.

32. DETR (2000b). *The Air Quality Strategy for England, Scotland, Wales and Northern Ireland – working together for clean air*. The Stationery Office.

33. A decade of dramatic improvements in air quality predicted – Meacher launches new air quality strategy to start new century: DETR Press Notice 032, 19 January 2000.

34. DTI (1994). *New and renewable energy: future prospects in the UK*. Energy Paper 62. HMSO. See paragraph 3.1.1.

35. Department of the Environment (DOE) (1993). *Renewable energy*. Planning Policy Guidance Note 22; Scottish Development Department (1994). *Renewable energy*. National Planning Policy Guidance 6 (now under review); Scottish Executive (1999). *Renewable energy technologies*. Planning Advice Note 45; Welsh Office (1999). *Planning Guidance (Wales) Planning Policy First Revision* (now under review); DOE (1996). *Renewable energy. Planning Guidance (Wales)* Technical Advice Note 8; Planning Policy Statements being prepared by the Department of the Environment in Northern Ireland on 'Protection of the environment' and 'Public services/utilities' may address relevant issues.

36. DTI (1999). *New and renewable energy: prospects for the 21st century*. See page 22.

37. Energy Technology Support Unit (ETSU) (1999). *New and renewable energy: prospects for the 21st century - supporting analysis*. See page 257.

38. DUKES 1999, table 7.5.

39. Between 1994 and the end of 1998, of the 18 wind developments which went before planning inquiries, just two small schemes won approval: Questions but precious few answers in renewable energy review. *ENDS Report*, No. 291, April 1999.

40. DTI (2000b). *New and renewable energy – prospects for the 21st century. Conclusion in response to the public consultation.*

41. ETSU (1999). See page 17 and figure 4.

42. DUKES 1999, chapter 6.

43. DOE, (1994). *Climate Change – the UK Programme*, HMSO.

44. DETR/Scottish Executive/National Assembly for Wales/Department of the Environment (in Northern Ireland) (2000c). *Climate Change: Draft UK Programme*. DETR.

45. Based on estimates for carbon savings arising from various policies set out in DoE (1997), *Climate Change – the UK Programme: The United Kingdom's Second Report under the Framework Convention on Climate Change;*
DETR/Scottish Executive/National Assembly for Wales/Department of the Environment (for Northern Ireland) (2000). *Climate Change – Draft UK Programme.*

46. DETR (2000c).

47. DETR (1998). *A new deal for transport: better for everyone.* Cm 3950. The Stationery Office.

48. DETR (2000c).

49. International Energy Agency (IEA) (2000); *Energy Policies of IEA Countries – 1999 Review*, OECD/IEA: Paris. tables B2, B4, B11.

50. IEA (2000); *Energy Policies of IEA Countries – 1999 Review*, table B4.

51. Office of Science and Technology, 1999, *SET Statistics 1999 – a handbook of science, engineering and technology indicators*. OST.

52. A similar trend occurred in the USA, where a decline in industry funding of energy-related R&D has been attributed to utility industry restructuring: Yeager, K.E. (1998). Rebuilding the commitment to R&D investment and innovation. *World Energy Council Journal*, July 1998, 80-85.

53. From £174 million to £139 million. Information supplied by Energy Policy and Analysis Unit, DTI, April 1999.

54. *R and d scorecard.* See http://www.innovation.gov.uk/finance/rndscore_1999/intex.html

55. Evidence from the University of Greenwich Natural Resources Institute, November 1998; Local Government Association, December 1998; The Royal Institute of British Architects, December 1998; Eryl McNally MEP (Bedfordshire and Milton Keynes), December 1998; The Rocky Mountain Institute, December 1998; Dalkia plc, December 1998; Environmental Change Unit and the Department of Engineering Science, University of Oxford, January 1999; BIFFA Waste Services, February 1999.

56. House of Commons Trade and Industry Committee. *Energy policy*. Volume I, paragraph 21(a). Session 1997-98, Fifth Report, HC471-1.
57. House of Commons Environmental Audit Committee. *Energy efficiency*. Volume I, paragraph 6. Session 1998-99, Seventh Report, HC 159-1.
58. United Kingdom (1999). *A better quality of life: a strategy for sustainable development for the United Kingdom*. Cm 4345. See paragraph 8.12.

Chapter 6

1. Department of Trade and Industry (DTI) (1999). *Digest of United Kingdom Energy Statistics 1999*. The Stationery Office. Cited as DUKES 1999. Tables 1.12 and 1.13.
2. Department of the Environment, Transport and the Regions (DETR) (1999a). *Fuel poverty: The New Home Energy Efficiency Scheme*.
3. The Eurowinter Group (1997). Cold exposure and winter mortality from ischaemic heart disease, cerebrovascular disease, respiratory disease, and all causes in warm and cold regions of Europe. *The Lancet*, **349**, 1341-1346.
4. DETR (1999a)
5. DUKES 1999, tables 1.12 and 1.13.
6. DTI (1997). *Energy consumption in the United Kingdom*. Energy Paper 66. The Stationery Office.
7. DUKES 1999, tables 1.11 and 1.13.
8. Energy Saving Trust (1997). *Energy efficiency and environmental benefits to 2010*.
9. Environmental Change Unit, Oxford University (1987). *DECADE 2 MtC* (Domestic Equipment and Carbon Dioxide Emissions Project – two megatonnes of carbon).
10. DUKES 1999, table 1.13.
11. DTI (1997).
12. DTI (1997).
13. HM Treasury (1998). *Economic instruments and the business use of energy*. A report by Lord Marshall. See paragraph 29.
14. Energy Technology Support Unit (ETSU) (1999). *Industrial sector carbon dioxide emissions: projections and indicators for the UK, 1990-2020*. Harwell.
15. ETSU (1999).
16. DUKES 1999, table 1B, page 21.
17. ETSU (1999).
18. Chancellor of the Exchequer's Budget Statement of 9 March, 1999; HM Customs and Excise (1999). *Consultation on a climate change levy*.
19. HM Treasury Press Release 7 on Pre-Budget Report, November 1999.
20. HM Treasury (1998), table c3.
21. DUKES 1999, page 238.
22. HM Customs and Excise (1999).
23. Chemical Industries Association (1997). *The energy efficiency agreement between the Chemical Industries Association and Government*.
24. House of Commons Environment, Transport and Regional Affairs Committee (2000). *UK Climate Change Programme*. The Stationery Office. See paragraph 71.
25. HM Treasury (1998), page 50.
26. Emissions Trading Group (1999). *Outline proposals for a UK emissions trading scheme*.
27. Information supplied by DETR, November 1999.
28. DUKES 1999, table 1.13.
29. DTI (1997).
30. DTI (1997).
31. DTI (1997).
32. DTI (1997).
33. DTI (1997).
34. Jonathan Fisher Environmental Economics (1998). *Prospects for energy saving and reducing demand for energy in the UK*. A report prepared for the Royal Commission on Environmental Pollution.

35.   DETR Energy Efficiency Best Practice Programme. New Practice Final Report 106, Energy Consumption Guide 19. Building Research Establishment Conservation Support Unit (BRECSU) and University of East Anglia. Garston.

36.   Information supplied by Chetwood Associates, architects, February 2000.

37.   Scottish Executive (2000), *Scottish Climate Change Programme Consultation.* Edinburgh.

38.   Evidence from the Royal Society for the Promotion of Health, January 1999.

39.   BRECSU (1996). *Review of ultra-low-energy homes.* General Information Report 39. Garston.

40.   HM Treasury (1998).

41.   DUKES 1999, table 1.13.

42.   DUKES 1999, table 1.13.

43.   DTI (1997).

44.   DETR (1999b). *Projections of households in England to 2021.*

45.   DTI (1997).

46.   Estimate supplied by ETSU, February 2000.

47.   BRECSU (1998). *The government's Standard Assessment Procedure for energy rating of dwellings, 1998 Edition.* Garston.

48.   Jonathan Fisher Environmental Economics (1998).

49.   Energy Saving Trust (1998). *Small scale multi-residential CHP and environmental benefits to 2010.*

50.   DUKES 1999, chart 9.4.

51.   House of Commons Environmental Audit Committee (1999). *Energy efficiency.* Session 1998-99, Seventh Report, HC 159-1.

52.   National Audit Office (1998). *The Office of Electricity Regulation: improving energy efficiency financed by a charge on customers.* The Stationery Office.

53.   Office of Gas and Electricity Markets (OFGEM) (2000). *Energy Efficiency Standards of Performance 2000-2002. Final Decisions.*

54.   DETR (2000a). *Energy Efficiency Standard of Performance 2002-2005. Consultation Proposals.*

55.   The government's estimate of the annual reduction in emissions resulting from this measure is 0.75 million tonnes of carbon (MtC) or 2% of the sector total: DETR/Scottish Executive/National Assembly for Wales/Department of the Environment (in Northern Ireland) (2000). *Climate Change: Draft UK Programme.* Cited as DETR (2000b). See paragraph 17, page 98.

56.   DETR (2000b), paragraph 18, page 99. The reduction in emissions is 2.7-3.8 (MtC) a year.

57.   Broad estimate based on DETR (1998), *English House Condition Survey 1996.* The rate of demolition is higher in Scotland than in England.

58.   See, for instance, chapter 7 of Northern Ireland Housing Executive (1998), *Northern Ireland House Condition Survey 1996.* Northern Ireland Housing Executive; Table A 9.13 of Scottish Homes (1997). *Scottish House Condition Survey Annex Tables 1996.*

59.   For example, the Metropolitan Borough of Calderdale was granted £95,000 at the end of 1998 by Calderdale and Kirklees Health Authority in order to improve, free of charge, the insulation and heating of old, cold homes occupied by pensioners in receipt of means tested benefits. The project was part of a Department of Health initiative which aimed to reduce the number of elderly patients needing hospital beds during the winter months, when bed spaces were in shortest supply. The scheme was advertised in the local press and by the end of 1999 407 homes had been serviced, at an average cost of £206 each. The main measures were loft and cavity wall insulation, draughtproofing and installing, servicing and repairing heating appliances. Information supplied by Andrew Cooper, Calderdale MB home energy conservation officer, January 2000.

60.   DETR (1999c). *Monitoring the implementation of the Home Energy Conservation Act.*

61.   Lord Chancellor's Department/DTI/DETR (1998). *The key to easier home buying and selling – a consultation document.* DETR Press Release 940 announced the government's intention of introducing the seller's information pack, 11 October, 1999.

62.   Information supplied by ETSU, February 2000.

63.   Environmental Change Unit, Oxford University (1987).

64.   Information from Market Transformation Programme website: http://www.mtprog.com

65.   Information from Market Transformation Programme website.

66. DETR (1999b). The projection for the increase in the number of English households between 1996 and 2021 is 3.8 million. Increases in the rest of the UK take the total growth above 4 million.

67. BRECSU (1996).

68. Information supplied by Linden Homes, February 2000.

69. Percentages supplied by DETR in oral evidence to the Commission, July 1999. Average estate house construction costs for owner occupation were some £500/m² in the final quarter of 1999, according to Lindsey Pullen of the Royal Institute of Chartered Surveyors' Building Costs Information Service. The typical new house has a floor area of some 90 m². The Commission estimates the combined annual gas and electricity bills for the average home built to the standards of the 1991 building regulations at £520, with a SAP of 70, a National Home Energy Rating of 7 and a floor area of 90 m². The estimate was based on the NHER Cost Table 1999. Information supplied by the National Home Energy Rating Scheme, Knowlhill, Milton Keynes.

70. Information supplied by the Building Regulations Division, DETR, May 2000.

71. Smith, P.F. and Pitts, A.C. (1993). *Buildings and the environment: a study for the National Audit Office.* University of Sheffield. Submitted as part of evidence to the Commission by the Royal Institute of British Architects.

72. Domestic CHP on the horizon. *ENDS Report,* No. 301, February 2000, 27.

73. DETR (2000c). *Planning Policy Guidance Note 3. Housing.*

74. Eighteenth Report, paragraphs 9.17-9.36.

75. DUKES 1999, table 1.13.

76. DETR (1999d). *Transport Statistics Great Britain 1999 Edition.* The Stationery Office. Cited as TSGB 1999. See table 2.3, page 64.

77. TSGB 1999.

78. DUKES 1999, table 1.13.

79. DETR (2000d). *Information Bulletin: 1998 UK air emission estimates, 30 March 2000.* See Table 3.

80. Passenger kilometres on national railways increased by 22% between 1994/95 and 1998/99: TSGB 1999, table 5.11.

81. United Kingdom (1998). *A new deal for transport: better for everyone.* Cm 3950. The Stationery Office.

82. Jonathan Fisher Environmental Economics (1998).

83. DTI (2000). *Energy Projections for the UK – Working Paper.* DTI EPTAC Directorate. All the projections quoted in this report from this working paper are for the central economic growth and higher energy prices scenario.

84. DETR (2000e). *Tackling congestion and pollution: the government's first report under the Road Traffic Reduction (National Targets) Act 1998.*

85. United Kingdom (1998).

86. TSGB 1999, table 2.7.

87. Standing Advisory Committee on Trunk Road Assessment (1999). *Transport and the economy.* The Stationery Office. See paragraph 6.36.

88. DUKES 1999, pages 235-237.

89. TSGB 1999, figure 2.6.

90. Chancellor announces further progress on meeting the UK's environmental commitments. HM Treasury Press Release, 9 November 1999.

91. DETR (1998). *UK Climate Change Programme: Consultation Paper.* See paragraph 131. This percentage estimate, and others in the section on transport, are based on government estimates of the reduction in carbon emissions achieved by this measure, making the assumption that energy consumption is proportionate to carbon emissions.

92. DETR (2000e), Scenario D, pages 30-31.

93. DETR (2000e), Scenario A, page 30.

94. House of Commons Environment, Transport and Regional Affairs Committee (2000), paragraph 30.

95. DETR (2000b), page 85.

96. United Kingdom (1998).

References

97.   Intergovernmental Panel on Climate Change (1999). *Aviation and the global atmosphere.* Cambridge University Press, Cambridge.

98.   DTI (2000).

99.   Jonathan Fisher Environmental Economics (1998);
        DUKES 1999;
        DTI (2000).

100.   ETSU (1999);
        DUKES 1999;
        DTI (2000).

101.   Jonathan Fisher Environmental Economics (1998);
        DUKES 1999;
        DTI (2000).
        DTI's 'business as usual' projection for 2010 ignores the voluntary agreements between the European Commission and vehicle manufacturers to reduce the carbon dioxide emissions from new cars; DTI estimates this could lower the transport sector's emissions by a further 4 MtC a year, approximately equivalent to a reduction of 3 GW in the rate of energy consumption.

102.   Jonathan Fisher Environmental Economics (1998);
        DUKES 1999;
        DTI (2000).

103.   Romm, J., Levine, M., Brown, M. and Petersen, E. (1998). A road map for US carbon reductions. *Science,* **279**, 669-670.

104.   Grubb, M. (1995). Asymmetrical price elasticities of energy demand. In Barker, T., Ekins, P. and Johnstone, N. (Eds). *Global warming and energy elasticities.* Routledge. See page 420.

105.   Lovins, A., Lovins, H. and von Weizsacker, E. (1997). *Factor four – doubling wealth, halving resource use.* Earthscan.

106.   Hawken, P., Lovins, A. and Lovins, H. (1999). *Natural capitalism – creating the next industrial revolution.* Earthscan.

107.   DETR (1999a).

108.   The latest projections for the number of households in England show a 3.8 million increase between 1996 and 2021; and a 4.1 million increase between 1991 and 2016, rather than the 4.4 million increase shown in the previous, 1992-based projections (DETR (1999b)).

109.   At the time of finalising this report, the government was supporting a private member's bill, the Warm Homes and Energy Conservation Bill, that would require the Secretary of State for Environment, Transport and the Regions to prepare and publish strategy for 'ensuring, by means including the taking of measures to ensure the efficient use of energy, that as far as reasonably practicable the homes of all households on lower incomes can be kept warm at reasonable cost.'

110.   The long-run price elasticities used by the DTI in its energy model and supplied to the Energy Advisory Panel in 1997 were -0.19 for the domestic sector, -0.09 for the service sector, -0.41 for the transport sector and in the range -0.07 (iron and steel) to -0.45 (textiles, leather and clothing) for the various manufacturing sectors. Thus a 10% increase in energy prices for households would bring about a 1.9% reduction in demand. DTI now estimates the long-run price elasticity for road fuel demand as -0.23, but also offers a projection based on an elasticity of -0.4 (DTI 2000).

111.   Evidence from the Energy Advisory Panel, October 1998.

112.   Motoring costs rose by 50% between 1989 and 1998 (before adjustment for inflation), rail fares by 66% and bus fares by 59%: TSGB 1999.

113.   Oral evidence, DETR, July 1999; Oral evidence, DTI, July 1999.

114.   Between 1970 and 1980 UK energy intensity declined at an average rate of 2.1% a year. Between 1980 and 1990 the decline averaged 2.0% a year. Between 1990 and 1998 the rate of decline fell to 1.2% a year. Rates calculated from DUKES 1999, table 1.12.

115.   House of Commons Environmental Audit Committee (1999).

116.   House of Commons Trade and Industry Committee (1998). *Energy Policy.* The Stationery Office. See paragraphs 144-148.

117.   DTI (1999). *The Energy Report.* The Stationery Office.

Chapter 7

1. Energy Technology Support Unit (ETSU) (1999). *New and renewable energy: prospects in the UK for the 21st century – supporting analysis.* Energy Technology Support Unit, Harwell. The term 'new and renewable' is used because the assessment covers fuel cells as well as renewable energy sources.

2. The model used by ETSU is the International Energy Agency's MARKAL, figured for the UK.

3   ETSU (1999), Figure 1 on page 178.

4. International Energy Agency (IEA)(1998). *World Energy Outlook 1998 edition.* Paris, IEA/OECD. These figures are for 1995 and are given as percentages in the tables on pages 412-413.

5. Figures for 1995 shown in Table 6.1 on page 64 in IEA (1998).

6. At La Rance in Britanny, with a capacity of 240 MW, built in the 1960s.

7. Department of Trade and Industry (DTI) (1999). *Digest of United Kingdom Energy Statistics 1999.* The Stationery Office. Cited as DUKES 1999. See table 5.4 (figures for 1998).

8. The EU average is 35%.

9   Royal Society and Royal Academy of Engineering (1999). *Nuclear energy: the future climate.* June 1999.

10. Between 70 and 135 years after closure of an AGR station, levels of radioactivity decline at a slower rate, reducing the advantages of extending decommissioning. The equivalent period for PWR stations is between 10 and 50 years beyond closure. Oral evidence from British energy plc, 7 May 1999.

11. Commission meeting with European Commission, Directorate-General XXI, Brussels, February 1999.

12. Sixth Report, 151-152.

13. Sixth Report, 367, 372, 389-90.

14. Sixth Report, 384-386.

15. Cummings, R. and Bush, R.P. *et al.* (1996). *An assessment of partition and transmutation against UK requirements for radioactive waste management.* Report DoE/RAS/96.007 for the UK Department of the Environment.

16. Sixth Report, 387-388.

17. House of Lords Select Committee on Science and Technology (1999). *Management of nuclear waste.* The Stationery Office, London.

18. DUKES 1999, tables 5.4 and 5.5 (figures for 1998).

19. Table A2.15 in Department of Trade and Industry. (1998). *The Energy Report: Transforming Markets Volume 1.* The Stationery Office.

20. European Commission (EC) (1997). *Energy for the Future: Renewable Sources of Energy,* COM(97)599. EC;
    ETSU (1999)

21. DUKES 1999, table 5.4.

22. Electricity Association (1999). *Electricity Industry Review 3,* pages 72-73.

23. ETSU (1999), pages 96 and 181.

24. ETSU (1996). Tidal Energy: UK Government Programme R&D Programme 1979-1994. ETSU-R-96. Harwell.

25. Department of Energy (1989). *The Severn Barrage Project: General Report: Energy Paper No. 57;* HMSO.

26. Evidence from the Severn Tidal Power Group, December 1998;
    information from DTI, February 2000.

27. Renewable Energy Advisory Group (1992). *Report to the President of the Board of Trade, November 1992.* Energy Paper 60. HMSO. See pages A36-A39.

28. ETSU (1994). *An Assessment of Renewable Energy for the UK.* ETSU, Harwell. See page 79.

29. REAG (1992).

30. Letter from Christopher Harding of the Severn Tidal Power Group to John Battle MP (Minister of State for Energy and Industry), 5 May 1999.

31. Information supplied by DTI, February 2000.

32. Oral evidence from British Energy plc, 7 May 1999.

33. REAG (1992), page A37.

34 DUKES (1999), table 5.4.

35. ETSU (1999), pages 184-185.

36. ETSU (1999), pages 186-187.

37. Electricity Association (2000). *Electricity Industry Review 4.* See page 56.

38. Capacity from wind turbines in Denmark was more than 1 GW at the end of 1997. IEA (1998). *Energy Policies of IEA countries: Denmark Review 1998.* OECD, Paris. See page 75;
Wind power capacity in Germany was 1.5 GW in 1996. IEA (1998). *Energy Policies of IEA countries: Germany Review 1998.* OECD, Paris. See page 123;
Onshore wind capacity in the UK in 1997 was 0.32 GW. ETSU (1999), page 166.

39. ETSU (1999).

40. A similar estimate is given by Brocklehurst, F. (1997). *A review of the UK Onshore Wind Energy Resource.* ETSU-R-99, ETSU, Harwell.

41. Commission visit to Denmark, June 1999.

42. Commission visit to Denmark, June 1999.

43. Information supplied by DTI, February 2000.

44. ETSU (1999).

45. Council Directive 85/337/EEC of 27 June 1985 on the assessment of the effects of certain public and private projects on the environment.

46. ETSU (1999), page 129.

47. Jackson, T. and Löfstedt, R. (1998). *Renewable Energy Sources.* A background paper for the Royal Commission on Environmental Pollution. Centre for Environmental Strategy, University of Surrey, Guildford.

48. Oral evidence from BP Solar, 4 December 1998.

49. Table 3 in Appendix B – Photovoltaics. In the report *Benign Energy: The Environmental Implications of Renewables.* http//:www.iea.org.tech/pubs

50. The value reported was 1,700 kWh per square metre.

51. Alsema, E.A. and Nieuwlaar, E. (2000). Energy Viability of Photovoltaic Systems, *Energy Policy* (special issue), **28**, in press.

52. Taylor, E.H. (1990). *Review of photovoltaic technology.* ETSU (ETSU-R-50).

53. Comprises an average pitch roof area of 70 square metres for 24.6 million domestic properties and roof and wall areas of non-domestic buildings. The total is reduced further by subtracting a proportion of surfaces which are likely to be shaded and those unsuitable for photovoltaics. ETSU (1999), page 133.

54. ETSU (1999) pages, 133-134

55. Presentation to the Commission by Dr Tim Jackson, May 1998.

56. ETSU (1999), page 119.

57. The average rate of electricity consumption in the public administration and domestic sectors in 1998 was 15 GW. DUKES 1999, table 5.1.

58. ETSU (1999), see page 29.

59. Estimates of accessible resources for domestic hot water, solar-aided district heating and water heating for non domestic building applications in 2025 are 1.4, 2.0 and 0.15 GW respectively. ETSU (1999), pages 32-33.

60. IEA Heat Pump Centre (1999). International Heat Pump Status and Policy Review – National Position Paper United Kingdom. Sittard, The Netherlands.

61. ETSU (1999), table 2 on page 83.

62. ETSU (1999), pages 96-97.

63. Evidence from South West Water plc, November 1998.

64. ETSU (1999), page 95.

65. Evidence from Thames Water plc, January 1999;
Evidence from Institute of Energy and Sustainable Development, De Montfort University, February 1999;
Evidence from Friends of the Earth, January 1999;
Evidence from Southampton City Council, January 1999.

66. Forum for the Future (1999). *Power for the New Millennium: Benefitting from Tomorrow's Renewable Energy Markets.* Forum for the Future. See page 17.

67. ETSU (1999) estimate that the maximum practicable resource for the UK in 2025 is 30 GW (declared net capacity). This assumes that photovoltaic cells are applied to all available (see description above) domestic and non-domestic buildings. Therefore to generate an average rate of 10 GW (declared net capacity) would require about one third of this area.

68. In 1995 installed capacity using energy crops appears to have been only 30 MW worldwide, all within the European Union (ETSU (1999), table 3 on page 72).

69.   ETSU R-82.
70.   ETSU (1999), page 77.
71.   Seventeenth Report, paragraph 5.29. For the evidence on which this conclusion was based, see box 5B and figures 5-II and 5-III.
72.   Information obtained from Project ARBRE during Commission visit, July 1999.
73.   ARBRE Technology, Yorkshire Water plc.
74.   Commission visit to Eggborough, July 1999.
75.   Annex 1, part 4 in EC Council Directive 1999/31/EC of 26 April 1999 on the landfill of waste.
76.   Figure for end September 1999, supplied by DTI.
77.   In March 1999 Commission Members visited a 38.5 MWe plant at Thetford designed to burn poultry litter, which is the bedding material from broiler houses.
78.   ETSU (1999).
79.   Information obtained from Project ARBRE during Commission visit, July 1999.
80.   Visit by Commission Member, September 1999, as part of a Commission meeting held in Northern Ireland.
81.   Visit by Commission Member, September 1999, as part of a Commission meeting held in Northern Ireland.
82.   REAG (1992), pages A29-A30.
83.   ETSU (1999), page 74.
84.   Members of the Commission visited a coppiced plantation in Yorkshire in June 1999.
85.   Information about Game Conservancy Trust research supplied by Project ARBRE, July 1999.
86.   Jackson, T. and Löfstedt, R. (1998).
87.   Press release from the Ministry of Agriculture, Fisheries and Food, Nick Brown announces a new direction for agriculture, 7 December 1999.
88.   Total area of agricultural land in the UK in 1994 was 17.3 million hectares of which 3 million hectares was used for growing cereals. Ministry of Agriculture Fisheries and Food (1994). *The Digest of Agricultural Census Statistics: United Kingdom.* HMSO.
89.   Berger, W.H. and Keir, R.S. 1984. Holocene changes in atmospheric CO_2 and the deep sea record. In: *Climate Processes and Climate Sensitivity. Geophysics Monograph Series,* volume 29. J.E. Hansen and T. Takahashi (Eds.), pages 337-351. American Geophysical Union, Washington D.C.
90.   REAG (1992), pages A47-A49;
      ETSU (1999), pages 187-188.
91.   The 1982 Review of UK Energy Research, Development, Demonstration and Dissemination.
92.   ETSU (1999), page 147.
93.   ETSU (1999), page 147.
94.   Information supplied by Wavegen Limited, 15 November 1999.
95.   Ocean Power Delivery: http://www.oceanpd.com/
96.   Information supplied by Dr. Richard Yemm, Ocean Power Delivery Limited, 16 November 1999.
97.   ETSU (1999), page 161;
      Evidence from Wavegen Ltd., March 1999.
98.   Convention on Wetlands of International Importance, Ramsar, Iran, 1971 (Amended in 1982 and 1987).
99.   REAG (1992), page A46;
      ETSU (1999), page 162.
100. ETSU (1999).
101. ETSU (1999).
102. ETSU (1994). *An Assessment of Renewable Energy for the UK.* ETSU, Harwell. See table 5, page 99.
103. ETSU (1999), page 158.
104. DTI (1994). *Energy Paper 62.* HMSO.
105. Thorpe, T. (1999). An overview of Wave Energy Technologies: Status, Performance and Costs. *Proceedings of an International One Day seminar, Wave Power: Moving Towards Commercial Viability.* Engineering Employers Federation, 30 November 1999.
106. ETSU (1999).
107. ETSU (1999), page 149.
108. ETSU (1999), page 157.
109. Evidence from Wavegen Ltd., March 1999.

110. ETSU (1999), page 141.
111. ETSU (1999), page 140.
112. ETSU (1999), page 139.
113. Projection submitted in support of oral evidence from British Energy plc, June 1999.
114. DETR/Scottish Executive/National Assembly for Wales/Department of the Environment (for Northern Ireland) (2000). *Climate Change – Draft UK Programme.* Cited as Draft Climate Change Programme.
115. UK Government (1995). *The prospects for nuclear power in the UK: Conclusions of the Government's nuclear review,* HMSO.
116. House of Commons Trade and Industry Select Committee (1998). See paragraph 2.53.
117. Royal Society and Royal Academy of Engineering (1999), page 49.
118. Draft Climate Change Programme, page 62.
119. Draft Climate Change Programme, page 58.
120. DTI (2000). *New and renewable energy: prospects for the 21st century. Conclusions in response to the public consultation.* See the paragraphs 'Obligation profile' on page 9 and 'Further obligations' on page 12.
121. Draft Climate Change Programme, page 58.
122. DTI (1999). *New and renewable energy: prospects for the 21st century.* See page 22. This downward trend is all the more striking in that 34 of the 61 projects accepted under NFFO-1 which have been commissioned were already in existence before being offered contracts.
123. DTI (1999), paragraph 30. For NFFO and Scottish Renewables Obligation the potential size of this would rise to a plateau of £150 million in 2003/04, declines after 2009/10, and finally runs out in 2018; the actual extent of the subsidy will depend on the market price of electricity.
124. DUKES 1999, table 7.5.
125. 'Green electricity' accreditation launched into murky waters. *ENDS Report,* No. 294, July 1999.
126. Between 1994 and the end of 1998, of the 18 wind developments which went before planning inquiries, just two small schemes won approval. Questions but precious few answers in renewable energy review. *ENDS Report,* No. 291, April 1999.
127. Evidence from British Wind Energy Association, November 1998.
128. Evidence from Friends of the Earth, January 1999.
129. Evidence from the Council for the Protection of Rural England (September 1998), the Countryside Commission (December 1998), the Countryside Council for Wales (December 1998) and the National Trust (December 1998).
    RSPB suggest that poorly sited wind farms (such as those on migration routes) can have adverse effects on the number of birds which strike rotor blades. This could be limited by avoiding development along these routes (November 1998).
130. Evidence from the Countryside Commission, December 1998.
131. Twenty-first Report, October 1998.
132. Oral evidence, March 1999. The functions of the Countryside Commission were taken over by the Countryside Agency on 1 April 1999.
133. Countryside Agency (1999). *Interim Landscape Character Assessment Guidance.* Land Use Consultants.
134. DTI (2000), page 20.
135. Draft Directive of the European Parliament and of the Council on the assessment of the effects of certain plans and programmes on the environment, 5685/00.
136. The Northern Energy Initiative (1999). *Energy for a new century: an energy strategy for the North East of England.* Sunderland.

Chapter 8

1. Department of Trade and Industry (DTI) (1999). *Digest of United Kingdom Energy Statistics 1999.* The Stationery Office. Cited as DUKES 1999. See table 1.1. This calculation includes energy losses in the electricity system and the energy used in refining oil and transporting hydrocarbons to users, but not for example the energy used in extracting fossil fuels from underground, providing fuel for nuclear power stations or constructing energy installations of all types. Nor does it include losses for thermodynamic reasons at the stage of end use, in particular in internal combustion engines in vehicles.

2. DUKES 1999, table 1.13.

3. DUKES 1999, comparison of tables 1.1 and 5.8.

4. DTI (1997). *Energy consumption in the United Kingdom. Energy Paper 66.* The Stationery Office. See page 15.

5. DTI (1997), pages 84, 44 and 111.

6. Measured in terms of the amount of electricity generated.

7. Dann, R.G., Parsons, J.A. and Richardson, A.R. (1998). *Microgen – co-generation for the home.* Paper for the 1998 International Gas Research Conference. BG Technology, Loughborough.

8. Gummert, G. (Hamburg Gas Consult) (1999). Using PEFC for the total energy supply of buildings. Presentation to Sixth Grove Fuel Cell Symposium, London, 13-16 November 1999.

9. Patterson, W. (1999a). *Transforming electricity: the coming generation of change.* Royal Institute of International Affairs / Earthscan.

10. Visit by Commission to Denmark, June 1999.

11. Information supplied by Birka Energi, April 2000; International Energy Agency (IEA) (1992). Heat pumps – an opportunity for reducing the greenhouse effect.

12. Seventeenth Report, paragraphs 5.24-5.29, box 5B and figures 5-II and 5-III.

13. This takes place at the Masnedø CHP plant, which consumes a 0.5 tonne bale of straw every 3 minutes.

14. Commission visit to Denmark, June 1999.

15. Information supplied by Energy Technology Support Unit, February 2000.

16. International Energy Agency (IEA) (1998). *World Energy Outlook 1998 Edition.* IEA/Organization for Economic Co-operation and Development. Page 412 shows that average annual growth rates for electricity (final demand) were higher than for mobility and other stationary uses between 1971 and 1995. Business as usual projections also suggest that electricity demand will have the highest growth rate between 1995 and 2020.

17. DUKES 1999, table 5.4.

18. DTI (1998). *Conclusions of the review of energy sources for power generation and government response to Fourth and Fifth Reports of the Trade and Industry Committee.* The Stationery Office.

19. Oral evidence from British Energy plc, May 1999.

20. Information provided by the Energy Technology Support Unit, February 2000.

21. Patterson, W. (1999a).

22. Maximum demand and capacity were 56 and 73 GW respectively. Electricity Association (2000). *Electricity Industry Review 4.*

23. Presentation by the National Grid Company plc, May 1999.

24. This figure was quoted by Dr Martin of Scottish and Southern plc during discussion at an international seminar on *Wave power – moving towards commercial viability,* Engineering Employers' Federation, Westminster, 30 November 1999.

25. Presentation by the National Grid Company plc, May 1999.

26. Patterson, W. (1999b). *Can public service survive the market? Issues for liberalized electricity.* Royal Institute of International Affairs Energy and Environmental Programme Briefing Paper (new series) **4**, July 1999.

27. Meeting by the Secretariat with the Institution of Electrical Engineers, 21 January 1999.

28. Presentation by the National Grid Company plc, May 1999; visit to Edison Mission's Dinorwig pumped storage scheme. June 1999.

29. The Commission visited the Dinorwig pumped storage scheme in June 1999.

30. Electricity Association (2000), page 88; Price, A., Bentley, S., Male, S. and Cooley, G. (1999). A novel approach to utility scale energy storage. *Power Engineering,* **13** (3), 122-129.

Chapter 9

1. Calculated from Department of Trade and Industry (DTI) (1999). *Digest of United Kingdom Energy Statistics 1999.* The Stationery Office.

2. DTI (2000). *Energy projections for the UK – Working Paper.*

3. DTI (1998). *Conclusions of The Review of Energy Sources for Power Generation and Government response to fourth and fifth Reports of the Trade and Industry Committee.* The Stationery Office. See paragraph 5.32.
4. Nuclear Utilities Chairmens Group (1994). *The Future Role of Nuclear Power in the UK: A background paper to the nuclear review.*

Chapter 10

1. House of Commons Environment, Transport and Regional Affairs Committee, 2000. *UK Climate Change Programme,* House of Commons. See paragraph 63.
2. The Advisory Committee on Business and the Environment has argued for a much greater proportion of the revenue from the levy to be devoted to such purposes.
3. A Finnish law of 1994 placed a tax on certain sources of energy at various different rates based on environmental considerations. A flat rate of tax was imposed on imported electricity, equivalent to the average rate of tax that domestically generated electricity attracted. In 1998 the European Court of Justice ruled that Member States could apply internal taxes on energy sources on environmental grounds. But in this particular case the way the tax had been applied to electricity imports into Finland breached EU Treaty principles which forbid Member States from imposing taxes on produces in excess of similar domestic products. The case is *Outokumpo Oy* (C-231/96).
4. House of Commons Trade and Industry Committee. *Energy policy* (Fifth Report session 1997-98). HC471. See paragraph 21(a).
5. Department of Trade and Industry (DTI) (1999). *The future of gas and electricity regulation. The government's proposals for legislation.* October 1999. See section 2.1.
6. House of Commons Bill 49, session 1999-2000, clause 1.
7. DTI (1999), paragraph 15.
8. DTI (1999), section 5.2.
9. DTI (1999), section 5.4.
10. House of Commons Environmental Audit Committee (1999). *Energy efficiency.* Session 1998-1999, Seventh Report, HC 159-1.
11. House of Commons Environmental Audit Committee (1999). See paragraph 65.
12. DETR (1999). *Government response to the House of Commons Environmental Audit Committee report on Energy efficiency.* See paragraphs 25-26.
13. Oral evidence by DETR, July 1999; oral evidence by DTI, July 1999.
14. DETR (1999).
15. House of Commons Environmental Audit Committee (1999). See paragraph 64.
16. The case for a body on broadly the lines we envisage has been spelled out in a report by Green Alliance, published in 1999.
19. Commission visit to Japan, March 1999, including discussions with the Ministry of International Trade and Industry and, with particular reference to fuel cells, the New Energy and Industrial Technology Development Organisation.
20. We do not agree with DTI's view (DTI (2000), page 17) that the problems raised by embedded generation should be categorised solely as a non-technological barrier to extensive use of renewable energy sources.
21. DTI (2000). *New and renewable energy: prospects for the 21st century. Conclusions in response to the public consultation.* January 2000.
22. Meeting with Chair and Members of the Energy and Natural Environment Panel, October 1999.
23. Advisory Committee on Business and the Environment (1999). *Carbon trusts: exploiting the potential of low carbon technology.* October 1999.
24. Royal Society and Royal Academy of Engineering. *Nuclear energy: the future climate.* Report of a joint working group chaired by Sir Eric Ash. June 1999. See chapter 12.

Appendix A

ANNOUNCEMENT OF THE STUDY AND INVITATION TO SUBMIT EVIDENCE

The Commission's study of energy and the environment was announced on 28 August 1997 in the following terms:

ROYAL COMMISSION TO STUDY ENERGY AND THE ENVIRONMENT

The Royal Commission on Environmental Pollution is to review energy prospects for the 21st century and their environmental implications. The aim is to identify the actions required in the years immediately ahead to develop a sustainable strategy for energy provision and use.

Growing concern over climate change has helped bring energy to the top of the environmental agenda. In December this year international negotiations will take place in Kyoto, Japan, to reduce emissions of greenhouse gases, particularly carbon dioxide from burning fossil fuels.

This study by the Royal Commission will compare the environmental consequences of different methods of providing energy. It will examine the scope for radical reductions in energy requirements.

The principal focus will be the UK and Europe. The global context will be considered in order to identify the constraints and opportunities likely to arise.

Rather than undertake new work, the intention is to draw to the fullest extent on analyses of particular aspects already carried out by other bodies, together with the Royal Commission's own work on energy use in transport.

As the first stage of the study the Commission Secretariat will assemble and collate existing material on some key topics. The Royal Commission is inviting interested organisations and individuals to draw relevant analyses and work in progress to its attention. It will also commission some studies by consultants.

The topics identified for initial study are:

(a) overall scenarios for future energy demand and supply in the UK, in Europe and globally;

(b) the environmental implications of such scenarios, especially in terms of pollution produced by the energy sector;

(c) technological, economic and social assessment of the scope for reducing demand for energy, including the possibility of radical changes in technology or in design practices under approaches such as Factor Four and Factor Ten;

(d) the potential contributions to energy supplies from various sources and the constraints on their development;

(e)   environmental, economic and social assessment, on a life-cycle basis, of alternative technologies for energy supply;

(f)   how governments can best interact with energy markets to ensure the development of those markets reflects environmental costs and risks;

(g)   the effectiveness of present institutions in framing and delivering energy policies that are environmentally sustainable.

Early next year the Royal Commission will define specific issues for investigation, and will invite written and oral evidence on these. It intends to publish its report in the first half of 1999.

On 23 September 1998 the Commission issued a news release in the following terms:

ROYAL COMMISSION TO INVESTIGATE IMPLICATIONS OF PHASING OUT FOSSIL FUELS

The Royal Commission on Environmental Pollution announced today what will be the main theme of its study of future energy prospects. The focus will be on the implications of considerably reducing, by the middle of the next century, use of fossil fuels as an energy source in the UK, or even phasing them out completely.

The Royal Commission is concerned both about the need to limit carbon dioxide emissions from burning fossil fuels, in order to avoid dangerous modifications to the world's climate, and about other environmental impacts of energy systems. It believes there are strong pressures for radical changes in the way energy is obtained and used. Its aim is to elucidate and assess what such changes entail.

Evidence is being invited on 23 specific issues. These cover alternative sources of energy, improvements in energy efficiency, the implications of climate change, social issues and international considerations. Evidence should be submitted by the end of November to the Commission Secretariat at Steel House, 11 Tothill Street, London SW1H 9RE.

The Royal Commission plans to publish its report on Energy and the Environment before the end of 1999. For the first time in such a study, information about progress will be available on the Energy section of the Royal Commission's web site at:

http://www.rcep.org.uk/energy.html

The list of issues was as follows:

Energy sources

1.   In the light of political, economic and social constraints, what key policies would be needed to force the pace of adoption of renewable sources of energy in the UK on the scale required to replace fossil fuels by the middle of the next century, and how could such policies be implemented?

2.   Are there environmental impacts of renewable sources of energy which would be critical limiting factors?

3.   Which renewable sources of energy are likely to offer the most scope in technical terms in the UK?

4.   Is there a realistic prospect of technologies (for example for sequestration of carbon at source of emission) that would help make some continuing use of fossil fuels as an energy source acceptable?

5. What might conventional nuclear power contribute? To what extent will its contribution be dependent on:

> innovations in technology?

> establishing valid disposal strategies for wastes?

> public attitudes?

6. Should fast breeder reactors or nuclear fusion be regarded as potentially viable energy technologies in the next century?

Improvements in energy efficiency

7. Can UK primary energy demand be stabilised by the middle of the next century? Can it be reduced over that timescale, and if so by how much?

8. What are the actual and potential drivers and barriers for reducing demand for energy? How are the drivers and barriers affected by the structure and regulation of the energy market? How could the drivers be enhanced and the barriers be reduced?

9. In comparison with other strategies, how attractive is reducing demand as a way of reducing the impact of energy on the environment?

10. What contribution can increased efficiency of generation and distribution make to reducing the environmental impact of energy?

11. What more needs to be done to integrate a concern for energy efficiency into professional training and practice in fields such as architecture, engineering and land-use planning?

12. How should considerations about energy efficiency enter into determinations of what represents the best practicable environmental option and into implementation of the EC Directive on Integrated Pollution Prevention and Control?

13. Where should lead responsibility lie for promoting energy efficiency, and are additional powers required?

Implications of climate change

14. What measures should be taken

> in the UK

> in the European Union

> in other parts of the world

in order to adapt to environmental changes that are inevitable as a consequence of higher concentrations of greenhouse gases in the atmosphere?

15. Is the factor which effectively limits utilisation of fossil fuel reserves likely to be requirements to reduce emissions of greenhouse gases, or the availability or distribution of reserves, or the relationship between the cost of exploiting those reserves and the cost of competing energy sources? How different are the respective limits on fossil fuel use likely to be imposed by these three constraints?

Social issues

16. How will different strategies to reduce the impact of energy on the environment affect different groups in society?

17. How can approaches be developed to reconcile reductions in demand for energy with greater equity in access to the services provided by energy?

18. What will be the health effects of different energy strategies?

International considerations

19. Are future trends in market prices likely to move the UK energy system in the desired direction, and if so how quickly? To the extent that interventions in markets will be required, how far does the UK have the ability to pursue its own energy policies?

20. Should the UK adopt policies to phase out use of fossil fuels in the absence of equivalent action by other countries?

21. How should the UK seek to influence the development of policies internationally to limit fossil fuel use? How can a sufficiently wide coalition be formed to obtain agreement on a global carbon tax?

22. Does research need to demonstrate specific national impacts of global climate change before the people in a given country will be prepared to support strong international action to counter it?

22. What scope is there for the UK to profit from exporting or licensing commercial technologies developed for clean energy supply?

23. What scope is there for the UK to profit from exporting or licensing commercial technologies developed for clean energy supply?

Appendix B

CONDUCT OF THE STUDY

In order to carry out this study Commission Members sought written and oral evidence, commissioned studies and advice on specific topics and made a number of visits.

Evidence

In parallel with the news releases inviting evidence, which are reproduced in appendix A, and advertisements placed in the *London, Edinburgh and Belfast Gazettes*, the Secretariat wrote direct to a large number of organisations.

The organisations and individuals listed below either submitted evidence or provided information on request for the purposes of the study or otherwise gave assistance. In some cases, indicated by an asterisk, meetings were held with Commission Members or the Secretariat so that oral evidence could be given or particular issues discussed.

Government Departments

ADAS
Department of Health
Department of the Environment, Transport and the Regions*
Department of Trade and Industry*
Foreign and Commonwealth Office
Ministry of Agriculture, Fisheries and Food
Office of Science and Technology
Scottish Office*

Parliamentary bodies

House of Commons Select Committee on the Environment, Transport and Regional Affairs*
House of Commons Environmental Audit Committee*
Parliamentary Office of Science and Technology*

European and international bodies

DG XI (Environment), European Commission
DG XII (Science, R & D), European Commission
Food and Agriculture Organization of the United Nations
Intergovernmental Panel on Climate Change, Working Groups I and III
International Atomic Energy Agency
International Energy Agency*
International Energy Agency Coal Research – The Clean Coal Centre
International Energy Agency Greenhouse Gas R&D Programme
International Maritime Organization
Organisation for Economic Co-operation and Development
United Nations Economic Commission for Europe
World Energy Council
World Health Organization
Wuppertal Institut für Klima, Umwelt, Energie GmbH

Other organisations

ABS Consulting
Advisory Committee on Business and the Environment
AEA Technology*
AMSET Centre
Anglian Water Services Ltd
Association for the Conservation of Energy*
Association of British Insurers
Association of Building Engineers
Association of Electricity Producers
BG plc
Biffa Waste Services Ltd
Biomass Recycling Ltd
Bolton Metropolitan Borough Council
Borough of Pendle
BP Solar*
BRE
British Association for Bio Fuels and Oils
British Biogen
British Cement Association
British Energy Efficiency Federation
British Energy plc*
British Medical Association
British Nuclear Energy Society
British Nuclear Fuels Ltd*
British Nuclear Industry Forum
British Petroleum Company plc
British Photovoltaic Association (PV-UK)
British School of Belo Horizonte
British Wind Energy Association
CAG Consultants
Cambridge Econometrics
Campaign for the Protection of Rural Wales*
Centre for the Study of Regulated Industries
Chartered Institution of Building Services Engineers
Chartered Institution of Water and Environmental Management
Chris Blandford Associates
Coalgas (UK) Ltd
Combined Heat and Power Association*
Combustion Engineering Association
Confederation of British Industry*
Confederation of United Kingdom Coal Producers
Consortium of Opposing- and Nuclear Free- Local Authorities
Construction Industry Council
Construction Industry Research and Information Association
Consumers' Association
Consumers in Europe Group
Council for National Parks
Council for Nature Conservation and the Countryside
Council for the Protection of Rural England*

Country Landowners Association*
Countryside Commission*
Countryside Council for Wales
Cummins Engine Company Ltd
Dalkia plc
De Montfort University, Institute of Energy and Sustainable Development, and Lincoln
   Renewable Energy Centre
East of Scotland Water
Eastern Group plc
Economic and Social Research Council, Global Environmental Change Programme
Economics for the Environment Consultancy Ltd
Electricity Association*
Electricity Consumers' Committees Chairmen's Group
Elm Farm Research Centre
Energy 21
Energy Advisory Associates
Energy Advisory Panel
Energy for Sustainable Development Ltd
Energy Saving Trust*
Energy, Technology and the Environment
Engineering and Physical Sciences Research Council
English Nature*
Environment Agency*
Environmental Services Association
Esso UK plc
ETSU*
European Wind Energy Association
EXO – Exothermics Ltd
Faculty of Occupational Medicine
Farming and Wildlife Advisory Group
Federation of Environmental Trade Associations
Foratom
Foresight Energy and Natural Environment Panel*
Forestry Commission Research Agency*
Friends of the Earth*
Friends of the Earth Scotland
GAIA Foundation
Gas Consumers Council
Geological Society
Global Climate Coalition
Global Commons Institute
Greenpeace UK*
Hadley Centre for Climate Prediction and Research, Meteorological Office
Haul Waste Ltd
Health and Safety Commission
Health and Safety Executive
Ian Pope Associates Ltd
ILEX Associates
Imperial College of Science, Technology and Medicine, Energy-Environment Policy
   Research Group

Institute for European Environmental Policy, London
Institute for Public Policy Research
Institute for Research in the Social Sciences
Institute of Arable Crops Research – Rothamsted
Institute of Biology
Institute of Directors
Institute of Economic Affairs
Institute of Energy
Institute of Grassland and Environmental Research
Institute of Petroleum
Institute of Physics
Institute of Wastes Management
Institution of Chemical Engineers
Institution of Civil Engineers
Institution of Electrical Engineers*
Institution of Environmental Sciences
Institution of Mechanical Engineers
International Project for Sustainable Energy Paths
International Sustainable Development Research Network
IT Power Ltd
Landfill Gas Association
Law Society
Lean Economy Initiative
Local Government Association
London Transport
Lye's Green Water
Magnox Electric plc
Mandix
Marine Conservation Society
Meteorological Office
National Consumer Council
National Council of Women of Great Britain
National Energy Action*
National Farmers Union*
National Grid Company plc*
National Home Energy Rating Scheme
National Power plc
National Radiological Protection Board
National Trust
Natural Environment Research Council (NERC)
Natural Resources Institute
NERC Centre for Ecology and Hydrology
NERC Institute of Terrestrial Ecology*
Network for Alternative Technology and Technology Assessment
New Product Research and Development
Newcastle City Council
North of Scotland Water Authority
North Yorkshire County Council
Norweb plc – United Utilities plc
Office for National Statistics

Office for the Regulation of Electricity and Gas
Office of Water Services
Open University, Energy and Environmental Research Group, and Technology Policy
  Group
Power Generation Contractors Association
PowerGen plc
RJB Mining (UK) Ltd
Radioactive Waste Management Advisory Committee
Ramblers' Association
Renewable Energy Club
Renewable Energy in the Urban Environment
Rocky Mountain Institute, USA*
Royal Academy of Engineering
Royal College of General Practitioners
Royal Institute of British Architects*
Royal Institute of International Affairs
Royal Scottish Forestry Society
Royal Society
Royal Society for the Protection of Birds*
Royal Society of Chemistry
Royal Society of Edinburgh
Royal Society of Health
Royal Statistical Society
Royal Town Planning Institute*
Sandwell Metropolitan Borough Council
Scottish Environment Protection Agency*
Scottish and Southern Energy*
Scottish Hydro-Electric plc
Scottish Natural Heritage*
Scottish Solar Energy Group
Scottish Power*
Severn Tidal Power Group
Severn Trent plc
Shell UK Ltd*
Shell Group Planning Unit*
Shropshire County Council
Silsoe Research Institute
Slough Heat and Power Ltd
Society of Occupational Medicine
Solar Century
Solid Fuel Association
South Midlands Renewable Energy Advice Centre
South West Water Ltd
Southampton City Council
Steel Construction Institute
Surrey County Council, Environment
Sustainable Agriculture, Food and Environment Alliance
SWALEC plc
Thames Water plc
UK Centre for Economic and Environmental Development
UK Nirex Ltd

UK Offshore Operators Association Ltd
UK Petroleum Industry Association Ltd
UK Round Table on Sustainable Development
UKAEA
Ulster Agricultural Organisation Society Ltd
University College London, Centre for Social and Economic Research on the Global Environment
University College London, Environmental Change Research Centre
University of Dundee, Centre for Energy, Petroleum and Mineral Law Policy
University of East Anglia, School of Environmental Sciences
University of Manchester, Faculty of Science and Engineering
University of Oxford, Environmental Change Unit, joint with Department of Engineering
Wavegen Ltd
West of Scotland Water Authority
West Wales ECO Centre
Women's Environmental Network in Wales
World Wide Fund for Nature UK*
WRc plc
Wycombe District Council
Yorkshire Water Projects Ltd

Individuals

Dr Mary Archer, National Energy Foundation
Mr W Bailey
Dr Ausilio Bauen, Imperial College of Science, Technology and Medicine, Centre for Energy Policy and Technology*
Dr R Barrass
Dr R Bentley, University of Reading*
Dr Brenda Boardman, University of Oxford, Environmental Change Unit*
Mr Philip Breeze
Dr Leonard G Brookes
Professor Melvyn Cannell, NERC Centre for Ecology and Hydrology
Sir Geoffrey Chipperfield, Energy Advisory Panel*
Professor Dame Barbara Clayton, University of Southampton School of Medicine
Professor M L Coleman, University of Reading*
Mr Jonathan Cowie
Professor Partha Dasgupta, University of Cambridge*
Professor J F Davidson, University of Cambridge, Department of Chemical Engineering
Professor Hans-Jürgen Ewers, German Council of Environmental Advisors*
Dr Nick Eyre
Mr David Hart, Imperial College of Science, Technology and Medicine, Centre for Energy Policy and Technology*
Professor Ian Fells FRSE, University of Newcastle upon Tyne
Dr Jonathan Fisher
Lord Flowers*
Dr Keith Guy, Air Products plc*
Dr Andrew Gilchrist, ETSU, AEA Technology
Professor David Hall, Kings College, London*
Professor G P Hammond, University of Bath

Appendix C

SEMINAR: ENERGY FOR THE WORLD WE WANT
2 JULY 1998

To assist the Commission in defining specific issues on which it would invite detailed evidence, a seminar 'Energy for the world we want' was held on 2 July 1998 at the Royal Institute of International Affairs, with a wide range of invited participants.

The programme for the day was:

Introduction to the Energy Study and the purpose of the day
Sir Tom Blundell, Chairman of the Commission from July 1998

Session 1: Shaping the kind of world we want
Rt Hon John Gummer MP, Former Secretary of State for the Environment

Discussion period

Session 2: Natural systems and human systems - working together?
Sir John Houghton, Co-Chairman of Scientific Assessment Working Group, Intergovernmental Panel on Climate Change, and Chairman of the Commission until June 1998

Discussion period

Session 3: Energy technologies for future needs
Michael Jefferson, Deputy Secretary General, World Energy Council

Discussion period

Session 4: Ground rules and how they are changing
Walt Patterson, Energy and Environment Programme, Royal Institute of International Affairs

Discussion period

Plenary session and Chair's closing remarks

In addition to the speakers and Members of the Commission, the other participants were:

Peter Beck (Royal Institute of International Affairs, Energy and Environment Programme)

Sir Geoffrey Chipperfield (Energy Advisory Panel)

Ute Collier (WWF UK)

John Constable (Esso UK plc)

David Cope (Parliamentary Office of Science and Technology)

Alex Galloway (Energy Saving Trust)

Richard Grant (British Gas plc)

Patrick Green (Friends of the Earth)

Michael Grubb (Royal Institute of International Affairs, Energy and Environment Programme)

Colin Hicks (Department of Trade and Industry)

Brian Hoskins (University of Reading, Department of Meteorology)

Emma Jones (Association for the Conservation of Energy)

Gary Kass (Parliamentary Office of Science and Technology)

Kevin Lane (Environmental Change Unit, Oxford University)

Nick Mabey (WWF UK)

Derek May (British Nuclear Fuels plc)

Doug McKay (Shell International)

John Mitchell (Royal Institute of International Affairs, Energy and Environment Programme)

Chris Newton (Environment Agency)

Douglas Parr (Greenpeace UK)

Peter Pearson ((Imperial College of Science, Technology and Medicine, Environmental Policy and Management Group)

Michael Schultz (Natural Environment Research Council)

Nicola Steen (Association of Electricity Producers)

Helen Stibbard (SustainAbility)

Appendix D

CARBON RESOURCES AND REMOVAL: TECHNICAL ISSUES

GLOBAL FOSSIL FUEL RESERVES AND RESOURCES

D.1 The limitation on our use of fossil fuels is unlikely to be the size of the available reserves of such fuels, but the degree to which their combustion leads to global warming by increasing the level of carbon dioxide in the atmosphere. The predominant view among scientists is that fossil fuels (coal, oil and natural gas) are, as that name presupposes, the outcome of biological processes in the distant geological past. For a meaningful discussion concerning quantities of fossil fuels, a number of terms need to be defined. The term 'reserves' refers to fossil fuels whose location is known and which can be recovered under certain assumptions concerning the available technology and the maximum price of the commodity. By contrast, 'resources' refers to the total amount of recoverable fossil fuel (identified reserves plus that which is yet to be found). Advances in technology increase the estimates of reserves as a proportion of total fossil fuel resources.

D.2 Oil companies have a detailed understanding of the geological conditions associated with oil deposits, which enables them to predict in which regions they are likely to occur. The world has been extensively mapped for large oil deposits which has led to a low and declining rate of discovery. No super-giant oil fields have been found for nearly a decade, and giant field discoveries have been in decline since 1970.[1]

D.3 There are differences of opinion about the size of the global oil ultimate, the quantity of oil that will ultimately be accessible to human exploitation. Pessimistic estimates of the conventional (non-heavy, low viscosity, easily recovered oil) global oil ultimate based on oil industry data are 2,000 Gb (gigabarrels), implying that global oil production will peak between 2010 and 2030. Over and above this, there is an estimated further 4,000 Gb of oil in the same deposits which cannot be extracted using current recovery techniques, but may be accessible due to improvements in technology. There are a further 3,000-4,000 Gb of heavy oil which would be much more expensive than the currently exploited deposits to extract and refine, in terms of both money and the requirement for energy.[2] Higher estimates for the global oil ultimate of 3,000 Gb, based on the utilisation of non-conventional oil reserves and improved technology for non-conventional oil production, might allow the peak for global production to be deferred until 2060.[3]

D.4 Natural gas (methane) reserves are likely to be available for exploitation for a longer period than oil reserves. It has been suggested that peak global production would not occur until 2090.[4] Identified global coal reserves are sufficient for over two hundred years at present rates of use.[5] There is a very large resource of methane on the deep ocean bed in the form of frozen methane hydrate,[6] but the technology to exploit that has yet to be developed.

D.5 Estimates of total global fossil fuel 'reserves' are between 829[7] and 1,501[8] GtC whilst total fossil fuel resource estimates (excluding methane hydrates) range from 4,166 to 4,678 GtC.

ENHANCING OCEAN SURFACE UPTAKE OF CARBON DIOXIDE

D.6   Changes in productivity of the oceans have in the past been major drivers of change in atmospheric carbon dioxide concentration. The world's oceans currently store approximately 40,000 GtC and exchange approximately 90 GtC with the atmosphere each year (see Figure 2-III).[9] Although the oceans have the theoretical capacity to absorb all anthropogenic carbon dioxide, this could only be achieved over a time-scale of several thousand years.

D.7   Although the surface layer of the ocean is saturated with carbon dioxide, the deeper ocean is not in equilibrium with atmospheric carbon dioxide, the limiting factor being the rate of carbon transfer between surface waters and the deep ocean. There are two ways in which carbon dioxide is transferred from the surface to the deep ocean; by mixing and the sinking of dead marine organisms which have taken up carbon from surface waters, and which are ultimately buried in ocean bottom sediments. The latter process, which has been referred to as the *biological pump*, can be promoted by fertilising the ocean with iron or macro-nutrients (nitrogen, phosphorous and silicon) to increase algal primary productivity.

D.8   One fifth of the world's oceans have 'high-nutrient-low-chloropyhll' (HNLC) waters in which it has been suggested that algal growth is limited by the availability of iron. Iron fertilisation experiments in the three main HNLC regions (the Equatorial Pacific, the Sub-Arctic Pacific and the Southern Ocean) demonstrated increased rates of algal productivity.[10, 11]

D.9   The effectiveness of biological productivity as a method of removing carbon from the atmosphere would also depend on the circulation patterns within the oceans. Circulation between surface and subsurface water in the Southern Ocean is relatively rapid.[12] As the Southern Ocean maintains a large pool of unused nutrients, it represents the most promising gateway for the transfer of carbon between the atmosphere and deep ocean. Modelling studies have suggested that the Southern Ocean plays a dominant role in maintaining natural levels of atmospheric carbon dioxide and that variations in iron availability in the geological past (through atmospheric dust transport) may have influenced glacial-interglacial variations in carbon dioxide levels.[13] Evidence advanced in support of this hypothesis includes analysis of ice cores, in which inferred elevated levels of atmospheric iron correlated with low atmospheric concentrations of carbon dioxide.[14]

D.10   The major limiting factor for algal growth throughout the remainder of the world's oceans is the availability of nitrogen. An objective for research has been to test the feasibility of establishing large kelp farms in the oceans through the addition of nutrients. Modelling studies have indicated that attempts to increase carbon uptake in this way would be expensive and inefficient.[15] In addition, there may be significant environmental impacts such as reduced biodiversity in surface waters, changes in community structure, the creation of oxygen deficient waters, and the generation of other greenhouse gases.

D.11   Although it has been suggested that iron fertilisation in the Southern Ocean has the potential to lower atmospheric carbon dioxide levels by 6-21%[16], the critical factor being the rate of vertical mixing, the IPCC[17] concluded that this was not a viable method for carbon sequestration. It would require fertilisation of 25% of the world's ocean continuously and indefinitely and even if it was entirely successful, would only reduce atmospheric carbon dioxide levels by 50 ppmv.[18]

fixation[34] leading to global nitrogen-induced carbon sequestration in forests, estimated to range from about 0.1 to 2.3 GtC per year. On the negative side, it has been suggested that higher temperatures may increase the loss of carbon dioxide in respiration and oxidation of soil carbon, thus offsetting some of the gains in photosynthesis. However, there is considerable uncertainty in this regard.

D.29   Results from recent soil warming experiments have indicated that a rise in soil temperature of $5°C$ does not lead to a long-term increase in carbon dioxide loss.[35] The increase in atmospheric carbon dioxide concentration and the increasing incidence of drought both reduce carbon dioxide uptake and loss of water by inducing closure of the stomata (the carbon intake valves) with the result that the efficiency of photosynthesis with respect to water use increases. A lowering of ground water levels, particularly in boreal forests, may also lead to enhanced carbon release through the oxidation of soil organic matter. In boreal peatlands, lower water tables lead to the oxidation of methane to carbon dioxide, which upon release has a lower net global warming potential.

References

1.   Oral Evidence from the Reading University Oil Group, 6 May 1999.
2.   Oral Evidence from the Reading University Oil Group, 6 May 1999.
3.   Oral evidence from Professor Odell, 6 May 1999.
4.   Oral evidence from Professor Odell, 6 May 1999.
5.   World Coal Institute (1998) *Coal Facts.* World Coal Institute.
6.   Some estimates suggest that the global methane hydrate resource exceeds all other fossil fuel resources combined. United States Geological Survey (1992). *Gas (Methane) Hydrates – A new frontier.* http://marine.usgs.gov/fact-sheet/methane-hydrates/title.html
7.   World Energy Council (1993). *Energy for Tomorrow's World – The realities, the real options and the agenda for achievement.* St. Martin's Press.
8.   Rogner, H.H. (1997). *Climate Change Assessments: Technology learning and fossil fuels – How much carbon can be mobilized?* Paper presented to International Energy Agency Workshop on climate change damages and the benefits of mitigation, 26-28 February 1997, International Institute for Applied Systems Analysis (IIASA).
9.   Intergovernmental Panel on Climate Change (1996). *Climate Change 1995: The science of climate change.* Cambridge University Press, Cambridge.
10.   Cooper, D.J., Watson, A.J. and Nightingale, P.D. (1996). Large decreases in ocean-surface CO_2 fugacity in response to *in situ* iron fertilization. *Nature,* **383**, 511-513.
11.   Turner, S.M., Nightingale, P.D., Spokes, L.D., Liddicoat, M.I. and Liss, P.S. (1996). Increased dimethyl sulphide concentrations in sea water from *in situ* iron enrichment. *Nature,* **383**, 513-517.
12.   Siegenthaler, U. and Sarmiento, J.L. (1993). Atmospheric carbon dioxide and the ocean. *Nature,* **365**, 119-125.
13.   Sarmiento, J.L. and Toggweiler, J.R. (1984). A new model for the role of the oceans in determining atmospheric P_{CO2}. *Nature,* **308**, 621-624.
14.   Martin, J. (1990). Glacial-interglacial CO_2 change: The Iron Hypothesis. *Palaeoceanography,* **5**, 1-13.
15.   Orr, J.C. and Sarmiento, J. L. (1992). Potential of marine macroalgae as a sink for CO_2: constraints from a 3-D general circulation model of the global ocean. *Water, Air and Soil Pollution,* **64**, 405-421.
16.   Ormerod, B. and Angel, M. (1998). *Ocean fertilisation as a CO_2 sequestration option.* IEA Greenhouse Gas R&D Programme, Cheltenham.
17.   IPCC (1996).
18.   IPCC (1996).

19.   Ritschard, R.L. (1992). Marine Algae as a CO_2 sink. *Water, Air and Soil Pollution.* **64**, 289-303.

20.   Ormerod, B. and Angel, M. (1998)

21.   Freund, P. and Thambimuthu, K.V. (1999). Options for Decarbonising Fossil Energy Supplies. *Combustion Canada '99,* 26-28 May 1999, Calgary, Alberta, Canada; http://www.ieagreen.org.uk/comb99.htm

22.   Goldthorpe, S.H., Cross, P.J.I. and Davison, J.E. (1992). Studies on CO_2 abatement from power plants. *Energy Conversion and Management,* **33**, 459-466.

23.   Freund, P. and Thambimuthu, K.V. (1999).

24.   Croiset, E. and Thambimuthu, K.V. (1999). A novel strategy for greenhouse gas abatement in coal-fired power plants: enriched oxygen combustion. *Combustion Canada '99,* 26-28 May 1999, Calgary, Alberta, Canada.

25.   International Energy Agency Greenhouse Gas Programme (IEAGGP) (1994). Carbon dioxide capture from power stations. Cheltenham.

26.   The oil industry also has experience of injecting mixtures of carbon dioxide and naturally occurring hydrogen sulphide, the primary objective being safe disposal of the hydrogen sulphide (information supplied by Dr. K. Thambimuthu, February 2000).

27.   Holloway, S. *et al.* (1996). *The underground disposal of carbon dioxide: Summary report.* British Geological Survey, Keyworth, Nottingham.

28.   IEAGGP. (1995). *Carbon dioxide utilisation.* Cheltenham, UK.

29.   Croiset, E. and Thambimuthu, K.V. (1999).

30.   Van der Meer, L.H.H. (1992). Investigations regarding the storage of carbon-dioxide in aquifers in the Netherlands. *Energy Conversion and Management,* **33**, 611-618.

31.   Malhi, Y., Baldocchi, D.D. and Jarvis, P.G. (1999) The carbon balance of tropical temperate and boreal forests. *Plant, Cell and Environment,* **22**, 715-740.

32.   Malhi, Y. *et al.* (1999).

33.   Vitousek, P.K. (1997). Human alteration of the global nitrogen cycle: sources and consequences. *Ecological Applications,* **7**, 737-750.

34.   Galloway, J.N., Schlesinger, W.H., Levy, H.H., Michaels, A. and Schnoor, J.L. (1995). Nitrogen fixation: anthropogenic enhancement-environmental response. *Global Biogeochemical Cycles,* **9**, 235-252.

35.   From the data of Professor Linder; information supplied by Professor Paul Jarvis, March 2000.

Appendix E

ILLUSTRATIVE ENERGY BALANCES FOR THE UK IN 2050

E.1   Scenarios were constructed to examine the practicability of making deep cuts in UK carbon dioxide emissions over the next half century. Four scenarios were selected to highlight the nature of the choices available for the UK, and are discussed in chapter 9. This appendix describes the methodology used to construct scenarios and contains a more detailed specification of some features of the four scenarios presented.

E.2   The Commission is aware of only one other attempt to construct scenarios for the UK energy system in 2050.[1] That adopted a different approach to the present exercise: it looked only at electricity and projected the proportions of electricity that would be generated from different primary energy sources over the period 1900-2050 under two scenarios: a 'business as usual', limited intervention' scenario and one which assumed 'a national plan ... aimed at minimising some adverse long-term environmental and economic effects'.

E.3   In the exercise carried out for the Commission the scenarios were highly simplified snapshots of the UK's overall energy system in 2050. The objective for the scenarios was to achieve a match between energy demand for different end uses and energy supply from different sources while reducing by about 60% UK carbon dioxide emissions from burning fossil fuels. The baseline taken for emissions was 1997, the most recent year for which final estimates of emissions were available at the time when the calculations were carried out.

E.4   The four scenarios presented incorporate alternative assumptions for levels of energy demand in 2050 (E.9-E.13) and for the ranges of sources from which energy would be obtained (E.14-E.25). They can be characterised briefly as follows:

scenario 1: no increase on 1998 demand, combination of renewables and either nuclear power stations *or* large fossil fuel power stations at which carbon dioxide is recovered and disposed of

scenario 2: demand reductions, renewables (no nuclear power stations or routine use of large fossil fuel power stations)

scenario 3: demand reductions, combination of renewables and *either* nuclear power stations or large fossil fuel power stations at which carbon dioxide is recovered and disposed of

scenario 4: very large demand reductions, renewables (no nuclear power stations or routine use of large fossil fuel power stations).

E.5   Within each scenario a match between demand and supply was obtained by iteration. The calculations were carried out in terms of rates of energy supply or use expressed in gigawatts (see the box on definitions and units on page 10), in most cases as annual averages. The initial constraint was to reduce the amount of energy obtained from fossil fuels by about 60%. To confirm that this would have the desired effect on emissions, an estimate was then made of the carbon dioxide emissions that would result from that particular mix of fossil fuels (E.37-E.38).

E.6   There were three main stages in the iteration:

in the first stage a preferred energy source was allocated to each of the specified end uses in the second stage shortfalls or surpluses in annual supply for each end use were reallocated, with electricity making up residual shortfalls in the supply of energy for end use in other forms

in the third stage estimates were made of the extent to which the postulated capacities of generating plant (E.7) would be unable to meet peak demand for electricity and would fail to meet demand for electricity at some other times because of the intermittent nature of many renewable energy sources. Calculations were then made of the amounts of energy that would have to be obtained from back-up plants, predominantly using fossil fuels, in order to fill such gaps; and the calculations made in previous stages were adjusted accordingly (E.30-E.32).

E.7   When the rate of energy supply from each energy source had finally been determined, calculations were made of the number and capacity of installations of each type (for example, the number and size of onshore wind farms) that would be requited to supply energy at that average rate, based on the proportions of time for which such installations could reasonably be assumed to operate (E.40).

E.8   To simplify the task of constructing scenarios:

it was assumed that the UK would not be either a net importer or a net exporter of energy in 2050;

non-energy uses of fossil fuels (which are included in the energy balances DTI compiles to represent the current situation) were disregarded;

no allowance was made for the possibility that the permissible level of UK carbon dioxide emissions from burning fossil fuels might be either raised or lowered by the trend in emissions from terrestrial ecosystems (3.15-3.22);

no allowance was made for the possibility that the UK might transfer obligations to reduce carbon dioxide emissions to or from other countries under the flexibility mechanisms incorporated in the Kyoto Protocol (box 4A).

DEMAND IN 2050

E.9   In order to specify energy demand, the baselines taken were total final energy consumption in 1998 and the proportions of total consumption that were attributable in 1998 to the major sectors of the economy (table E.1).[2]

Table E.1

Final energy consumption by sector 1998

Sector	annual average rate (GW)	proportion (%)
industry	46	22
transport	70	34
domestic	60	29
services	24	12
others	5	2
total final energy consumption	205	100

Table E.7

Number of generating plants required in 2050 under the four scenarios

	scenario 1	scenario 2	scenario 3	scenario 4
large onshore wind farms (100 turbines each)	50	25	2	25
small onshore wind farms (10 turbines each)	510	250	16	252
large offshore wind farms (100 turbines each)	180	177	180	88
photovoltaic roof installations (average peak output 4kW)	15 million	7.5 million	0.75 million	0.75 million
wave power units (1 MW capacity)	7,500	7,500	7,500	7,500
tidal stream turbines (1 MW capacity)	500	500	500	500
tidal barrage	1	1	1	1
new small scale hydro	4,500	4,500	4,500	2,200
CHP plants fuelled by energy crops (capacity 1-10 MW)	290-2,900	290-2,900	42-420	42-420
CHP plants fuelled by agricultural and forestry wastes (capacity 0.5-10 MW)	53-1,050	53-1,050	53-1,050	34-688
CHP plants fuelled by municipal solid waste – (capacity 8-60 MW)	3-20	3-20	0	0
baseload plants: *either* nuclear *or* fossil fuel with carbon dioxide recovery and disposal (capacity 1,200 MW)	46	0	19	0
domestic (micro) CHP units using gas (2 kW)	0	1.7 million	1.8 million	2.4 million
fossil fuel plants to back up intermittent renewables (capacity 40 MW)	1,000	760	475	460
fossil fuel plants for meeting peak electricity demand (capacity 400 MW)	120	70	65	55

Appendix E

References

1. Boyer, S.T. (1994). Factors affecting an energy and environmental strategy for the UK for the year AD 2050. Unpublished MSc thesis, Cranfield University School of Mechanical Engineering.
2. Department of Trade and Industry (DTI) (1999). *Digest of United Kingdom Energy Statistics 1999.* The Stationery Office. Cited as DUKES 1999. See table 1.1.
3. DTI (1997). *Energy consumption in the United Kingdom.* The Stationery Office.
4. Data for 1998 taken from DUKES 1999, tables 5.4, 7.4 and 1.9.
5. Energy Technology Support Unit (ETSU) (1994). *An assessment of renewable energy for the UK.* ETSU, Harwell.
6. ETSU (1999). *New and renewable energy prospects in the UK for the 21st century – supporting analysis.* ETSU, Harwell. See page 134.
7. Presentation to the Commission by Dr Tim Jackson, May 1998.
8. ETSU (1999) used conversion efficiencies for energy crops (future technology) and AFW of 44% and 31% respectively. It was assumed that a similar conversion efficiency of 31% had been used for MSW.
9. Out of the total energy loss of 27%, conversion accounts for 20% and internal energy use for 7%.
10. ETSU (1999), page 74 and table 7.
11. Grubb, M. J. (1993). Integration of renewable energy sources. In Jackson, T. (ed). *Renewable energy: prospects for implementation.* Butterworth/Heinemann, Oxford.
12. The resource-cost curves published in ETSU (1999) are based on output and conversion losses are therefore taken into account already.
13. Information supplied by Professor Laughton, Westfield and Queen Mary College, London, December 1999.
14. The Onyx CHP plant (near Basingstoke) and the SELCHP plant (south-east London) are able to operate as a CHP plants, but as the network is not in place they currently provide electricity only. Information supplied by John Collis of Onyx and by SELCHP, February 2000.
15. DUKES 1999, table 5.9.
16. Turhollow, A. F. and Perlack, R. D. (1991). Emissions of CO2 from energy crop production. *Biomass and Bioenergy,* **1,** 129-135;
    ETSU (2000). *Estimation of carbon dioxide and energy budgets of wood fired electricity generation systems.* B/U1/00601/05/REP. Harwell;
    Forestry Authority Research Division (1994). *Modelling of carbon and energy budgets of wood fuel coppice systems.* Prepared for ETSU on behalf of DTI;
    Bauen, A. (1999). *Gasification-based Biomass Fuel Cycles: An Economic and Environmental Analysis at the Regional Level.* Unpublished PhD thesis, King's College London.
17. IEA Greenhouse Gas R& D Programme (IEAGGP). *Carbon dioxide capture from power stations.* IEAGGP, Cheltenham. See page 9.

Appendix F

MEMBERS OF THE ROYAL COMMISSION

CHAIRMAN

Sir Tom Blundell FRS*

Sir William Dunn Professor and Head of Department of Biochemistry, University of Cambridge and Professorial Fellow of Sidney Sussex College

Director General, Agricultural and Food Research Council 1991-94

Chief Executive, Biotechnology and Biological Sciences Research Council 1994-96

Member, Advisory Council on Science and Technology 1988-90

Honorary Director, Imperial Cancer Research Fund Unit in Structural Biology, Birkbeck College, University of London 1989-96

Professor of Crystallography, Birkbeck College, University of London 1976-90

MEMBERS

Sir Geoffrey Allen PhD FRS FREng FIC FIM FRSC FinstP#

Executive Adviser to Kobe Steel Ltd

Chairman of URGENT Steering Committee, Natural Environment Research Council

Chancellor of the University of East Anglia

Chairman, Science, Technology and Mathematics Council

President of the Institute of Materials 1994-95

The Reverend Professor Michael Banner MA DPhil

FD Maurice Professor of Moral and Social Theology, King's College London

Chairman, Home Office Animal Procedures Committee

Chairman, Government Committee of Inquiry on Ethics of Emerging Technologies in the Breeding of Farm Animals 1993-95

Dean, Fellow and Director of Studies in Philosophy and Theology, Peterhouse, Cambridge 1988-94

Member, Agriculture and Environment Biotechnology Commission

Member, Church of England Board for Social Responsibility

Professor Geoffrey S Boulton OBE FRS FRSE#

Regius Professor of Geology, and Vice Principal, University of Edinburgh

Member of Council, Royal Society

Member of the Scottish Higher Education Funding Council

Member of Council, Scottish Association for Marine Science

Professor Roland Clift OBE MA PhD FREng FIChemE FRSA

Professor of Environmental Technology and Director of the Centre for Environmental Strategy, University of Surrey

Visiting Professor Chalmers University of Technology, Goteborg, Sweden

Member, UK Ecolabelling Board 1992-99

Chairman, Clean Technology Management Committee, Science and Engineering Research Council 1990-94

John Flemming MA FBA
Warden, Wadham College, Oxford
Chief Economist, European Bank for Reconstruction and Development 1991-93
Chief Economist, Bank of England 1980-91
Member, Advisory Board on Research Councils 1977-90
Chairman, National Academies Policy Advisory Group Working Party on Energy and the Environment 1993-95
Chairman, Hansard Society/Economic Policy Forum Commission on the Regulation of Privatised Utilities 1995-97
Treasurer, British Academy
Chairman of Management Committee, National Institute of Economic and Social Research

Dr Ian Graham-Bryce DPhil FRSC FRSE+
Principal and Vice-Chancellor, University of Dundee
Convener, Committee of Scottish Higher Education Principals
President, British Crop Protection Council
Head of Environmental Affairs Division, Shell International 1986-94
Director, East Malling Research Station 1979-86
Member of Natural Environment Research Council 1989-96

Sir Martin Holdgate CB PhD FIBiol
President, Zoological Society of London
Chairman, Energy Advisory Panel 1993-96
Director General, International Union for Conservation of Nature and Natural Resources 1988-94
Chief Scientist, and Deputy Secretary, Department of the Environment 1976-88
Chairman, International Institute for Environment and Development 1994-99

Professor Brian Hoskins CBE FRS
Professor of Meteorology, University of Reading (Head of Department 1990-96)
Chairman, Expert Panel on UK Strategy in Global Environmental Research 1996
President, Royal Meteorological Society
Past President, International Association of Meteorology and Atmospheric Sciences

Professor Richard Macrory Barrister MA
Professor of Environmental Law, University College London
Board Member, Environment Agency
Specialist Adviser, House of Commons Select Committee on the Environment, Transport and Regional Affairs
Editor-in-Chief, *Journal of Environmental Law*
First Chairman of UK Environmental Law Association 1986-88
Chairman, Merchant Ivory Productions Ltd
Honorary Vice-President, National Society for Clean Air and Environmental Protection

Printed in the UK for The Stationery Office Limited on behalf of
Her Majesty's Stationery Office
Dd 5067591 6/00 65536 Job No. TJ001591